Other Books by Margaret Halsey

WITH MALICE TOWARD SOME
SOME OF MY BEST FRIENDS ARE SOLDIERS
COLOR BLIND

The Folks
at Home

by

MARGARET HALSEY

19 52

SIMON AND SCHUSTER

To My Father

A Man of Character

TABLE OF CONTENTS

———

The Folks at Home

I

The Upward Step

Except for the circumstance that I am now entering my fifth decade of it, I have no particular qualifications for writing about American life. But aside from being a female, I have no particular qualifications for being a mother, either. I am, however, the parent of a four-year-old daughter; and this book is, in a manner of speaking, some thinking out loud I am doing in her behalf. The American society—through its newspapers, picture magazines, movies, comics and radio-television—is soon going to move in on my little girl. She will very shortly be old enough to ask naïve and devastating questions about the behavior of the tense and anxious grownups. When that time comes, I should like to be prepared with a few unhurried and non-evasive answers.

By profounder thinkers than I, it has been noted that

there are certain widely accepted and pretty much un-questioned beliefs—notably about money—on which most of American living is based. It occurs to her father and me that instead of buying our daughter the customary television set, we might (in terms of her whole life) per-form an equally benevolent service by taking hold of some of these beliefs and giving them a quick flap, to see whether any moths fly out. If a cat may look at a king, certainly a parent may look at an entrepreneur.

What is the real nature of American life? The query may not be as complex as it seems at first. The pressures and tensions—admitted even by the advertisements to be characteristic of American living—are universal. That is to say, they operate with splendid impartiality on "haves" and "have-nots," talented and untalented, conservative and liberal, minority and majority, management and labor, Democrat and Republican. This harsh democracy of ten-sion would seem to imply that there is some kind of least common denominator which is producing it. If such a least common denominator exists, the people who most need to know about it are the parents of small and grow-ing children.

I am forty-two years of age and my daughter is four, which probably makes me the Oldest Living Mother of a Small Child. Since a rather longer interval than is cus-tomary intervened between my birth and my daughter's, I am perhaps more conscious than other mothers of four-year-olds of how times have changed. Like many of my contemporaries, I grew up in the long, cold shadow of

Victorian dutifulness. This kind of upbringing was not without its advantages. In its way, it prepared people to accept responsibility. But customs and conventions are perpetually evolving and developing; and in our enlightened age, it is generally agreed that children need love.

Now that I have a daughter of my own, I am glad the emphasis in child care has switched from demanding obedience to giving affection. It seems to me to represent a large step forward in man's upward struggle toward the stars. We now have permission to love our children, as even fairly recent vintages of parents did not. But it does not seem to be enough. I think most parents would agree that bringing up children in the present-day United States is both a tentative and a taxing job. Indeed, the enormous American literature on child care is mute evidence that most American parents do not function parentally with easy and joyous self-confidence.

The books on child care, however, usually concentrate solely on the children. They rather take for granted the country in which the children are living. The following chapters grew up out of a notion that perhaps some kind of interpretation of the American scene could be made which would bring the task of raising children into somewhat clearer focus. For those of my readers who have no children, or whose children are ravaged old characters of twenty-five, the interpretation of American life which ensues will provide either the pleasurable feeling of recognition or the possibly even more pleasurable feeling of discovering a human being who is completely and utterly in the wrong.

Until I was thirty-eight, all I knew about parenthood was what one could pick up from having had two of them. To be sure, during a period of temporary affluence, I did what so many affluent Americans do—laid my dreams and my childhood (my version of it) in the archepiscopal laps of a couple of classical Freudian analyists. In the beginning of these experiences, I was entranced by the delightfully heart-rending picture of sensitive, appealing little me being trodden all over by brutal, Oedipal giants. But when at long last it began to dawn on me—celerity on the pick-up is not one of my strong points—that the giants had themselves once been children in the slightly untender atmosphere of the American nineteenth century, the magic went out of it. Freud's hot little vacuum of parent and child was not for me.

This is not to say that I do not contemplate with reverence and awe the courage and the sovereign intellect of Sigmund Freud. There are few Americans or Western Europeans who do not owe something to that unbowed head. But one swallow does not make a summer; and one man does not make a science. I was trained—conscientiously trained—for a life that World War I extinguished four years after I was born; and I have spent most of my adult years trying to keep my footing among a long series of unheralded novelties. I have been able to get a certain amount of scientific help in this balancing act, but it has come from the relatively inexpensive method of reading

4

here and there among the published works of the many—
and sometimes acidly divergent—scientists who picked up
and branched out from where Freud left off. It was not,
however, until four years ago, when I achieved a child of
my own, that I began to see that this unnerving gap between childhood and adult life was not as peculiar to me
as I had thought it was. It happens to all Americans. It is
going to happen to my little girl, unless her father and I
can think of something to do about it.

Since I have been a parent, I have noticed that there
are two major particulars in which my daughter's early
life has no kinship whatsoever with my early years. One
of these particulars lies in the circumstance that when I
and my contemporaries were four years old, it was not
possible to make very much money out of children. There
were no comic books, no radio, no television, and the
movies were still in a fledgling state. Except for oatmeal
and library books, children were not consumers. Today,
however, her father and I are by no means the only people who love our daughter. Almost literally, she is worth
her weight in gold to private enterprise. Or, at least, she
soon will be. People with older children than mine, who
have already had the experience of sharing their parental
responsibilities with the American businessman, do not
seem wholly comfortable about their new partner.

On the other hand, children of my daughter's age are
no longer so intensively conditioned as they once were to
fear and despise the human body. The current practice is
to let them more or less take their own time about toilet

5

training; nor are they customarily pilloried and condemned for evincing a cheerful interest in their excreta. They see more of their own and other people's living tissue than was formerly the case, and if their innocent inquiries about sex are met with "HUSH! You mustn't *say* that!" it is not because the authorities on child guidance want it that way. I have been rather dazzled, in the course of my maternal duties, at how much protoplasm has come up in the world since I was four years old.

It seems to me quite possible to underestimate the potentiality for good which lies in the freedom of many present-day children from the old-fashioned shame and fear about their bodies. It is freely admitted by all of us that American life is full of tension; but one point about this tension I have never seen raised except in social-science treatises whose vocabulary clearly indicated they were not for the retail trade. That point is that a whole generation of Americans approximately my age had the rug pulled out from under them. These Americans spent their early, formative years—which are now considered very important, but which were just run-of-the-mill then —being indoctrinated with the sinfulness of the flesh and the desirability of chastity. Then, when they reached maturity and what were alleged to be the years of Reason, Freud broke over their unprotected heads. All of a sudden, so to speak, the stakes were changed. All of a sudden, the dictum became—to paraphrase the children's derisive chant—"The last one to be sexually responsive is a bedbug!"

This is an exaggerated way of stating that in the first fifty years of the twentieth century, a revolution was taking place in people's thinking. Revolutions are usually untidy and they usually mean that somebody gets hurt. What might be called, very roughly, Freud's Revolution has at length achieved a certain amount of respectability, but it has had a by-product which may need more attention than it gets.

Freud's Revolution has meant that American business and American government are at the present time in the hands of an age group which started life by being made to feel unworthy if it *was* sexual, and arrived at maturity in time to receive a strong, painful and contradictory hint that unworthiness consists of *not* being sexual. This harsh dividing line between the goals of childhood and the goals of adult life is typical of much American living and extends into other areas besides sex and other generations besides mine. It is the key to a good deal of American unhappiness, and American unhappiness is what all compassionate parents want to shield their children from.

In this endeavor, there is one way in which we have a headstart. Childhood has now come to be recognized as a part of living, and is not brushed off, as it once was, as a mere disciplinary prelude to "real life." When one stops to think how slowly, as a general rule, ideas give place to other ideas, this emancipation appears to be a very considerable triumph for the Western European and American mind. In the current emphasis on nuclear fission, it

7

is easy to forget that there are other sciences besides physics; and very possibly we are not sufficiently grateful to the schoolteachers, writers, psychologists, lecturers, thinkers, researchers, anthropologists, philosophers, experimentalists, pediatricians and parents whose combined efforts have given the children lebensraum.

Nobody—at least, nobody important to American middle-class parents—is going to quarrel with the statement that children need love. But this uncontroversial tenet raises a rather troubling question: Where are they going to get it? American children do not live in test tubes and agar solutions. They live in the United States. And in the United States, at the present time, the press, the radio and the popular magazines are hissing and seething and steaming with hostility. Nor is all this hostility directed solely against the Russians. Indeed, as the target for tonight, the Russians very often play second fiddle to such of our countrymen as have not been lucky enough to secure the endorsement of the American communications industry.

It may be that, since I earn my living as a writer, I am oversensitive to changes in vocabulary. It is nevertheless dismaying that the fallible human being—the mortal man who may or may not be right—is disappearing from the American language. People whose opinions and decisions are not popular are more and more referred to in the kind of terms that used to be reserved for cannibals. This fashionable abusiveness passes for patriotism; but the fact is that the disappearance of the fallible human being from

8

the American vocabulary creates unease. It creates unease, moreover, in a far wider area of feeling than the mere region of politics. Some of my best friends are fallible, including me.

However, in matters of political opinion, perhaps a certain amount of hatred is to be expected. What counts, as far as parents and children are concerned, is the extension of this prevalent hostility into the field of entertainment. By their champions, the comics are defended on the ground that they give the child reader a safe, vicarious outlet for his aggression. Nobody, nobody at all, contends that the comics are not all a-bristle with aggression. In a wildly overexcited but by no means wholly dismissable pamphlet, *Love and Death,* a New York printer writing under the pseudonym of G. Legman points up with documentation which cannot be denied the extent to which hostility, violence and aggression have imperceptibly crept into the entertainment with which we adults solace our idle hours.

The traditional man from Mars, if he knew nothing of the American Republic except the so called "mass communications," would certainly be justified in thinking that there is not enough loving-kindness afloat in the contemporary United States to see a crippled old lady across an Indian trail. We live from crisis to crisis, and our sense of dignity is undermined by the recurrent suspicion that at least some of these perils are manufactured—fictional dangers promoted by newspaper publishers, public-relations firms, and men who want to be President.

9

And yet in the midst of this thunderous, denunciatory and singularly unaffectionate atmosphere, the parents and teachers keep up a little cricketlike chirping about children needing love. Are we fools? In spite of the evidence, I do not believe so. But if we are not, then it must be taken as proved that the outward and immediately visible appearance of American life is misleading.

In the old, Pre-World-War I days, respectable, middle-class American parents did what was known as "planning for the children's future." Two factors have intervened, in the years since, to put a considerable crimp in that forward-looking activity. One is that we no longer have the extended periods of peace and prosperity upon which such planning was based. Depressions, inflations and wars succeed each other much more rapidly than they used to. The other factor is that Freud's Revolution has brought it home to the middle class that a child's *present* is his future. It is now generally agreed, by the people we consult about our children, that what a child is going to do about marriage, work, money, friendship and parenthood is to a large extent determined a good many years before he is actually old enough for those performances.

In a nutshell, this means that parents have much more influence on their children than had previously been supposed—twenty or thirty or forty years ago. "Bad blood" or natural "orneriness" is no longer enough to account for the disappointing child. Nowadays everybody turns a gimlet eye upon the cringing mother and father. But to have influence is to suggest that the influence is going to be used in some direction or other. Which direction? This opens up—for parents, at least—an area of great confusion. During the Kefauver Investigation, a Miss Virginia Hill made an extremely favorable impression on television, but the parents of little girls have an understandable reluctance about bending the twig toward that point of the compass. Mr. Whittaker Chambers was embraced by large sections of the press as a hero and a shining patriot, but not many mothers and fathers were disposed to point him out to their children and say, "Go and live a life like that man's." Miss Rita Hayworth, though combining in the highest degree the sterling attributes of beauty and solvency, seems to the alerted parent a forlorn and exploited piece of protoplasm. Senator McCarthy has brought a self-respecting nation almost to its knees, but the average parent hopes rather fervently that no child of his will ever get so spectacularly out of touch with the Marquis of Queensberry.

The conscientious parent of the present day has to be something more than the dutiful saver of pennies for tuition. He has to have more knowledge of both himself and his children than is involved in turning out "well-trained"—to use a word which once had great currency—offspring. Parenthood has become a more complex job than the mere practice of thrift and the inculcation of discipline. What renders the task even more difficult is that it can no longer be done in privacy. It has to be achieved with the whole United States in the living room. Our children are consumers, and it is no more possible to keep producers away from them than it is to divert hummingbirds from honeysuckle.

The United States is my little girl's environment, and it has developed into a much more intense and intrusive environment for children than it was when I was small. As an environmental factor, it deserves at least as much thought and attention as her diet, her schooling, her teeth and her supply of playmates.

It will not be disputed by anybody that what characterizes the American family, as a rule, is the Upward Step. Except for old, rich, long-established families—which are not the concern of this book—we tend, generally speaking, to put horny-handed Grandpa behind us as fast as we can. The familiar pattern in American life is that parents give their children more dentistry, more schooling, more clothes, more recreation, better furniture and a better-balanced diet than they, the parents, themselves had. The Upward Step was a feature of both my husband's family and mine, and we both have reason to be grateful for it. It is nevertheless neither unjust nor unfair to suggest that any given institution has the vices of its virtues.

The Upward Steps of all the American families, taken together, constitute the American standard of living; and for my own part, having once resided for a year in Europe, I am not disposed to abandon that standard of living while I still have strength to put plug in socket. But one serious disadvantage of the Upward Step is that it means parents and children cannot live in the same world. The child starts off on a higher social and economic level than the one his parents inhabited when they were children. Consequently, parents and child do not share a common experience of childhood. To the child, his parents' childhood seems remote, unfamiliar and rather meaningless—if, indeed, he can bring himself to believe that they had one at all. Nor does the gap ever close. If the child grows up into a conscientious, purposeful American who has advanced himself in life, his relationship with his parents in maturity is as necessarily superficial as it was when he was young.

It has been customary, for a long time, to blame this separation of parent and child upon the immigrants. The immigrant child—it has been said—was ashamed of his father, because the old man spoke broken English, and he hastened to put as much distance as possible between himself and his sire. The immigrant child, however, did not disavow his father simply because the progenitor had an imperfect command of the language. He disavowed his father because—since the father was operating in an unfamiliar environment—that father had very little prospect of making lots of money. In those extremely rare instances where the immigrant father, while continuing to speak nothing but fluent Magyar, nevertheless made a million dollars out of a strudel recipe, the children did not feel it necessary to disown him. Poppa became, not a dirty old foreigner, but a charming eccentric.

The immigrants did not impose the Upward Step on the United States. It was the other way around. The United States imposed the Upward Step on the immigrants. The immigrants copied and compounded a kind of behavior they found here upon their arrival. By 1925, the enormous flood of immigration which characterized the nineteenth century had slowed to a mere trickle. The foreign-language press became a dying industry. The Upward Step, however—although it has been a quarter of a century since we had any immigration worthy of the name—is still doing business at the old stand.

The consequence of the Upward Step is that most Americans never form the habit of looking back. They concentrate on the present and the future. And what does this constriction of life into two, instead of three dimensions mean—in terms of human happiness? We have the evidence of two thousand years of literature that the goal toward which human beings have always gravitated—in their quest for contentment and fulfillment—has been knowledge of self. Modern human beings do not go to psychoanalysts because they have symptoms. In a sense, everybody has symptoms. People go to psychoanalysts because they have symptoms they do not understand. It is not the symptoms, but the inability to interpret them, which wears out the springs in those couches.

If knowledge of self is the basis and foundation of happiness, what happens in a forward-thrusting society like ours where the high standard of living involves the loss of the parents? All the books and all the authorities on present-day American parenthood are agreed upon the great influence exerted by parents on children—not only in their actual behavior toward the child, but in their behavior toward each other and in the whole general picture of the kind of people they are. The very large American literature on the subject of child-rearing asserts over and over again that to a certain extent, the children *are* the parents. The children imitate the parents; they identify with the parents; they take over many of the parents' atttitudes and beliefs so thoroughly that they cannot, in later life, completely divest themselves of those attitudes and beliefs—even when they very much want to. The inability of many Southerners to conquer their fear of Negroes, though they may be completely convinced intellectually that it is unnecessary baggage, is a case in point. So is the inability of many women to surrender in sex, although they may be utterly persuaded in their minds that frigidity is an unhealthy symptom.

Even rebellion against the parents is an inverted tribute to their influence. But in our onward-and-upward society, this influence is exercised upon the child by people who start out, and who remain, comparative strangers. Father may possibly, as the early Freudians claimed, bestride his narrow world like a Colossus; but he is also, in our country, The Boy We Left Behind Us. Knowledge of self is indispensable to happiness. Such knowledge does not have to be articulate. It can be unconscious, as it is in a cow or a tiger; but it must be accurate. Knowledge of self, however, is impossible without a fairly exact understanding of the people who had so much to do with forming the self.

In this connection, psychoanalysis has performed a major service to Americans of our time in directing attention to the parents. If my own experience of analysis was a waste of time and money, it was because my particular practitioners were so enthused about infantile sexuality and so happily bemused with incest, that they left out of the picture its most important element. The behavior of my parents—and, indeed, of most people's parents in the United States—could be usefully interpreted only in light of the fact that they were doing what everybody else in that place and at that time was doing. They were getting ahead. Psychoanalysts themselves sometimes have a partiality for getting ahead, which may be why some of them fail to understand that the American family cannot be treated solely as an arena for Greek tragedy.

My husband and I sometimes speculate on what, in twenty or thirty years' time, our daughter will think of us. My own parents saved their money, gave their two children the college educations they had not had themselves, and achieved an independent old age. They lived up faithfully to the standards of their time and place, and those standards, being American, were not the easiest thing in the world to meet. But their lives, being American lives, did not give them much leisure for meditation, and I doubt if it ever crossed their minds to wonder what their children thought of them. In their generation, the important thing was the parents' opinion of the children, not vice versa. So far as my husband and I are concerned, we are not so much interested in our child's thinking well of us as we are interested in her thinking *something*

16

about us. And that something, for the sake of her peace of mind, should be as near to the truth as possible.

I cannot hope to convey to my daughter anything of the quality of my own childhood. She is growing up in an American suburb not very far in miles from the respective suburbs where her father and I grew up. But forty years, and the ever-increasing urbanization of American life, have changed the territory beyond recognition. Where her father and I saw open fields, swamps, stretches of woodland and rather amateurish brooks, she sees paved streets, legions of houses, blue spruce and supermarkets. The outward change is no more spectacular than the inner one. Freud's Revolution rendered my childhood—like those of many of my contemporaries—obsolete almost before it was over. I cannot bring up my daughter the way I was brought up. Like most American middle-class parents, I have to bring her up on theories and out of books. I do not regret it, although it seems to me hard on the parents. It represents a step forward in human progress. But it means that my daughter's knowledge of me is a knowledge of my experience in reading books and talking to pediatricians, and not of my experience in being a child.

However, though I cannot convey to my daughter anything of my own outmoded childhood, it has occurred to me more than once in the last four years that I might possibly be able to convey to her something of the quality of her parents' adult life—which is, after all, her present environment. The parents influence the children, but the society influences the parents. My husband and I belong to that large group of Americans who were born in roughly the first twenty or twenty-five years of the current century and whose tribal focus and spiritual pivot was the Great Depression. Twenty or thirty years from now, could my—or anybody's—child go to a library and glean an accurate impression of mid-century America from reading the mid-century "mass communications"? It is my belief that she could not. For one thing, the American press—and its sister institutions—is not wholly free from the vice of self-deception. After the 1948 election, the more intelligent and mentally flexible publicists —like Mr. James Reston, of *The New York Times,* and Mr. Elmo Roper—admitted with commendable frankness that the Delphic oracles and Cumaean sibyls got off the beam because they had been infatuatedly talking to each other, instead of listening to the voters. For another thing, the word "communications" is misleading. "Communication" in the dictionary sense means a two-way exchange. But who ever argues with a movie? Who talks back to *Time* and *Life*? To assume that nobody wants to is taking too much for granted.

If I wish to do a little bit more for my daughter than merely to be the springboard from which she bounces into a penthouse, I shall have to try to give her some glimpse of the pressures that were operating on her mother and father at the time her mother and father were operating on her. This does not mean that anything said about American life in the following pages is to be construed as written by one who has made a conquest of it. On the contrary. I am not "mature," "adjusted," "well-integrated," "relaxed" or free from "anxiety"—to employ the terms which the self-help books have brought into popular usage. Like most of my fellow countrymen, I was not raised to be mature; I was raised to be successful. By the time maturity got on the best-seller list, I was too old to go back and begin all over again. I was also skeptical enough to wonder about the pure, unalloyed bliss of being mature in a slightly unripe society. When it comes to being mature, it does not pay to get too far ahead of United States Senators, as Mr. Owen Lattimore found to his cost.

This is therefore not a book which contains any answers. The most I can aspire to is enough good luck occasionally to frame the right questions. I have lived all my life in a transitional society, and I cannot claim to have risen above that hard conditioning. My mother and father, for example, were the products of a world ignorant of contraceptives. In that world, the behavior of men and women toward each other was sternly regulated by the fact that every act of sexual intercourse might produce a new life to be taken care of. Sex was not a matter in which there was much room for experiment. Since my mother and father brought me up, the pre-contraceptive world is by no means wholly unfamiliar to me. On the other hand, all the time I have been old enough to take responsibility, contraceptives have been in general use—even, sometimes, among people whose religion forbids them—and males and females have not had to regard each other as potential dynamite.

The era is well within my memory span when the American middle class believed in work even more than it believed in God. Any kind of work, without reference to its purpose or to what had to be jettisoned in order to get it done.

> "Satan finds some mischief still
> For idle hands to do."

But within the last twenty or twenty-five years, this passionate belief in the absence of idleness has been under attack from two very different quarters. On the one hand, the psychologists have pointed out that work can be compulsive—that it can be just as much of an escape from reality as taking drugs. (It is with me.) On the other hand, the gangsters, publicity men and alumni who buy football players—the "shrewd operators," as they are indulgently called—have caused it to be bruited about that anyone who works is a fool, since money in lavish amounts can be garnered without it. This is quite an egg-dance through which to pick one's way, and I sometimes think rather wistfully of Thoreau's very practical remark on his deathbed— "One world at a time."

If the question is raised—What is the real nature of American life?—can that question be answered wholly without bitterness? Frankly, no. Not by me. In fact, I do not think it ought to be answered completely without bitterness, although bitterness is very much out of fashion at the present time. The only bitterness which is allowed any

I have very little reliable information, therefore, about my parents and their times; and most of what I know, I have had to deduce from the imprint left on me. Consequently, I should like to leave some kind of record for my little girl, which she could read in twenty or thirty years time, and which might at least partially illuminate for her the climate in which her personality unfolded. Like a good many other people, I find the present-day United States a rather disturbing and unmanageable place in which to live. In two or three decades, I may be unable or unwilling to remember what times were like when my daughter was a small child. Or, on the other hand, I may be sunk in senile delusions—muttering into my beard that those were the good old days.

When my daughter began to talk, it was frequently suggested to me that I should keep a notebook and write down the cute things she said. On thinking it over, however, it seemed to me that the real pay dirt would be to keep a notebook and write down what the grownups were saying. Since this book is being written, in part, for a reader in the distant future, it may be necessary for me to take issue occasionally with some of the popular prejudices which are now very much in evidence on the surface of American life and which I am convinced are going to look utterly foolish in the strong, cold light of history. Her father and I are not averse to being considered intelligent, at some future time, by the young person we are engaged in rearing. In pursuit of this fair guerdon, it may not be possible to avoid stirring up the all-too-easily-aroused hostility of some of our more emotional citizens.

My second objective in writing this book is to try to work out a sort of philosophy of parenthood which could be used as a basis for the numerous decisions that are such an inescapable part of being a parent. Should we, for instance, buy our little girl things we do not approve of just because all the other children have them? All parents are agreed that they would like to bring up their children to be good human beings; but on the subject of what constitutes a good human being, there is at present a great deal of confusion. The Elizabeth Bentleys and Louis Budenzes have received favorable mention in the press as models of deportment; but since it is not going to be made easy for our children to join the Communist Party, they may find it a little difficult to achieve moral stature by leaving it and then reminiscing punitively about their former associates.

In approaching American life, with a view to pulling together out of it some kind of useful and workable philosophy of parenthood—to say nothing of some not-too-taxing method of getting from the cradle to the grave—two subjects are of primary importance. One of these is money, and the other is the middle class. On the subject of money, I am self-confessedly a little dogmatic. What I know about money, I learned the hard way—by having had it. As to the middle class, I was born and raised in it, and all I ask of World History is that I be given the chance to stay in it. I like middle-class decorum and responsibility, and I do

26

not mind middle-class banality (on those occasions when I am perspicacious enough to recognize it).

However, it must be added that I have not always been this effulgently benign about that station in life to which it pleased God to call me. Twenty years ago, when I was first out of college, all the young folks with git-up-and-git were splashing around with joyous bitterness in the wash from H. L. Mencken. When it was the intellectual fashion to take the hide off the bourgeoisie, I went right along with the crowd. I had at that time, toward the middle class, the unfaltering contempt it is possible to entertain only toward relatives. What happened to change my attitude was a circumstance beyond my control. I learned to appreciate the middle class by being unexpectedly pitchforked out of it.

When I was twenty-eight, I had the experience of seeing my first book suddenly become a popular best seller. The book had not been planned or written with that toothsome fate in mind. In fact, it had never been any part of my plan to be a writer at all. All the time I was in school, my English teachers said that I wrote well. When they occasionally mentioned to my father that I ought to be a writer, he said amiably, "There's no money in it." This does not mean that my father was a dull, insensitive clod. Any householder on our street would have said exactly the same thing—and with equal amiability. On the social level where I grew up, writers were people like Dickens and Thackeray, not people one knew.

This was, of course, before the days of the Book-of-the-Month Club, the Literary Guild and the munificent salaries paid to Hollywood scriveners. This was the Andrew Carnegie Benevolent and Philanthropic Public Library Era. In that era, and in the middle class, there was a sort of vague notion that authors lived in garrets on cheese rinds and bread crusts, in return for which deprivation, they became very famous after they were dead. It is not surprising that, with this background, I did not entertain the notion of being a writer. I have always had an unconquerable prejudice against enjoying things posthumously.

After I got out of school, I went to work and in a few years I married. I married an English teacher who agreed with all the others that I wrote well, and this particular English teacher had a piece of equipment not usually vouchsafed to the members of that profession. He had a brother who was a publisher. Very shortly after we were married, my husband got an exchange professorship in England and we went to live in Devonshire for a year. In Devonshire, I soon found time hanging heavy on my hands. The house we rented was very competently taken care of by a maid, and on my dizzy social eminence as a professor's wife, I could not lay hand to broom without ruining the British caste system. (This was prewar England, of course.) Only two activities were open to me. I could take calves'-foot jelly to the deserving poor, or I could ride to hounds. The poor, however, did not seem overly enthusiastic about the ministrations of even the English ladies, and I had a rather clearly defined impression that they could muddle through without me. As to the horses, their ability to dispense with the Frau Professor was in the nature of a fine art. The horses terrified me.

At this juncture, my brother-in-law suggested that I occupy myself by keeping a diary of my experiences in England, and he gave the discussion a serious note by sending me a small advance. It did not occur to me, when I was writing it, that the book would sell. The casual reflections of a somewhat inexperienced young woman, willing to eat her head off any place but in a stable, did not seem very promising commercially. The most I hoped for was that the volume would do well enough so that the publisher would not be out of pocket for the advance. When I returned to the United States and handed in the manuscript, the publisher said he would not be out of pocket. He said the book was to be called *With Malice Toward Some,* and he said that it would sell. In this opinion, he was alone. No one else shared his optimism. But he was right. He was very, very right; and overnight I was catapulted into the ranks of the Terribly Solvent.

This was the American Dream—the sudden, juicy, delicious, enthralling, entrancing, exhilarating acquisition of money. It cannot be said that I rose magnificently to the occasion. I was confused. The Upward Step I had been used to for three generations; but this was not a step—it was a pole vault. I had not gradually built up a public by writing several books over a long period of years. I acquired a public between Sunday night and Monday morning. They had not had any chance to get to know me, nor

29

I them, and the glances I cast in their direction were more than a little uneasy. I did not know just exactly what they wanted of me, but whatever it was, I was pretty sure I could not do it. I knew that as far as writing was concerned, I was a talented amateur and not a professional; but this was a guilty secret I could not induce anyone to share with me. The money *proved* I was a professional. Actually, the money proved nothing except that I was a fool for luck—and it was at this point that I began to get the first intimation of a kind of split or division in American life which is to be dwelt on at more length in subsequent chapters.

My vision at this time in my life was the reverse of hawklike, but I could see that it seemed to be taken for granted that what I had inadvertently accomplished was just a beginning—that having polevaulted out of middle-class obscurity and the middle-class income group, I would bend every effort to make the vault stick. The obvious way to do this was to write a couple of sequels to or variations on the original Opus of Opulence, while my name was still "hot," and ultimately to end up in Hollywood or radio as a prosperous fugitive from self-contempt. But I was written out. The vein had not been very large in the first place, and whatever had been in it was gone. If, as I suspected at the time, I was a one-book writer, I wanted to be the kind of one-book writer who writes only one book.

It was not until some years later that I was able to understand where I got this faintly un-American notion. It came from the way I was brought up. It was, in fact, a cultural heritage, since my upbringing was not a system invented by my mother and father especially for me. A great many other Americans my age and older were reared in approximately the same way. I am not nostalgic for my childhood, but my childhood is certainly nostalgic for me. Owing to my early conditioning, I was unable to reap a big, fat harvest of self-confidence from the "fame" attendant upon the first few months of the book's sale. I kept having an uneasy recollection of the woman who lived next door to us saying—apropos of someone whose name was much in the papers—

> "Fools' names and fools' faces
> Always appear in public places."

Nor could I embark with nonchalant grace upon a new and splendid standard of living, on the assumption that I was so full of successful books, I would have no trouble paying for it. Up to the time of the pole vault, I had had too narrow and self-protective a life to have acquired any children or any debts—I have since relaxed my vigilance enough to achieve both—so the money from my first book was, to me, capital. If there was one thing above another that was bred into my bones, it was that respectable people NEVER go into capital—and this applies to emotional, ethical and spiritual capital, as well as financial.

However, I did go into capital—both kinds. I did all the things the fallible human beings usually do, under pressure. I got a divorce, which is standard. I went to a psychoanalyst—which is standard, too. I listened to all kinds of advice. I had to listen to advice, because I was not writing. I was in the uninhabitable position, for an American, of being a demonstrated money-maker who was not making money. Countless schemes were advanced to make it "easy" for me to write. It was suggested frequently that since my first book had been a somewhat rough-and-ready commentary on the English, the next step was to buy a ticket to some other hapless commonwealth and give it the benefit of my bracing and salubrious remarks. But I did not want to.

People with strict Victorian upbringings—and our tribe is still quite a way from having died out—often tend to be very compliant outwardly and very rebellious inwardly. After my first book came out, I tried—in fact, I put myself through all sorts of agonizing contortions—to do what seemed to be expected of me, as far as writing was concerned. A long time afterwards I realized that for all the seeming docility, I had never, underneath, had the slightest intention of going anybody's way but my own.

In retrospect, it is fairly easy to see what, in the years after my first book was published, I was actually doing and what was actually happening to me. While the book was still fresh in people's minds, I was what is known on Broadway as "a property." In this capacity, I encountered somewhat dramatically certain basic American beliefs about money and human beings which, had I remained in modest circumstances, I would have experienced only as a long, dull ache—a chronic perplexity and a permanent sense of disjointedness. It is to these basic American beliefs about money that I am particularly anxious to draw my daughter's attention.

What I was actually doing, in those years which should —theoretically—have been a time of pure felicity, was hanging on blindly to the notion of writing as a talented amateur. Some dim, unformulated instinct warned me that the status of the average professional writer in the United States leaves a little something to be desired. Either he gets paid too much for writing harmless, lukewarm insipidities, or he tries to tell the truth as he sees it and starves to death—which, of course, removes him from the ranks of the professionals. I wanted to keep my independence—my amateur standing, as it were—and to be free to write or not write, when and upon such topics as I myself should choose. Since I did not, at the time, understand this myself, I naturally experienced a little difficulty in communicating it to other people.

I did not depart from the company of the Terribly Solvent with the same meteoric suddenness which characterized my arrival in that sphere, but I departed. There are various ways, and I used most of them. Also, I married again—on this occasion not in such unchastened ignorance of what holy matrimony requires in the way of give and take. By that time, the United States was at war. My husband was in the Army; the air was full of talk about democracy—a distinguishing characteristic of American society being that it is the most verbal in the world; and I went to work in a very minor administrative capacity at the widely celebrated Stage Door Canteen.

It is possible that there is some one basic factor in American life which would explain why American tension affects the whole population and not just parts of it. There is a hint of such a factor in the circumstance that any given American has to switch back and forth a thousand times a day from the fact of his life, as his five senses know it, to the fiction of his life as it is uninterruptedly portrayed by the press, radio, movies, television and popular magazines. Very few American men know—much less marry—women who look like movie stars. No American of either sex, however, gets much chance to forget what a movie star looks like. The kitchens and bathrooms we see in the magazines and the cinema are stainless, radiant and without flaw. The ones we actually occupy contain the usual sediment of living.

We know of our own knowledge that we are human beings, and, as such, imperfect. But we are bathed by the communications industry in a ceaseless tide of inhuman, impossible perfection. Upon ordinary human beings, this inescapable bath of perfection has one of two effects. Either they feel permanently dejected and unworthy because they have failed to live up to what (they assume) everybody else has been able to live up to, or else they knock themselves out trying to earn sufficient money to command such perfection. In either case, their capacity for enjoyment is irretrievably crippled.

The Stage Door Canteen was a good example of the unnerving discrepancy between the fact and the fiction of American life. Through the mistaken generosity of the communications industry, it was publicized throughout the length and breadth of the land as a place where the celebrities of stage, screen and radio—the Flowers of the Forest—donned percale aprons and made sandwiches for the servicemen with their own hallowed digits. The Flowers of the Forest, however—at least, those of them who would have significance for a Pfc. from Selma, Alabama— do not lead the kind of lives which permit them to put in long hours of humble toil. They move around a lot, and they have contractual obligations.

Actually, the Stage Door Canteen made a very meaningful contribution to American life. It was one of the very few canteens in the country—I know of only two others— where Negro servicemen were entertained on the same terms as white servicemen. The purpose of the Canteen was recreational. So far as Allied victory was concerned, this purpose was something less than the keystone of the arch. The Canteen, however, gave a certain resolute and full-bodied air to itself by entertaining all the servicemen and not just the white ones. To pull off this democratic coup in a prevalently discriminatory Republic was a triumph of no mean proportions. But the public prints, with a few honorable exceptions, ignored it.

I do not mean to suggest that the Flowers of the Forest lay down on the job. They did not. They came when they could, and they very sensibly stuck to their last, which was to be diverting, and eschewed the fabrication of sandwiches. But the AUS was something more than a pint-sized Army, and there were not enough Flowers to go

35

around. My point is not concerned with anybody's individual behavior, but with the fact that the Canteen illustrated, in miniature, the necessity Americans are under to live in two worlds at once. The fiction about the Stage Door Canteen was, at that time, familiar to everyone. The fact—that it was only mildly glamorous, but it was boldly democratic—almost never got into the papers. The people who went there, however—both civilian and military— could scarcely help being aware of the reality, no matter what they might have just finished reading in a magazine or newspaper. The permanent conflict between fact and fiction of which this is an infinitesimal sample means that the people who are caught in the middle—150,000,000 of them—have to live out their lives on permanently unsure ground.

If the Flowers of the Forest did not draw the tea, empty the ashtrays and dance with the lonely servicemen, who did? These indispensable services were performed, nobody will be surprised to learn, by people from the middle class. The entertainment industry, which founded and ran the Canteen, is as well stocked with middle-class people as the Air Force is with ground crews. The vigilant reader has no doubt already noticed that I have made no effort to define what I mean by the middle class, and beyond describing it as a rough grouping which excludes both racetrack touts and cartelists, I do not intend to. Anyone who uses the phrase at all, knows what he means by it and does not want to be told by me. I think, however, I shall not be strewing around any Apples of Discord if I say that the people in the middle class are the people whose formative years were not spent in the corrosive shadow of far too much or far too little money. I have rather lightly waived definitions and delimitations because essentially, being in the middle class is a feeling as well as an income level.

During the four years of its existence, three million servicemen passed through the Stage Door Canteen, so the people who worked there had the opportunity to become acquainted with quite a sizeable handful of their fellow countrymen. In addition, it was more or less inevitable to develop a large correspondence with the servicemen. Since the Canteen was for enlisted men, and was not open to officers, the clientele was not generally the product of what the class magazines call Gracious Living. We got more comic-strip readers than lean-minded strategists. For me, as for many other people there, the Canteen was a developmental experience. I saw more Americans—Caucasian and otherwise—than I had ever seen in my life. It did what all the plans, schemes and conferences—as well as the expensive psychoanalysis—had failed to do. It took me back to writing.

In those days, as I have said, the air was full of talk about democracy. At the Canteen, and so far as the servicemen were concerned, the air was also full of anti-Semitism. About the crudely anti-Jewish remarks tendered me by servicemen, I could not very well take a holier-than-thou attitude. I was myself brought up to be anti-Semitic. In my childhood, Jews were usually referred to as kikes; the remark, "That's the Jew of it for you," was current and prevalent; and it was taken for granted that the Jewish confraternity consisted of a threatening multiplicity of Fagins whose aim in life was to humiliate and destroy the seraphic congregation of the Gentiles. This is what I was taught, and there was no one around who questioned or contradicted. My instructors were not evil people. They were simply passing on what they themselves had never heard questioned. The anthropologists call it cultural conditioning.

It was not until I grew up and moved out into a more complex environment that I met any Jews, and they were so unlike Fagin that I refused to believe they were Jewish. When I could finally be convinced on the point, it was my wont to tell them with sweet condescension that, of course, they were not like the other Jews. Some years later, the pukka sahibs made me buy that one back by telling me with sweet condescension that, of course, I was not like the other Americans. Two factors changed me from being anti- to what I might almost call pro-Semitic. One was actually meeting Jews and having the evidence of my eyes and ears that they were not like Fagin. The other was meeting Gentiles whose opinion I valued and who disapproved of anti-Semitism. My early training in anti-Semitism had been external and more or less automatic, and since I came from the sheltered and non-embittered middle class, I had no pressing emotional reason for clinging to it.

If many of the servicemen were anti-Semitic, I understood perfectly well what had made them that way. I could

38

not, however, be happy about it or dismiss it from my mind. In the ordinary way, one can simply stay away from people whose views produce discomfort. But I was working in a canteen, and I was pinned to the spot. No profounder morality or ethics exist in my character than can be picked up through a routine processing by the Episcopal Church and the public schools of Yonkers, New York, but I felt a deep personal involvement in the meaning of the war. In those days—as we all wistfully remember —we had the type of armed conflict about which it was possible to have a wholehearted, unhesitant, one-piece feeling. Under the influence of such a feeling, I blew the dust off my typewriter and wrote, around the theme of anti-Semitism, a novel called *Some Of My Best Friends Are Soldiers* which I hoped was persuasive rather than angrily didactic. It was quite different in content and attitude from my first book, but there was quite a difference between the peacetime and the wartime world.

Until I worked at the Stage Door Canteen, I was not aware that the position occupied by ethics and morality in the United States is a somewhat odd one. It was to be expected that some parts of the population would be openly hostile to the Canteen's racial equality. What was surprising—at least, to me—was the number of people who were patronizing about it. Theoretically approving, they nevertheless referred to it with tolerant amusement as a "good cause." Up until that time, I had not noticed that when an American uses the phrase "good cause," he invariably condescends to it. The condescension is not

39

studied or deliberate. It is simply that that is the way everybody inflects those words. But what lies behind the condescension? What explains it?

If good causes are mildly amusing with the faintest dash
of contemptibleness, are bad causes admirable? Patently,
no. Or, is the feeling that there should be no causes at all?
This probably comes closer to it. And yet here we all are,
living day in and day out, from one end of life to the
other, in a country whose social structure is mainly a series
of "good causes" elevated into political institutions. One
would think that such a hidden contradiction might cause
trouble. It does. Here is another intimation of a rift or
split in American life—another hint of a universal difficulty which would explain why American tension afflicts
all classes and groups so uniformly.

Apropos of contradictions, it would seem logical that
since I was brought up to be anti-Jewish, I would also
have been reared to take the traditionally unflattering
view of Negroes. But in the sparsely settled suburb where
I grew up, Negroes were so incredibly remote that it was
not necessary to have any opinions or feelings about them
at all. In our neighborhood, nobody had servants. A
woman, generally Polish, who came in once a week to do
the laundry or the heavy cleaning was the extent of our
experience with caste and class. Until I got to college and
took sociology courses, nobody tried to influence me in
any direction at all about non-Caucasians. I was pretty
much of a clean slate. The professors made a theoretical
equalitarian of me, but when I went to the Canteen, I was

like most white Americans in that I had never met any Negroes socially.

If it had been as easy as it sounds to run an unsegregated canteen, there would have been more of them. The pressures of the time were on the side of segregation. To resist these pressures, and to keep on resisting them, required unflagging work by a considerable group of Negroes and whites. It seemed to me unfair that the Flowers of the Forest should get so much credit for being patriotic, while these devoted people were overlooked. There was the further circumstance that in several years of dealing with all shades and brands of anti-Negro feeling, these people had acquired a body of valuable experience. Since there were plenty of other situations where this experience could be used, it seemed too bad for it to vanish into thin air when the war was over. For these reasons, I wrote a third book, *Color Blind,* which was about the Stage Door Canteen's little-known but extremely helpful contribution to the practical ethics of the Western Republic.

Six years elapsed between the publication of my first and second books, and in those six years the United States changed from a nation at peace to a nation at war. In time of war, a nation re-examines its morality. It has to. People do not fight because they have know-how. They fight because they have convictions. The change from peace to war, with its consequent re-emphasis on ethics, explains how I could start out as a carefree humorist and end up writing about anti-Semitism and racial equality.

It is only recently that my wish not to belong to the

41

strenuous circles of the Terribly Solvent has become conscious and articulate. Unconsciously, however, I must have entertained it for a long time. For, if an American writer wants to stay in the middle class, anti-Semitism and racial equality are two subjects that will do it for him. At least, they would some years ago. This was before the time of *Gentleman's Agreement* and the Hollywood movies on race. On the other hand, and fortunately for me, the American spirit is sufficiently troubled and the American ethos sufficiently ingrained, so that I have not up to now had to drop out of the middle class via the trap door at the bottom.

If I were reading this book instead of writing it, politeness might constrain me from asking out loud what exactly happened to the money from that first book; but the question would certainly pass through my mind. The final bit of the glittering pile got used up last year, when my husband and I bought—or, at least, started to buy—a six-room house in the suburbs so that our little girl could have fresh air and a good public-school system. I lived on my emoluments for some years. I did not live lavishly, as lavishness is understood in the environs of Madison Avenue and 57th Street, but I did not put myself to the trouble of saving wrapping paper and the string from packages. I took expensive vacations. There is nothing to make a vacation costly like the fact of having very little, except the Inner Woman, to take a vacation from.

A considerable amount of the money I gave away—a procedure which resulted, in almost every instance, in a measure of bitterness between me and the donees. I have always been rather slow and laborious about sizing up my fellow men, and when I was younger, I was willfully prone to see in people what I wanted to see, and not what was actually there. What went wrong between me and the recipients of my bounty was the circumstance that in a money society, there is one thing you cannot successfully do with money. You cannot give it away. It is too important. My beneficiaries, though convinced that they were delighted with the windfall, were unconsciously ill at ease with themselves for having taken it. As for me, my own unconscious attitude was that I had bought the creatures and they were mine. If anyone had pointed this out to me at the time, I would have denied it hotly. No one did point it out to me, however, because I had money; and when you have money, people are inclined to be a little careful what they say to you. Unpalatable truths take longer to catch up to the well-heeled than to the indigent.

Another large segment of the money I sank into psychoanalysis. It was analysis of the now somewhat obsolete type which a witty friend of mine refers to as Oedipus-Bedipus. At the time, I considered this a very wise and shrewd investment—an opinion in which the analysts heartily concurred—but on looking back at it, I am inclined to think that this was the only part of the money which was really wasted. With the rest of it, I may be said to have purchased experience; and as everybody knows, that comes high.

However, all that is now, in every sense of the word, water over the dam. Currently, I am engaged in thinking,

43

as parents do, about my daughter. In this connection, both money and the middle class must be regarded as subjects of major importance. Money, and its place in the American scheme of things, deserves extended treatment. As to the middle class, when I say that all I want is to be able to stay in it, the wish is accompanied by a considerable apprehension that it may not be granted. As our inflations succeed each other with ever-increasing rapidity, it costs more and more money to stay in the middle class. It is also beginning to take more and more courage to come out in support of middle-class standards of virtue.

We in the United States are now going through the painful process of seeing virtue redefined. Ex-Communists, confessing their own and other people's sins in a blaze of publicity, have taken the place once occupied (with considerably more reticence and self-sufficiency) by Nathan Hale. The middle-class virtues of responsibility, honesty and decorum are passing out of the hands of the middle class. They are not passing into the hands of any other class. They are just passing. Period. Why? Perhaps an exploration of the basic nature of American life, as opposed to the immediately visible surface, will provide an explanation.

The Five O'Clock Shadow
over the United States

———

V IEWED FRESHLY, and as if one had never till this
moment seen it before, the most visible thing about
the United States is that it is a business and "success" society. The point deserves special emphasis. Our Republic
is not a pastoral, not a military, not an agricultural, not a
nomadic, not a clerical, but a business civilization. Nor is
there anything random, casual or accidental about the
United States as a business society. It is thoroughly well in-
tegrated—organized from top to bottom for the maximum
efficiency of commerce and industry, for the maximum
efficiency of making money. We are so accustomed to the
infiltration of business into every single area of human
living that we take it for granted. It seems to us the nat-

ural, the inevitable—indeed, the only conceivable—way for a nation to be organized. How far this is from the truth, however, is evident the moment we stop to reflect that most of the rest of the world does not live the way we do.

There are, of course, other business societies—England, Holland, Belgium and France, for instance. But ours is the only culture now extant in which business so completely dominates the national scene that sports, crime, sex, death, philanthropy and Easter Sunday are money-making propositions. This statement is not to be interpreted as critical or derogatory. In this book, there are no villains, although the heroes may not be just exactly the people we have been asked to regard as heroic. Mechanistically considered, the American business society has been a brilliant and unparalleled success. No view of that society can be valid which does not acknowledge that its distinctive quality— its unique triumph and the thing which sets it apart from other societies—is the actual and potential freedom from drudgery which it has bestowed on the human race. Not that the United States invented the business society. We borrowed it from Western Europe. But with the passion and energy which have always characterized American activity, we developed it to lengths which left the originators gasping.

I am more intense than casual about this semi-divine gift of freedom from drudgery because I am one of its direct beneficiaries. I do my own housework. From 9:00 A.M. to 2:00 P.M. a woman—for whose calm and stable and generous character I can never be sufficiently grateful—comes in to take care of my little girl while I address myself with what scraps of diligence I can muster to my typewriter. This woman does the breakfast dishes, makes the beds and tidies up, but her principal job is to take care of my daughter. The shopping, cooking, heavy cleaning, gardening, mending, moth-proofing and curtain-making, I do myself. (Or leave undone, and fret about.) In these activities, I can count on some slight assistance from my husband. My husband, however, is in the academic world; and although he is not a full professor, he has a full professor's absent-mindedness. His grasp of abstract concepts is superb, but rakes and mops are likely to drop with a clatter from his limp and meditative fingers.

Drudgery—or rather, the absence of same—is part of my daily living. Moreover, I am old enough to remember when people cleaned rugs by throwing them over a clothes-line and beating them with a stick. Cooking on a coal range, boiling clothes in big tubs, making Javelle water to bleach them, heating flatirons, and washing down wood-work with soap which then had to be rinsed off were, when I was growing up, the usual procedures. A day does not pass, therefore, that I do not feel profoundly grateful to the American business society for its production and distribution of the vacuum cleaner, the steam iron, the pressure cooker, the automatic laundry, the home permanent, the electric sewing machine and the luxurious detergent. It is indisputable that the geographical and cultural entity which we call the United States has smoothed the way and lightened the burdens of millions of its own people, and

47

has made physically possible, at least, the amelioration of toil for all the rest of the planet.

But James Watt did not invent the steam engine in order to make a fast buck. And in the United States, the Industrial Revolution began as a creative and continent-conquering impulse. However, it became very evident, very quickly, that there was money to be made from these inventions. A great deal of money. And so business took over. Big Business. The unparalleled dominance of business in American life is not in the least bit affected by the fact that nonindustrial pockets are to be found here and there in the American scene. On his summer vacation, the American sometimes goes to a little fishing village or a farm community or a North Woods settlement, and he suffers a considerable wistfulness as he observes the placid inefficiency—by industrial standards—which characterizes these backwaters. The entertainment industry occasionally selects for the full treatment one of these nonindustrial pockets, on the assumption that the life which is lived there represents the American Way. But the American Way is the business way—the high-pressure, producing-and-consuming, making-a-profit way—and the quiet back-waters provide nothing in significant quantities except grass roots, grass and nostalgia. They have no influence at all on the prevailing moral and psychological climate of the United States, which is the climate of a business society.

So much emphasis is placed, by the American press and radio, on "free" or "private" enterprise and the "independent" businessman, that it is hard for Americans to think of themselves as living in a society at all. The official picture of us is the picture of a collection of invulnerable hermits, piling up money in a state of contented anarchy. However, the picture is not true. Compared to the business societies of Western Europe, ours is a somewhat lawless one. Gangsterism, the Ku Klux Klan, the Vigilantes, the institution of lynching and our universal evasion of the Prohibition Amendment are evidence that our business society has a strain of recklessness not apparent in, for instance, the English business society. In its April, 1948, issue, *Fortune* ran an article comparing English and American banking and pointing rather pridefully to the fact that American banking is more reckless than its British counterpart. But the American business society actually is a society—even though we do not usually think of it that way—and as such, it does the two things that all societies, of any description, do.

For one thing, it moves. It changes. There is no such thing as a society that does not move. Sometimes, like those of the Pueblo Indians, societies move with glacial slowness; but they always move. Yet at this point in American history, both the responsible and the irresponsible press are in accord on one point. They are agreed that from the economic, political and moral standpoint, the United States is a nation in aspic—changelessly, movelessly and immutably good. Or with only such minor and disarming faults as nobody need bother with. Only in the field of mechanical progress—only in the matter of flying

49

from New York to London overnight, or buying I.B.M. machines for the universities to mark the True-or-False tests—is it conceded that there is any movement, or any need for movement, in the American scene. However, the American business society moved from a nineteenth-century laissez-faire economy to the New Deal and the concept of the welfare state. This transmutation took place in spite of passionate insistence by most of the news-gathering industry that it could not and would not happen.

Save for feeling comfortably superior to the people who had to get around in surreys with a fringe on the top, Americans are not encouraged to look backward and digest the past. It nevertheless requires no great, wrenching effort of the intellect to accept the fact that the American business society, like all societies, moves. Also like all societies, it never leaves the people in it alone. Any society —advanced or "primitive"—perpetually influences and puts pressure on its individual members to be something or do something they would not have thought of by themselves. A society has to do this, if it is going to keep itself going as a distinct and recognizable community. Consequently, all societies, with no exceptions, impose a certain degree of standardization upon their component human beings. Some impose more than others, but a certain minimum of regimentation—traffic lights, for instance, for a people that moves on wheels—is necessary, or the civilization could not exist at all.

It is not surprising to find, therefore, that a clerical society puts pressure on its individuals to be religious persons; a traditionally agricultural society influences its individuals to be good farmers; and a business society endeavors to mold its individuals into the pattern of the successful businessman. Thus, a clerical society fosters prevalent attitudes among its people of humility and passivity; an agricultural society turns out more people who are patient and stable than people who are not; and the "typical" man in a business-success society is aggressive, competitive and skeptical. The climate, the general atmosphere, of a business society, therefore, is predominantly aggressive, competitive and skeptical.

To be sure, since the American business society has what might be called a tie-in sale with Christianity, the psychological attitudes it encourages are not so bluntly labeled. They are described as "being on the ball," "going places," "getting ahead," "being a live wire," or being "hardheaded." Sometimes, in fact, American business encourages people to be aggressive, not by celebrating aggression as such, but by heaping scorn on the nonaggressive and noncompetitive. Such persons are spoken of as "never having met a payroll," "muddleheaded," "starry-eyed," and "unrealistic."

The sensitive American may perhaps wince a little at hearing his country described as prevailingly aggressive, competitive and skeptical, but it should be kept in mind that these qualities are not necessarily bad. They are good or bad according to the situation in which they are used. In one context, American aggression, competitiveness and skepticism have produced for the United States a body of technical achievement unrivaled in human history, and that achievement has made life cleaner, safer and more comfortable for millions of people who would have had harder—and shorter—lives before the American industrial machine got rolling. Furthermore, no single person or group of persons, however influential, creates a social climate. Social climates are created unconsciously and unwittingly. Our social climate is created by books, movies, plays, newspapers, gossip, hearsay, radio, ritual, comics, tradition, television, magazines, lecturers, old wives' tales, schools, churches, house organs, parental training, advertising, habit, custom, convention and conversation.

Nobody, literally nobody, rises above the society he lives in. The people who seem to have the most to do with molding American opinion—the so-called policy-makers—are just as much victims as victimizers. In fact, they are likely to be much more the inadvertent captives of the society and its climate than some of the humbler folk whose thinking they aspire to direct. Aggression, competitiveness and skepticism are—in the United States—what the social scientists call prevailing cultural attitudes. Nobody can take much credit for a cultural attitude when it is good, and nobody can be blamed for it when it is bad. Cultural attitudes are almost literally in the very air we breathe. They are as catching as the measles, and they imply no more personal responsibility than is suggested by succumbing to a germ or getting sunburned in the sunlight.

Since American business has always been considered

more or less sacred—by Americans, at any rate—and since at the present time it is regarded as especially blasphemous and "Communistic" to hint at any flaw in it, perhaps I had better assure those of my readers who are getting nervous that I was raised by a Roosevelt-hating Republican and I was myself trained for a business career. My father, though aggressive as a buzz saw and skeptical as Pontius Pilate, was not in business. But he had a profound admiration for the business society's efficiency and, himself endowed with a good head for figures, its arithmetic seemed to him downright seductive. For his first-born, the undersigned, he had even more—and more personal—affection. In consequence, nothing could be more natural than that a business training seemed to him the one sure and certain guarantee of my prolonged security, safety and general welfare.

It was not my own choice. My father handed down to me a considerable measure of his own aggressiveness, but neglected to pass on his mathematical gift. As a young person, I was considerably confused on the subject of what I wanted to be or to do, but the nearest thing I had to a clear idea on the subject was a notion that I would like to teach English. It was the English that attracted me, rather than the teaching—but I did not know that at the time. The idea that I might merely get married and continue the human race was not, in our household, given much attention. My father was all his life wistful about people who had had a chance to get more education than he had, and I was under a good deal of pressure to get high marks in school. When I got them, I became too promising a

53

sprig to be heaved without a second thought into the cistern of domesticity. Marriage was not ruled out, but it was clearly secondary.

On the subject of my career, therefore, I was not extensively consulted. This does not mean that my father wanted to ride roughshod over me, or that he did not have a considerable capacity for being fond of people. He died of arterio-sclerosis—an infirmity in which, toward the end, the mind wanders. I went into his room one afternoon, four days before he died, and said, "Hi, Pop, it's Margaret. Do you know me?"

He shot me a bright glance.

"No," he said, "but I'd like to buy you a beer."

Twenty-five years ago, the idea that "Father knows best" had more currency and more prestige than it does now. Also, my father's grueling early years had left him with a permanent habit of anxiety—some of it wore off, in the later years of his life—and one of the things he was anxious about was his children. My approach to business, therefore, is not the approach of one who ever twinkled in the bright firmament of liberal arts. When I went to college, I took a course called Secretarial Science, and my curriculum was principally concerned with typing, shorthand, office practice, personnel management, statistics, double-entry bookkeeping, business law and similar down-to-earth subjects.

If it has been established, as I hope it has, that this writer is not a "sensitive" artist condescending to business, we may now safely return to the topic of the American business society and the fact that it is undeniably flying distress signals. The tension in American life is a puzzling phenomenon. There seem to be so few visible reasons for it. It is too easy, and it accomplishes nothing, to explain it as based solely on fear that the Russians will drop atom bombs on us. We have the evidence of all our major novelists—Dreiser, Hemingway, Faulkner, Fitzgerald, Sinclair Lewis and Mark Twain—that American tension was a recognized infirmity long before the atom bomb was invented.

From the point of view of its practicing fathers and mothers, our country seems less a nation in aspic than a nation in trouble. Within the past decade, 350,000 schoolteachers have been forced out of the profession by the meagerness of their salaries and in some cases by overbearing interference in their personal lives. To the non-white American, it is cold comfort that the Congresses which failed to pass any civil rights legislation were elected by the secret ballot in a two-party system. (In fact, that makes it worse.)

In the United States, three out of every five marriages end in divorce.* One out of every ten Americans spends part of his life in a mental home. We have the highest crime rate in the civilized world. Every year, 35,000 Amer-

---

* To be sure, this figure is a little swollen by the fact that just as we have six-goal polo players, we have three-divorce movie stars and crooners. But it is significant that some of our most conspicuously successful people—who would seem to have the most reason for being placidly satisfied with themselves and their lives—are dogged in their matrimonial careers by what the poet refers to as divine discontent.

icans are killed—this does not include the injured—in automobile accidents. Juvenile delinquency is with us, as it is not with the other business societies, high on the list of admittedly unsolved problems. The American statistics, in short, which have to do with people's personal lives—as distinguished from the cheerful digits on freight-car loadings—show a disturbing pattern of failure, collapse and breakdown.

Obviously, something is out of kilter. Possibly the typically American characteristics of aggression, competitiveness and skepticism are operating in some area where they are not the ideal equipment. And this is just the case. The sanctioned hostility of the American business society achieved its fullest formulation and acceptance in the days of the robber barons, who said, and got away with it, "The public be damned." But the days of the robber barons are over. This is the era of the smooth operator, the public-relations firm, and the sales-sensitive litany that the customer is always right. (This dictum, coldly considered, is certainly the most "unrealistic" statement the Western Hemisphere has yet produced.) With the advent of mass communications, it became just as impossible for the businessman to be aggressive, competitive and skeptical within the privacy of his business as for parents to bring up their children without intrusion in the privacy of the home.

The result is that the "typical" man in our business society, the successful businessman, has an almost impossible role. He must produce the results of hostility without showing any hostility. In a system loosely described as

56

freely competitive, he must produce results—i.e., financial success—which can only be achieved by unco-operative, self-absorbed devotion to his own advancement; but he must produce these results without at any time appearing to be selfish. The Smiler with the Knife, in short. What happens to the apostle of the business society who has a deficient supply of hostility was poignantly set forth in Arthur Miller's play, *Death of a Salesman*.

The American businessman has been much laughed at and, less frequently, has been regarded with pity and compassion—as in *Babbitt*. But to get to the roots of American tension, it is necessary to view him as being just as much the result of social molding and social pressures as the Aleutian Indian. The Aleut is nudged and jostled by his society into being as competent a hunter and fisherman as the state of his reflexes will permit. But all he has to do to the seals and walruses and polar bears is to kill them. He does not also have to make them like him. By disillusioned young novelists and anguished fugitives from the communications industry, American business is often alluded to as a jungle. The fact is that if it really were a jungle, it might be easier to live in. Pythons are not world-weary, and tigers are not cynical.

When privacy disappears from a society, as it is disappearing from ours, it disappears for everybody—for robber barons, divorcées, parents, and up-to-the-minute businessmen, as well as for professors suspected of having Communist sympathies. The businessman in the business society would seem to be the ideal example of the person well

suited to his job—the round peg in the round hole, in fact.
But even during the business day, the American businessman is compelled to operate under a psychological handicap; and when the business day is over, and he goes
home to "relax" with wife, children and friends, his troubles multiply. When the business day is over, the socially
trained and socially produced businessman must perforce
try to turn off his aggression, competitiveness and skepticism as he would turn off water in a faucet. And, of course,
it cannot be done. The weight and pressure of a whole
society—and a very well-organized one, at that—cannot
be eluded merely by putting on a hat and walking away.

It is perhaps time now to make an explanation which I
ought possibly to have made a little earlier. In this book,
I am consistently using the word "society" where a social
scientist—an anthropologist, a sociologist or a psychologist
—would use the word "culture." The professionals make a
distinction between a society and a culture—the society
being merely the sum total of the human beings in any
given group and the culture being the things those human beings think and say and do. Since I am talking about
what American human beings think and say and do in
their business-dominated country, I should properly refer
to the American business culture instead of the American
business society.

However, when I was growing up, the word "culture"
meant having a sepia photograph of the Coliseum by
moonlight hanging over the umbrella stand in the front
hall; and I have never been able to teach myself to think

of the word in any other way. In the belief that many of my readers may suffer from the same disability, I have chosen to say "society" instead of "culture," although it is technically incorrect. Since it is impossible to be at once scientific and cosy, I have elected to be cosy.

I trust I will be forgiven by the social sciences for this gaucherie—the more particularly since I am very much in their debt. When orthodox psychoanalysis failed to help my insomnia and anxiety, I turned to the public library. In the works—among others—of Abram Kardiner, Margaret Mead, Ruth Benedict, Lewis Mumford, Ralph Linton, Clyde Kluckhohn, Karen Horney, Karl Menninger, Harry Stack Sullivan, Erich Fromm, Wilhelm Reich, Ashley Montagu and David Riesman, I was able to pick up a good many helpful hints and illuminating insights about the forces which gave my life its own particular direction and which may be expected to have their bearing on my little girl.

It is not that all these writers are in sweet, harmonious agreement with each other. They are not. But their writing is a part of that great body of discoveries about what is carelessly called "human nature" which has derived from the pioneering of Sigmund Freud. This body of discoveries has been overshadowed by nuclear fission, but it is nevertheless the proudest and most significant achievement of the last seventy-five or eighty years. It is also the hope—the only hope—for the future. It is a well-known fiction of American life that this is the atomic age. It is a little-known fact of American life that we have in our libraries the definite knowledge of how to turn out good human beings. A little of this knowledge has seeped into the books on child care. A little, but not enough.

That there is nothing in this book which has not already been said in other books, by other writers, will already have become apparent. Scientists, however, are under the necessity—if they are to be clear and true and exact in their results—of developing and using scientific language. The dabbler, the amateur, on the other hand, can afford to be a little more informal; and having myself come many a cropper on things like "acculturation" and "parataxic distortion," I am not inclined to leave them about for other people to stub their toes on.

Very little knowledge of people in other countries is required for seeing that the American family is distinctive in two ways. First, it has more comforts and conveniences than families in other lands, and second, it is more brittle and more fragile—more likely to break under pressure. On the surface, it would appear that modern American inventions have taken family life out of the home and transferred it to more public places. But that is only on the surface.

No civilization yet devised has been able to dispense with the institution of the family. The family can, and does, take on many forms. It was one thing in Sparta—in fact, it was not much in Sparta, and Sparta did not stay the course—and quite another thing in Mandarin China. But in essence, what the family stands for is some kind of clearly defined, well understood, workable relationship between the older people in a society and the younger ones who will eventually take their places. If the race is to continue, if the young of the species are to be raised to maturity, the family in some form or other must exist. It cannot be by-passed.

But the psychological attitudes which are indispensable in the American market place are disastrous to family life. Family life, to be comforting to its participants, has to be based on love, trust and faith. It requires yieldingness, generosity, sympathy, altruism, tenderness—all the qualities, in fact, which lead straight to bankruptcy. Here is the basis of American tension. Here is the reason why bringing up children in the United States, if the parents are conscientious and responsible, is a task pervaded with anxiety and strained uncertainty. American tension is not caused by labor unions, taxes, government spending, Communists in the State Department, nuclear fission, machine technology or turbulence in Asia. It is caused by the fact that the American family is tragically out of gear with the profit structure which has mushroomed up around it. That is why the tension is so general in all classes of society and in people of the most widely divergent views and interests.

Most Americans, without being aware that they have made a choice, follow the directions indicated by the business society and lead family lives of strain, perplexity and unspoken disappointment. (It is, of course, not necessary to be in business to be shaped and influenced by the business society. Merely being alive in it will do the trick.

61

Doctors are frequently businessmen. So are lawyers. So are designers.) Usually, we are not explicitly conscious of the tension in our family lives, but our behavior reveals it. We do not stay home. We stream out in our millions to ball games or movies—where people do not have to talk to each other, and sharing is limited to a bag of popcorn. Or, if we do remain under our own rooftrees, we avoid close family contacts by turning on the radio or television. And we worry about our children.

The heart and core of American chronic unhappiness is the fact that the American family is failing in its job of turning out stable human beings. It is not failing because it has too many machines. It is failing because Americans do not dare to cultivate in themselves those characteristics which would make family life creative and rewarding. To do so, would ruin them financially.

As has already been noted, the business society very often instills profit-making qualities in its members, not by applauding aggression, etc., but by heaping scorn and ridicule on the nonaggressive and noncompetitive. People whose jobs are indispensable, but unlikely to prove stepping-stones to fame and fortune—preachers, teachers, nurses, subway motormen, telephone operators, school janitors, truck drivers, railway switchmen, postmen, milkmen—are spoken of as "public servants," with the emphasis on the "servant." The note of irritated condescension is particularly apparent when members of these callings go on strike. A very good job can be done of bolstering up private enterprise merely by the reiterated assertion that public enterprise is the province of fools and weaklings.

However, the crucial disadvantage of aggression, competitiveness and skepticism as national characteristics is that these qualities cannot be turned off at five o'clock. They can be repressed, of course, after the business day is over. In fact, they usually are. But this means that the people who do the repressing are restless, haunted and uncomfortable without knowing why. They smoke too much, eat too much, drink too much, buy too much, marry too much, take too many sleeping pills and drive too fast. Stark tragedy would be easier to bear. Time ultimately dims the pain of bereavement, but a permanent, undiagnosed tension yields to nothing but death.

As every schoolboy knows, repressed emotions do not evaporate. They merely find their way to the surface in devious and twisted forms. The single most important problem of the American business society can be quite simply stated—though not quite so simply resolved. That problem is the aggression, competitiveness and skepticism which have no place to go after five o'clock, and which spill out in all directions—not only conventionally against Russia and the Communists, but also against liberals, Negroes, government employees, schoolteachers, artists and children. It is a point worthy of special note that this surplus hostility—this unemployed aggression—is directed not only against people who are openly hostile to the business society, like the Communists, but also against people who are merely indifferent to it.

It may seem surprising to mention children as one of

the groups toward whom the surplus hostility of the business society is directed. This does not mean that the individual American is hostile to any individual child. On the contrary, he may be markedly generous in his personal contacts with children. But that does not alter the fact that the position of children as a group, in a commercial society, is not wholly advantageous. A commercial society urges its citizens to be responsible for things, but not for people. It is the unquestioned assumption of a mercantile culture that things need and deserve attention, but that people can take care of themselves and no one else has to be, or ought to be, responsible for their welfare. Senator Taft is perhaps the best-known exponent of this viewpoint; but it does not suffer from lack of articulate supporters.

However, even as thoroughgoing a business civilization as that of the United States produces a certain percentage of people who cannot take care of themselves—not, at least, on the terms dictated by the business society. Such people are taken care of by our business society, because it has no choice. It has no traditional sanction—as the agricultural societies of India have—for letting them starve to death, on the ground that they earned their fate in a previous incarnation. Also, these helpless people are consumers, even if they are not producers as that word is understood commercially, and a business society stands in perpetual need of markets. The people who cannot take care of themselves, therefore, are taken care of by a business society; but they are taken care of grudgingly and with constant

64

complaints about how much it costs and how inferior and undesirable such individuals are.

The largest group of people in the United States who cannot take care of themselves is the children. It would be going too far to say that Americans take care of their children grudgingly, since children are much more appealingly helpless than violin players, the aged or the unemployed. But human relationships in the United States are characteristically tense and unrelaxed; and the parent-child relationship is no exception to the general rule. Nor is a nation which has lost 350,000 schoolteachers in a very strong position to argue that its children are the closest thing to its heart.

Schoolteachers have already been mentioned as one of the groups toward whom the overflow, after-business-hours aggression—the Five O'Clock Shadow over the United States—is directed. Schoolteachers, by the very nature of their calling, cannot have market-place qualities. The successful exercise of their profession calls upon them to go squarely across the grain of the American business society. The nature of their job requires that they cultivate the Bankruptcy Qualities—yieldingness, generosity, sympathy, altruism and tenderness. It is easy enough to recall the hostility of American business to the professors in President Roosevelt's Brain Trust. That hostility is an example par excellence of the business society's reaction to people who use their rich, creamy intellects for noncommercial purposes.

The low prestige of schoolteachers in this country stems

from the fact that children are an embarrassment to a business civilization. A business society needs children for the same reason that a nomadic or a pastoral society needs them—to perpetuate itself. Unfortunately, however, children are of no use to a business society until they have almost reached physical maturity. In a religious society, children can be taught about the infant Jesus almost as soon as they can toddle. In an agricultural society, children can feed hens and herd cattle when they are as young as six or seven. In a nomadic society, children can build fires and skin carcasses as soon as their hands have the necessary co-ordination. But it would be dangerous to have kindergartners playing around in a factory, and youngsters of six or seven would be utterly disruptive in an office.

In non-money societies, children begin to participate in the main job of the society at a very early age. They grow up with it, so to speak, and the goals of the society are always an integral part of their lives and memories. But in a business society, an impassable gulf exists between the child and the functioning adult—which is one reason why parenthood in such a society involves a good deal of uncertainty and groping. We are so used to the absence of children in business that it does not strike us as unnatural. But in terms of a society which is to produce contentment and serenity in its citizens, this absence is more than unnatural—it is highly disadvantageous.

Children are basically more responsive to people than to things, since it is people who take care of them and fill their needs. A business society, therefore, always has in its

66

children a large group of individuals who cannot make money and who do not understand (or want to understand) the profit motive. In short, they are subversives, and they belong right at the head of the Attorney General's list.

In describing children as an embarrassment to a business society, the word "embarrassment" is used advisedly. The children of a business society cannot begin to take part in that society until they are adolescent or even older. What is to be done with them in the meantime? It would seem logical to train them to be aggressive, competitive and skeptical, since those are the qualities they will be expected to manifest when they grow up. But there is not room in the American home—or in any kind of home, for that matter—for those single-minded drives which are so much appreciated in corporations and business firms. So the business society does not give its children a formal and conscious training in the market-place qualities, though a considerable measure of those qualities—an ever-increasing measure, these days—filters across the chasm between the child and the functioning adult. In competitive America, for instance, the ironic spectacle can often be observed of children competing to be happy; and Little Johnnie must frequently accept the obligation to be the most "secure" child on the block, or risk seeing his family fall on their sword.

The children of the American business society do not have a formal and conscious education in profit-making behavior, but a formal and conscious education they do have. And this education involves another one of those hidden contradictions which lie at the root of American tension and chronic anxiety. By a sort of historical accident, the children of the United States—while they are waiting to participate in the business society—are given a stylized education in the Judeo-Christian ethic. They are taught that people are more important than property; they are taught the brotherhood of man; they are taught that blessed are the meek; they are taught that no man can serve both God and Mammon. Nothing more unsuitable for their lives as grownups could possibly be devised, but it was either that or nothing. The business society draws a blank when it comes to children.

To refer to the American child's education in the Judeo-Christian ethic—or Christian morality, or the good life—as "stylized" is to suggest that there is a certain absence of passion in this indoctrination. And there is. The United States is a highly verbal society, and the Judeo-Christian ethic is its official morality; but, as I discovered at the Stage Door Canteen, the United States is also a country where "good causes," "crusaders" and "reformers"—American morality in action, that is—are felt to be embarrassing and slightly ridiculous. It might be anticipated, therefore, that the training of American children in the Judeo-Christian ethic would frequently be dilatory and ineffective and would not make a lasting impression on them.

But children are literal-minded and unskeptical. At least, they start out that way. Furthermore, it takes them a long time to learn how to distinguish between fact and fiction. To the child of tender years, a story he reads in a book is just as much a reality as an experience which actually happened to him. He does not differentiate between the two. A child does not decline to believe in the Easter Bunny for the silly, grown-up reason that he happens never to have seen it. If the presents are on the breakfast table Easter Sunday morning, the existence of the Easter Bunny may be taken as proved.

The ethical instruction of American children is sometimes mechanical, but that does not stop the credulous children from trustingly taking the instruction right into their blood streams. The cynical comment that in the United States, the Judeo-Christian ethic is more honored in the breach than in the observance is the comment of an adult, not of a child. Unlike the children of the so-called primitive societies, who participate in the adult world, the child of a business society does not move in business circles. He has no opportunity to see what his spiritual pastors and masters are compelled to do to Christian ethics when they move into the spinning orbit of business and profit.

Gunnar Myrdal called his famous book on race relations *An American Dilemma,* but *the* American dilemma is that conscience is not formed when one is grown up. Conscience is formed in childhood; and the American conscience, shaped unalterably in the American childhood, gives no spiritual sanction to aggression, competitiveness and skepticism. Quite the opposite, in fact. The American conscience, which is no more wholly escapable than childhood itself, sanctions the Bankruptcy Qualities. Hence business activity—no matter how intensive, expansive and apparently successful—cannot produce in the American businessman that automatic, involuntary self-respect which is the basis of real contentment and relaxation.

Happenings abroad have been allowed to obscure the fact that the central problem of our society is not the atom bomb or the Russians, but the ruinous clash of interest between American business and the American family. The Russians are an outside and complicating factor in a situation which, quite in its own right, is painfully reminiscent of the ignorant armies on Mr. Matthew Arnold's darkling plain. Without at all denying the need for the highest intelligence and integrity in handling Russo-American relations, the fact remains that were the entire Slavic Empire to sink into the sea tonight, our basic internal dilemma would be quite unaltered in the morning.

IV

One Nation, Divisible

————

M Y FATHER was a great admirer of American business, and in this he did not differ from many of his countrymen. He also labored under several illusions about American business—and himself in relationship to it—and he never really took its measure. In this, too, he was by no means alone. When my father finished his training as an architect, he worked briefly for a firm of architects and then went into Civil Service. He stayed in the Civil Service for the rest of his working life—thirty-five years—engaged in the not-too-depressing job of building schools for the children of the city of New York. When he retired, in 1937, he was Deputy Superintendent of School Buildings for the metropolis. This was the highest he could go, since the office of Superintendent was a political patronage plum.

My father's job necessitated his having a great deal of contact with building contractors, and these contacts— combined with the fact that he invested his modest savings shrewdly and with skill—gave him an unshakable impression that he knew all about the American business society. And he did know a good deal about American business in its nineteenth-century incarnation. He knew about the kind of business that was still small enough to be, as it was for him, a matter of personal relationships. But the fact that the business society moves—the fact that the small, independent businessmen he knew both socially and professionally were increasingly ingested by large corporate bodies —this fact escaped him.

While my father was working, he received every year at Christmas a collection of expensive and impressive gifts from some of the building firms to whom he let out contracts. Every year he sent them all back—it being his belief that it was not proper or suitable for a man in his position to take them. I once mentioned this in passing to an acquaintance of mine who is highly placed in the public-relations industry. My acquaintance stared at me slack-jawed and said, "You mean he called that *business*!" My father thought that American business was the greatest thing ever invented, and he esteemed it so highly that he went to considerable trouble to have his older daughter trained to take part in it. But he died without ever having perceived the fundamental irony of his position. The irony was, briefly, that for himself, he turned his back on it. When it came to tossing the total of his working years

72

into American business, the old man wasn't having any.

My father was not a businessman, although he thought he was. He was a man with a clear-cut sense of morality and a knack for totting up sums. It is for the privilege of living for a couple of decades in the same house with that clear-cut sense of morality that I am most deeply indebted to him. My father was, like everybody else, an incomplete man and an imperfect man. In some ways, he failed his children. I wish he had been around more when I was a small child. In his old age, I got to know him very well; but it would have been better for both of us if I had had the chance to know him when he was a young man. Nevertheless, in the kind of job he had, he was indirectly a sort of parent or provider for a great many children besides the actual fruit of his loins; and it was the nature of his job which furnished the firm and solid basis of his self-respect. To his great admiration for American business, I did not, fundamentally, pay much attention. My father was like most parents in that what he taught me, he taught me by the way he lived and not by what he said.

In orthodox psychoanalysis, a great deal of emphasis is placed on the analyst as a parent figure; but the reason analysis was of no help to me was that it had no ethical content. The work I did at the Stage Door Canteen was much more therapeutic. The strict Freudians would say that if I gravitate toward morality like filings to a magnet, it is because of my identification with my father. I am not inclined to dispute the statement. I think, however, I would enlarge it. It is my belief that most people, given

half a chance, also gravitate toward morality like filings
toward a magnet. It is getting half a chance that is the
stumbling block.

The mention of stumbling blocks brings us once again
—by a natural association of ideas—to American anxiety.
Americans themselves freely admit to the tension which
pervades their lives. Even the professionally jubilant advertisements allude to it. But before discussing this tension, it is necessary to make a distinction between American unhappiness in particular and human unhappiness in
general. American unhappiness is chronic, rather than in-
termittent. It was not induced exteriorly by famine or
high explosives, but seems to spring from somewhere
within the American character. And it is inward-turning
and passive. The sufferers (another word that is used advisedly) tend generally to seek relief in such things as spec-
tator sports, drinking or looking at television, rather than
in reading the classics or taking the five-and-twenty-mile
walks with which Mr. Pickwick was accustomed to stabilize himself. From a certain amount of human unhappiness
—death, bereavement, illness—we cannot hope to protect
our children. Indeed, we do not want to. But it is possible
that American unhappiness, if sufficiently dissected and
anatomized, need not be passed on in its gnawing entirety
to the next generation. Some part of it, at least, might
die with us.

The basic cause of American tension is the fact that
Americans are taught as children to give and compelled as
adults to grab. (The latter activity is sometimes euphemis-

74

tically described as being "red-blooded," but it does not always feel that way to the people who have to do it.) This about-face in American life is described by the social scientists as a split in the culture. What that technical phrase really means is that there are two Americas. There is the business America, and that is the one which meets the eye. Then there is what might be called the anti-business America, or the child's America, or the family America, or the America of the Judeo-Christian ethic. The anti-business America is more or less subterranean, but that does not mean it cannot make itself felt. These two Americas are a part of each individual's life, just as childhood and adulthood are a part of each individual's life, and these two Americas are mutually exclusive, diametrically opposed in their aims and interests, and completely irreconcilable.

Disunity in American life is often interpreted as meaning that responsible Republican newspapers do not approve of the Republican Senator McCarthy, or that liberal Democrats are appalled by the Southern wing of the party. But the real disunity in American living goes far deeper than politics, although in politics—as in everything else—it finds a blurred and clumsy expression. The real disunity in American life is the disunity *in the individual American*. We are all accustomed to hearing about something which is called "our way of life." Actually, we have not one way of life, but two. We have not one American society, but two. They are in direct contradiction to each other, but we all have to live both of them. Or, to put it more exactly, we have to keep perpetually switching

75

back and forth from one to the other—sometimes almost from minute to minute.

The rift in American life is not a matter of civil war—of the North and the South facing each other across the Mason-Dixon Line. It is not a matter of joining liberal or conservative political parties. If it were, American living would be comparatively simple. The split in American life is a split in the mind and heart of any given American. The trouble is not that we have two conflicting ways of training people, but that any given American is trained in both ways. The trouble is not that we have two contradictory societies, but that those two societies inhabit the same piece of protoplasm—the same hard-pressed chunk of living tissue.

The perpetual dilemma of the American is that if he follows the rules of the business society, his conscience is uneasy and he feels unfulfilled and harassed; but if he follows the rules of the Judeo-Christian ethic, the business society calls him a subversive—which, in its terms, he is—and throws the book at him. The wonder is not that our business society, queen among business societies, is also the most anxiety-ridden. The wonder is that we have been able to maintain even such a perilous balance as we have. If the hackneyed phrase about "our way of life" means anything, it means that the human nervous system is able to absorb an awe-inspiring amount of punishment without retreating into lunacy.

One has but to look, and the split in American life reveals itself in a thousand ways. It shows up in the fact that

76

our political structure is to a large extent a series of "good causes" turned into law, and yet "good causes" in the United States are popularly regarded with skepticism, condescension and defensive amusement. It is a part of the fiction of American life that everybody likes, respects, enjoys and admires business activity. Whereas the fact is that the American not only receives no direct childhood training *for* business—he actually receives a specific childhood training *against* the qualities which furnish the driving-power of business and "success." As a recipe for nervousness, confusion and nameless dissatisfaction, this situation is hard to beat.

It may seem that a contradiction is involved by affirming in Chapter III that the United States is a business society and stating in Chapter IV that the United States is not a single, but two societies existing (or trying to) side by side. However no real contradiction is involved. Of the two American societies, the business society is the dominant one and the most conspicuous one. It sets the hurried tempo of American living and creates the psychological and emotional climate in which we all move. It does this through the communications industry, which is just that—an industry. And not a cottage industry, either, although it sometimes, with demurely downcast lashes, likes to pretend it is.

The American business society, nevertheless, is confronted for all its dominance by a minority problem of which civil rights for Negroes is only one small part. It is haunted, hamstrung and held back by a collection of minorities, numbering in the tens of millions, who are

77

either dubious about the profit motive or (as is more usually the case) indifferent to it. Chiefest among these minorities are the children the business society must have if it is not to die out, and the women who bear and rear them. Also included in this huge concourse of dissidents and revolutionaries—of people who cannot or will not take care of themselves on the basis of every man for himself and devil take the hindmost—are the aged, the artistically talented, the sick, the schoolteachers, the unemployed, nurses, government employees, social workers, unaffluent ministers of God, self-sacrificing doctors and various modest servants of the common good.

In speaking of civil rights for Negroes as only one part of a huge minority problem, I do not at all wish to play down the crucial importance of equality for all races. My daughter, however, is four years old; and it seems to me quite possible that, if God spares her, she may live to see the day when Negro Americans and Caucasian Americans can inhabit the same pleasant suburbs on terms of amiability. Neither she nor anybody, however, will see the day when the business society is able to assimilate its women and children. The most implacable reality of our time is not the hydrogen bomb, but the fact that children need love. And the only place they can get it, in a steady enough supply to be of any use, is from the indigestible legions of the unbusinesslike.

It is of no consequence whether the United States is described as two societies, businesslike and unbusinesslike, or whether it is described as a business society with a permanently insoluble minority problem. What is important is that nobody likes the business society, because it is not a thing anyone *can* like. The business society can be listened to and obeyed without question—and by millions of people, it is. But it cannot command loyalty, as the Judeo-Christian ethic can command loyalty, because—with its basic philosophy of disguised self-seeking—it is unable to return loyalty.

The crucial question about a business society is not how the square pegs get along—the business failures, the creative artists, the "confused liberals." The crucial question about a business society is how the round pegs get along. There are always square pegs in any society, and they always make heavy weather of it. There are neurotic Hopi Indians and paranoic Bantus. The danger sign in the business society, however, is that the round pegs make heavy weather of it, too. If the business society were a fundamentally healthy arrangement—if it were able to sustain and satisfy people in their total personalities and not just as money-makers—that fact would show up in the statistics. If it were humanly possible to *like* the business society, the businessmen would like it. That liking would be reflected in there being much less alcoholism, divorce, suicide, impaired sexuality, psychosomatic illness and nervous collapse in the upper income brackets than in the lower. In a money society, that is what one ought to find.

But one does not find it. American tension is universal and all-inclusive. It cuts across party lines, income lines,

79

color lines, geographical lines and every known classification of the American people. The square pegs are afraid of the business society—and with reason. It is punitive. Heretics, rebels, dissidents and people who ask embarrassing questions, it serves up to columnists on the half-shell. As a rule, and with some notable exceptions, the square pegs either cower in silence or make unwilling and shamefaced attempts (like other men, they have dependents) to appease the business world.

But the square pegs are not important.* It is not fair to judge a business society except in terms of the businessmen it aspires to, and does, produce. It is not fair to judge a business society except in terms of the round peg in the round hole—the businessman in the business society. And if the square pegs are afraid of the business society, the round pegs are afraid of finding out they are afraid of it. The cruel burden of the round pegs is that they can never rid themselves of the *temptation* to be square pegs. This is the split personality which a split society—two societies masquerading as one—inevitably produces.

It is part of the fiction of American life that business is a very satisfying and rewarding activity. It is a fact of American life that American business has produced in a good many citizens of the United States a considerable measure of bitterness, disappointment and disillusion. I cannot claim to be one of the disillusioned ones, but there were certainly two things I did not learn in my comprehensive and well-planned business course. They took me by surprise.

* Save that there are so many of them.

80

The first was that there was going to be a depression. I was released from the groves of Academe in 1930, and at that time Ph.D.'s from the Harvard School of Business had the jump on me in the coveted chance to get a job emptying wastebaskets. With some brief but scary intervals, I managed to keep working during the lean years; but my first impression of the American business society was not that it callously failed to appreciate sensitive literary folk. When first it dawned upon my ken, American business was having a little trouble absorbing even the unlettered, unlyrical business folk like me. I remember that during the cold winter of 1931, it was my custom to buy an apple every morning on the way to work from one of the unprosperous fellows who sold them in those days. But after a few weeks, the personnel manager asked me not to bring the apple into the office. It was, he said, bad for morale.

A second thing I did not learn in my business course was that if I were going to be a "success"—and in the United States, who wasn't?—I would have to compete with males as a male. From this unequal contest, I shrank. I have the usual American sympathy *for* the underdog, but no particular yearning to *be* one. In addition, my genes, chromosomes and hormones—to which I am pathetically attached—set their faces firmly against any such abdication. My business training and experience proved, eventually, valuable—though not quite in the way my father had anticipated. They gave me a permanent skepticism about the phrase, "confused liberal." In the springtime of my life, I saw so many confused conservatives as to have formed

81

the impression—never since moderated—that confusion is basic and fundamental in American life and not to be laid at the feet of any one school of political thought.

The basis, then, of American tension is the split personality from which we all unavoidably suffer. Two conflicting societies, officially designated as one, inevitably produce human beings who must willy-nilly try to go in two directions at once. The question which naturally arises is how we happen to have gotten into this dilemma in the first place. If we now have two societies, instead of one, it is because the United States has not always been, as it is today, a country organized extensively and intensively for the pursuit of trade, commerce, money and profit.

Until the beginning of the Industrial Revolution, the United States was a predominantly agricultural society. As such, it gave a good deal of leeway and freedom to the ancient and traditional morality which the settlers and colonizers brought over from Europe with them. This does not mean that the early Americans were better people than we are. They were not—as Indians, slaves, indentured servants and certain ill-fated citizens of Salem, Massachusetts, could very well testify. To say that the Judeo-Christian ethic comes down to us from our agricultural past is not to suggest that that past was idyllic and pastoral. On the contrary, it was in many ways harsh and brutal, and very little research is needed to uncover Colonial customs —flogging and the stocks, for instance—which by our standards are needlessly cruel. The early Americans were not better people than we are. There were, however, fewer of them; they were not mechanized; and they lived in an agricultural society. (Despite certain commercial centers on the Eastern seaboard, like Salem and Boston, the prevailing occupation of pre-industrial America was the transformation of the wilderness into tilled land.)

In an agricultural society, the family tends to be larger and more interdependent and close-knit than the family as we know it today; and the other social groups—the church, the city, the town meeting, the market—are smaller and more personal than our social groups. Relationships between human beings are more intimate. In present-day, mass-production America, the opinions we form of our great lovers or our great industrialists are not based on personal contact with them—or even on contact with people who know them well. What we think of our great lovers or our great industrialists is decided for us in the paneled offices of public-relations firms or over the luncheon table in tensely sophisticated restaurants. Practically speaking, the man of distinction in an agricultural or frontier society must try to *be* good; whereas in a business society he need only *appear* to be good. It seems like an easier goal, of course, but it sometimes appears to leave the conquistadores spitting out ashes.

In our inherited morality—and in sharp contrast to the business society—protection of the weak is a cardinal point. In a frontier society, such as ours used to be, protection of the weak is important. It means, in fact, protection of almost everybody, since, confronted by untamed Nature, all men are to some extent feeble and "unbusinesslike."

It may seem somewhat startling to mention protection of the weak as having been important on the American frontier, since a good many history books, orators and editorial writers create just the opposite impression. Kit Carson, Daniel Boone, and Lewis and Clarke are often mentioned as the spiritual godfathers in aggression of the modern American businessman. But frontier America was the godfather of business America only in so far as it took away from the aborigines the land which was rightfully theirs. The wagon trains, on the other hand, in which the early Americans went West, and the various "bees" at which they built houses and cleared land for each other were examples of co-operative, not competitive, behavior. The American pioneers had a simple choice—co-operate or die.

American morality, therefore, had a chance to get established in the ante-business United States because in those years of our history protecting the weak was a useful way of behaving. A second reason for the establishment of this morality was that, in pre-business America, people had to be dealt with as individuals, since there was no way of reaching them in the mass. (Not, that is, as we understand reaching people in the mass.) This does not mean that agricultural America, in treating people as individuals, always treated them well. It did not, by a long shot. But it had no way of pressuring or manipulating people, sixteen or eighteen hours a day, to make them behave like part of a market, or part of a labor supply, or part of something called "public opinion." This enforced emphasis on individuality provided a favorable climate for the Judeo-Chris-

84

tian ethic, which views man not as a consumer, but as a total, twenty-four-hour personality.

It is the twenty-four-hour aspect of living which accounts for the fact that Christian morality, before the Industrial Revolution, had a chance to get itself embedded into American tradition and, to some extent, into the Declaration of Independence and the Constitution. In an agricultural or a pioneering society—or even a trading society based on wind and sail—the working day does not end at five o'clock. The distinction between work and non-work is not as painfully sharp as it is in our business society. Home and livelihood, instead of being miles apart both geographically and emotionally, are often combined. Hence the pre-business Americans adopted the Judeo-Christian ethic as the official American morality, not because their Nobility Quotient was higher than ours, but because that ethic fitted into the way they had to live.

It is still our national morality, although the United States is now a business and not an agricultural society. However, so far from dovetailing with the business society and thriving in its climate, it is at loggerheads with business. Why, then, when the United States evolved into a business society, did not that business society develop its own ethic? Because it could not. One needs ethics to live, because living is an around-the-clock proposition, but one does not need ethics to make money. In fact, they are a handicap. The business society is interested in training its citizens to make money, and, in this objective, it is often successful. Many of them do make money, and the ones who do not obligingly regard themselves as failures who have wasted the precious gift of life. But if we are to have a national morality at all—if we are not to descend into a bottomless pit of anarchistic self-seeking—then the only morality available is the leftover morality from our agricultural past. In other words, we are compelled to have not one, but two societies.

If the child of a business society could live in the business world—if it were physically possible for children to start dabbling in business at the age of four—the Judeo-Christian ethic would probably have disappeared from the United States many years ago. However, the American business society would have disappeared with it. Without family life in some more or less stable form, no society can keep going. Fortunately, it is not possible to be an American businessman without first having been a child. Hence, our official national morality has been able to function as a brake on a business society which—for all its very real contribution to the lightening of mankind's burden—has a strong drift toward suicide.

In speaking of ethics and morality, I recall that I have mentioned my father as a man with a clear-cut sense of both. I should not like to give the impression—as to some of my readers, I might—that this meant he was an unlikable person. Indeed, quite the opposite is true. People liked him because they knew where he stood. There was no shabby compromising, no ambiguity and no tattletale gray about him. He was all black and white. In the kind of job he had, he could afford the luxury of being forthright; and he was supremely competent in his job. Since he had nothing to hide and nothing to defend, he was free to be friendly and outgoing to his fellow human beings. Not only was he generous in giving compliments, but—what is rarer—he was poised and dignified about receiving them.

Like all Americans, he lived under tension. His harrowing adolescence had left its mark on him, and he was definitely inclined to irascibility. But although "Civil Service" is usually construed to mean a timorous drudge—burrowing like a mole toward the inglorious haven of a pension—my father was an extremely self-confident person. Oldsters will remember that during World War I, there was such a burst of feeling against the Germans that German music was not played by orchestras, and people whose names had been Schmidt hurriedly changed them to Smith. My father's father was of English ancestry, but his mother was an Austrian; and his mother had given him the Christian name of Reinhold. During the height of the anti-German feeling, a committee of citizens called on my father and suggested that if he wanted them to believe in his patriotism, he would have to change his name from Reinhold to Reginald. My father told them to go jump in a lake; and although the committee had behind them considerable of the popular feeling in our community, they shambled uncertainly out of our house like a flock of sheep. My old man was not the Reginald type.

This does not mean that he was fearless. He knew what it meant to be afraid. He was desperately afraid of poverty and deprivation. He was afraid—until the time came for him to do it—of dying. And one of my most vivid memories, as a small child, is of seeing him go past my bedroom door one night when we had all been awakened by a noise in the cellar. The old man was not approaching the problematical situation below stairs with eagerness and joy. Will power conquered natural prudence; but not, as I could tell from his face, by a handsome margin. (It turned out there was nothing and nobody there, and we never did find out what had disturbed us.) I have seen fear in my father's eyes—and I probably did not see it as often as it was there.

By the Freudian analysts, Reinhold was lightly brushed aside as an anal-erotic; and it is certainly true that he was grimly methodical, compulsively neat and a sufferer from constipation. But that was by no means the whole picture of the man. He would not take presents when he was working, but he felt free to take them upon the occasion of his retiring. And when he retired, he received so many presents that the American Gothic house he bought for his declining years is still cluttered with the tributes—some of them in touchingly bad taste.

I have often wondered about the really surprising outburst of affection and gratitude which my father received at the termination of his working life. I finally concluded that what lay underneath it—aside from his passion and energy and slightly rhetorical Victorian charm—was the fact that he had mastered the fine old art of taking responsibility. He was utterly trustworthy. He knew—without knowing that he knew it—that there are times when you have to do the right thing, no matter what it costs, simply because the right thing has to be done. For this kind of reliability, people are intensely grateful.

My father, though staunchly provincial in his tastes and arbitrary in his morality, was inclined as a general rule to like his fellow man. But Franklin Delano Roosevelt he loathed. Like many other Republicans, he voted for Roosevelt the first time. But my father had had it hard about making a living, and the genial way in which F.D.R. dispensed the public funds caused him almost physical anguish. Since I voted for Roosevelt all along, the relations between me and my father were not always the relations of two fluting, cooing doves. He disliked Heywood Broun, too, and although I never had the privilege of meeting the late, great columnist, my father always referred to him irritably as, "Your friend, Heywood Broun . . ."

However, Reinhold had a clear-cut sense of morality; and what impressed me most about that sense of morality —of what is right and what is wrong, and doing good for others—was the fact that it paid off. He was pleased and surprised by the financial success of my first book. Nevertheless, despite his admiration for American business, he never had the slightest interest in the fast buck. The slow buck was his line of country. It was the second and third books, with their definitely ethical slant, which made him feel that he had reared a child he could afford to respect.

Because of the fashion in which he had instinctively

89

brought up his children, my father never had in his family a Hollywood swimming pool which he could either adjust to or stay away from. That I was able to get to know him well, in the closing decade of his life, was partly due to the fact that he and I were living on approximately the same economic level. He had worked his way up to the middle class, and I had worked my way back down to it. It is a source of great regret to me that I did not get around to parenthood in time for my little girl to have a chance to know him. He had a quality which is, I am afraid, disappearing from the American scene. It is a quality which it would be well worth the trouble to try to recapture. He had style.

When my maternal grandmother was a little girl in Scotland, she used to have to recite a poem which began:

> "Satan is glad
> When I am bad,
>
> "And hopes that I
> With him will lie,
>
> "In fire and chains
> And dreadful pains,
>
> "With many more
> Who cursed and swore,
>
> "And all who did
> What God forbid. . . ."

This formidable nursery rhyme went on for pages and pages, and my grandmother and her brothers and sisters had to repeat it from memory every Sunday, in the intervals between attending three church services and eating scratchy meals of cold food. (The Sabbath could not be defiled by lighting a fire.)

Most people would probably agree that this hair-shirt approach to a somewhat gangsterish Deity scarcely deserves the title of an ethic. The official national morality of the United States of America—the Judeo-Christian ethic, as the phrase is used in this book—means a certain kind of behavior. It means behavior based on the belief that people cannot always take care of themselves, and that they are not necessarily inferior and valueless if they cannot. It describes, for example, the action of a group of high-school teachers—in a town near New York—who opened a teen-age civics club to Negro young people, in spite of the implacable hostility of certain influential groups in the community. Since these teachers had tenure, they could not be dismissed, but they were stripped of all the after-school activities at which they had been accustomed to earn a little money to supplement their meager incomes. It describes the conduct of the young white people who co-operated with the teachers in spite of strong pressure put on them by some of their parents to remain inert and passive.

It describes the doctors who eschew lucrative practices and devote themselves to the crucial, but poorly paid and unappreciated, field of public health. It describes the minister and his wife in Hood River, Oregon, who fought a winning battle to compel the American Legion to put back on its Honor Roll the names of the Japanese-American soldiers who fought in World War II. It describes the men and women who have held themselves responsible for trying to get wages of more than twenty-five cents an hour for Spanish-American agricultural workers. It describes the career of Lillian Smith, who gave the cachet of good breeding to morality in the South. It describes the people who accept the low salaries and near-opprobrium of government service in order to have a sense of contributing to the American nation.

It describes my Uncle Will, who spent fifty years reinvigorating failing Episcopal parishes in upper New York State where "the hungry sheep looked up and were not fed." It describes the social workers who have been fighting for recognition of the eight million healthy Americans who are unemployed because they are over fifty-five years of age. It describes the hardy souls who tried to protect the forests of the Alaskan Indians from the American timber interests. It describes a great many schoolteachers and workers in the P.T.A. It describes the tenacity of Laura Z. Hobson in writing *Gentleman's Agreement,* although the smart money said it was a quixotic project. It describes Miss Frieda Hennock, a member of the Federal Communications Commission, who singlehandedly won twenty-five per cent of television facilities for the education of American children. It describes the Secretary of State who would not turn his back on Alger Hiss. It describes, in short, a great deal of uncelebrated—and sometimes markedly unpopular—American behavior which is nevertheless one half of our divided society.

This book has no villains, but the foregoing examples no doubt illustrate that its heroes (as previously indicated) may not be quite the people the American public has been invited to consider heroic. From the above-mentioned list, one thing is readily apparent, and that is, that the keystone of the Judeo-Christian ethic is action, not passivity. That ethic—trustingly accepted and never wholly shaken off by the American child—was designed as a guide to actual behavior. It does not mean talk. It does not mean good intentions. It does not mean good will. It does not mean reading newspaper editorials. It does not mean full-page, semi-sacred advertisements which can be taken off the income tax. To define the Judeo-Christian ethic satisfactorily, it is necessary to consider the real nature of an ethic, and the real nature of an ethic is that it does not become an ethic *unless and until it goes into action.*

The business society, like the American ethic, also means action and not passivity. Here, one would think, is ground for some sort of compromise. But no compromise is possible, because two totally different kinds of action are meant. Action, in our traditional morality, is directed toward the welfare of others. Action in the business society is directed toward one's own profit. When the Judeo-Christian ethic goes into action in the midst of a business society, it always, ultimately, means money out of somebody's pocket. Out of the stockholder's pocket. Out of the

93

taxpayer's pocket. And money out of pocket in a business society is—for reasons to be discussed in the next chapter —an alarming experience, emotionally.

For this reason, and in spite of the fact that the Judeo-Christian ethic is one of our two American societies, no solution to our split personalities can be looked for in regular attendance at church. The American—wishing to be a decent fellow, but afraid of what will happen to him if he declines to put his whole soul into earning money—sometimes turns with his problem to organized religion. But organized religion, in a dominating business society, can do only one of two things. It can either assure the communicant with uneasy bluster that God Himself likes money —a theory which convinces nobody—or it can give him an apologetic, halfhearted invitation to go out and get himself crucified.

If the American were really to do on Monday what he has been reminded of on Sunday—to sell what he has and give to the poor, for instance—he would lose most, if not all, of his friends and acquire a set of vindictive enemies. Furthermore, his gesture would in all likelihood be wasted. Crucifixion is beyond most people's capacity. It takes a unique personality to make it meaningful, so that the sacrifice does not run uselessly down the drain. The business society can be successfully defied only by people who have no illusions about it and who have something good and solid to take its place. Most Americans are temperamentally unsuited to crucifixion and most Americans, through no fault of their own, have a good many illusions

94

about the business society. Hence, to say that organized religion is of little help to us in our dilemma is only to repeat a point which cannot be too much emphasized—i.e., that the split in our society is not a split between clergy and laity any more than it is a split between conservatives and liberals.

It is a split, produced by contradictory pressures, in the single human being—and the clergy are no more exempt from it than anyone else. To run a church, you need real estate; and to possess real estate in even the most modest way is to operate within point-blank range of the business society. To have a church, you need a congregation; and if the congregation is being urged during every waking hour to make and spend money, you cannot very well tell them, literally, to go to hell and restrict your preaching to cherubim and seraphim.

The Judeo-Christian ethic is not nowadays administered to children in quite the hearty doses in which my contemporaries and I received it thirty or forty years ago. But those people who were instructed in it twenty or thirty or forty years ago are still alive. They are still voting. They are still reading the newspapers. And they are suffering an agony of confusion and bewilderment because the middle-class virtues of honesty, decorum and responsibility are disappearing with what seems like incredible speed.

In a recent profile in *The New Yorker,* President Truman was quoted as saying that the Truman Committee, which was said to have saved the taxpayers fifteen billion dollars, never released anything to the papers until it had

95

been established with certainty that no innocent citizen would be maligned. Any thinking we do on behalf of our children is a waste of their time and ours unless it is done as honestly as possible; and honesty compels us to admit that in the ten years since the Truman Committee, we have had a change of moral climate. Maligning innocent citizens has become an established American institution. False charges are made; false charges are printed in the newspapers; false charges are read by the newspaper readers. Even if nobody believes them—and some people do— they are still there in black and white, a bizarre and tax-free legacy for the adolescents and the young people.

Although they do not phrase it in quite the same way, both the professional philosophers and the man in the street are agreed that the most invulnerable bulwark against Communism is a solvent, self-respecting middle class. The American middle class, however, is at the moment groggy and reeling because its old landmarks of morality have disappeared into a murky gloom labeled, ironically enough, "security." Leaving aside the question of who is going to be safe from what, when Senator McCarthy enjoys no less imposing a sponsor than Senator Taft, a still more urgent question presents itself. At least, it is more urgent to parents. That is the question as to why our traditional notions of ethics and justice and fair play went down with such a splintering, powdery crash under what appeared to be pressure from the Communists.

The answer may very well be that the Communists did not have much to do with it. The answer may possibly be closer at home than we imagine. The answer may lie in the fact that all societies move, and business societies, because of their relentless emphasis on "getting ahead," move very fast. The answer may possibly be found in the fact that "our way of life" is not one way of life, but two. The American ethic and American business have always been diametrically opposed and utterly hostile in their views of life and human nature. However, while we still had some surviving remnants of our agricultural past, it was possible to evade or sidestep the clash between them. The American could get through life somehow—give a little, take a little—without being caught squarely between the upper and the nether millstone.

Economists of every shade and stripe, however, are all agreed that a business society must constantly expand. And the more the business society expands—the more it invades the newspapers with advertising, the home with television and the movies with dehumanized heroines—the closer it comes to a knock-down-and-drag-out fight without official morality. And, as a matter of fact, that is exactly what is happening. What appears—to us who are older, at least—as a horrifying decline of public and private morality is in essence a death struggle between the business and the anti-business America. The real nature of American life, as distinguished from the fictional version of it, can be summed up in a single sentence. The American business society, with its relentless pressure on people to be aggressive, competitive and skeptical, has expanded to the point where it must either wipe out the Judeo-Christian

97

ethic or submit to such drastic modification, in terms of ethics and compassion, that it will scarcely be recognizable.

This book is being written in the hope of evolving some kind of philosophy of parenthood which would make the job of raising a child, in these disturbing times, a little more definite and purposeful. In any such philosophy, the first thing that has to be taken into consideration is the fact that the United States is blanketed with an exceedingly dangerous illusion. That illusion is the idea that the American business society and the American ethic have somehow been harmoniously blended into a single society which we can refer to as "our way of life." No such blending has ever taken place. Nor will it. The American business society has not one enemy, but two—the Communists *and* the Judeo-Christian ethic. With what amounts to a genius for confusion, it treats them both as the same thing.

By lumping its two enemies together as identical, American business is wreaking an immensity of havoc on one of them. The Communists do not suffer when compassionate and ethical behavior is described as "left-wing," "radical," "socialistic" or "Communistic"; but the anti-business America is in a state of rout and panic because anyone who has ever lifted a finger on behalf of the square pegs is in danger of losing his livelihood. The point has been firmly established—not to everybody's satisfaction, but beyond any single man's power to buck it—that having had left-wing sympathies during the Great Depression means a permanent corruption of character.

Under the guise of rooting out corrupt character, the

American business society is rooting out character altogether. This, naturally, cuts the ground right out from under the Judeo-Christian ethic, whose stock in trade is character—and, moreover, character capable of sympathy and of action. Furthermore, what might be called our un-Communist scandals would seem to indicate that the business society is succeeding in its blind but purposeful attempt to wreck the American ethic and to establish the United States on a basis of all-out cynicism. It is anybody's guess whether or not we will be able to contain Communism; but the basketball fixes, the revelations of the Kefauver Committee, and the sale of narcotics to teen-agers indicate with dreadful clarity that we have not been able to contain the profit motive.

This does not mean, however, that the business society is composed of evil men. It is not. The business society is composed of harried protoplasm. That protoplasm manages to struggle through what is called the business day (though not exactly with what William Blake describes as "comfort in morning, joy in the noontide"); but it is caught off base by the fact that there is no such thing as the business night. To this awkward situation, different businessmen react differently. Some of them have nervous breakdowns; some of them muddle bravely along in a sort of partially paralyzed way; and some of them retreat into reckless and destructive cynicism.

It certainly cannot be said that cynicism in the United States is on the wane. The basis of cynicism, however, is not innate evil, but ignorance—sheer, genuine, three-ply, naïve, stumbling, fumbling ignorance. The particular ignorance which is involved in present-day American cynicism is just this: That the profit motive, carried to its logical conclusion, can end up in nothing but the destruction of American morality. But when American morality goes, the American business society goes with it. This, much more than the Russians, is the taproot of that cold fear with which every man and woman of us is so horrifyingly familiar.

However, there may be, in our present unenviable situation, a silver lining. If there is one, it consists of the possibility that American business may not have made, under the surface, as much headway against the American ethic as at first appears. The business society is not really equipped for the long pull. It has certain fatal weaknesses. While it gives the rules for victory—in terms of "getting ahead"—it provides no armor for defeat. Indeed, as many a successful businessman has found to his sorrow, it drops no hint as to what to do with the victory once it has been attained. If the business society is to survive, the businessman who is its ideal product has to be made of self-reproducing protoplasm. But in his capacity as self-reproducing protoplasm, the business society wants no part of the businessman. Considered in terms of women, children and the family, the business society's chances for survival are not impressive. The Judeo-Christian ethic, on the other hand, does not need our or anybody's business society for its continued existence; and the Judeo-Christian ethic will not touch the profit motive with a twenty-foot pole.

The rift in a split society has to be healed in the area where it originally takes place. And that area is in the mind and heart and feelings of the single American—"businesslike" or "unbusinesslike." We have no handy or convenient factions with which we can associate ourselves. Clergyman and layman, liberal and conservative, businessman and child are all in the same boat—the S.S. Schizophrenia. But in our children, the sentimentalists say, we have a chance to start all over. And we do—provided, of course, that we blaze a trail for them by at least making a stab at starting all over ourselves. In this connection, the first question that needs attention is the issue on which the business society and Christian morality are hopelessly and incurably divided—the question of money.

V

The Eggcup Civilization

———

MY LITTLE GIRL is going to have it repeatedly suggested
to her—by every form of hint, inflection, innuendo
and implication in the language—that money is the Great
Simplifier. Against that treacherous dogma, she will need
a little armor. I cannot provide it for her except out of my
own experience. For me, the money which accrued from
my first book was in a manner of speaking a simon-pure
event. Since I was not in debt and had no dependents, it
provided no exquisite sense of release from pressure. Nor
did it represent the consummation of ambitious strivings.
While I had been reared, like all Americans, to be successful, the goal had been a temperate and middle-class
success and nothing—to use a very much overworked word
—fabulous.

This manna from heaven, consequently, could not have

landed with its lethal kerplunk on anyone less prepared for it. Mine is a plodding rather than a towering intellect, so it took me more time than it should have, perhaps, to find my way around the leafy little bower of greenbacks into which I had tumbled. The first thing I noticed was that the possession of money, in a business society, relieves one of the necessity of ever having to explain one's self. The mere clothes you wear—not to mention the restaurants you eat in or the vacations you take—tell people all they want to know about you. It is a great economy of effort; but the drawback is that explaining one's self to people —especially if the dumb brutes show any sign of catching on—is one of the more entrancing of life's experiences. There is nothing like mink for enforcing anonymity.

A second thing I began to notice—rather more slowly —was the inseparability of money and guilt. Only those rare Americans who were brought up as Druids or taught to worship Pallas Athene have escaped hearing that the rich man has as much chance of getting into heaven as the camel of going through the needle's eye. When I was a child, this stern mandate used to worry me. I wanted to be rich, since it was my understanding that rich people did not have to save for a rainy day or go without things in order to go to college. But I also wanted to go to heaven. When I was a child, however, it was not an immediate problem; and I figured that the powerful grownups prob- ably had an answer to it, since they had an answer to everything else.

But a thing exists, the philosophers tell us, in terms of

103

its opposite; and the presence of money inevitably suggests the absence of it. It is banal—it is extremely banal—to say, "Why should I be drinking Martinis in Twenty-One when small children are getting rickets from not having orange juice?" It is banal, but it is also inescapable. One can reason, if one wishes, that the adult poor are only getting what they deserve; but that still leaves the unnerving possibility that some day, some way, somehow, one is going to be held responsible for their children. Even when money is deliberately set out for and purposefully earned, the underprivileged children keep rearing their disturbing heads. In our country—all the talk about free enterprise, individual initiative, risk capital and the survival of the fittest to the contrary and notwithstanding—money and guilt are Siamese twins.

While my first book made a good deal of money, it did not make enough for me to live on opulently for the rest of my life. What I had achieved was not money, but the access to money—beach rights on a river of gold. Very few Americans live in the eerie world of permanent wealth so acutely portrayed by Scott Fitzgerald. But a comparatively large number of Americans get the opportunity to dabble in the stream. And for any good, red-blooded citizen of the United States, the beach rights ought to be enough. His own power and drive and energy and American training can be counted upon to do the rest. I had, therefore, the entrée to money. I had a "name" and it could be traded upon. At least, it could if I kept it in the newspapers where people would see it. Also, presumably, I had a talent—and the fact that it was a hesitant, rather self-indulgent, one-cylinder talent was something I soon learned not to mention. That was heresy. It did not strike the right note of cheery self-confidence.

Fourteen years have passed since I woke up one morning to find myself in the chips. After such a long interval, it is hard to write about the experience without sounding as if I were, at the time, both shrewd and composed. As a matter of fact—and for the benefit of my daughter, who is supposed to be finding out what her folks were really like, in their unbelievable youth—I was confused, disoriented and rudderless. The confusion would have been evident to any moderately perceptive observer, but moderately perceptive observers are not what the freshly successful are usually surrounded with. This is not to say that I was homeless. It was not that I had no place to go. Quite the contrary. The Terribly Solvent welcomed me with open arms. In a business society, the more solvent you are, the guiltier you have to feel about the shabby, flabby two-year-olds who are not yet out on a paper route. Hence, new recruits to the Society of People Who May Possibly Be Heels are accorded a more than royal reception. The saints may rejoice over a repentant sinner, but it is not a patch on the rejoicing of sinners upon acquiring a new transgressor.

The Terribly Solvent demanded, naturally, that I should go on being terribly solvent. Or, to be more exact, they demanded that I should *want* to go on being terribly solvent. Because they are not ungenerous people, they would have forgiven and pitied me if I had tried and failed. But one, and only one, responsibility was dumped into my lap. I did not have to be beautiful. I did not have to be a clear thinker. I did not have to take an interest in politics. I did not have to be kind to animals. I did not even have to write well. But when it came to maintaining my status as a "success," I had to be in there giving it the old college try. However, like others of my fellow-countrymen who had old-fashioned, non-permissive upbringings, I am somewhat allergic to pressure. It is sometimes enough to be told I have to do something, for me to make up my mind not to do it.

There remained, of course, the More-or-Less Insolvent with whom I had spent my whole life—but I was cut off from them because something had happened to me which they had not experienced. You cannot go around to people who are supporting their aged parents and worrying about shoes for the children and ask them to feel sorry for you because you are a bird in a gilded cage. So, over all, the affluent years of my life were rather more tentative than blissful, and only the wish to shield my daughter from certain prevailing falsities induces me to recall their difficulties. From those difficulties I finally dredged up, after a period of some years, the conviction that there might be something to be said for the Downward Step. I learned—by infinitesimal accretions of knowledge, which were painfully slow in building up—that if my life were truly to belong to me, instead of to a couple of other fellows, I would have to get back to my roots. Instead of divorcing the middle class and leaving it behind me, I would have to

return to it. That this conclusion needed quite a bit of ferreting out, in a country geared to getting ahead, goes without saying.

Even in a money society, it is not necessary for the average
person to know very much about interlocking directorates;
but it is of primary importance to know a little something
about interlocking directors. After all, you could so easily
turn out to be the mother of one. And it is a curious paradox that in a money society, the one thing nobody medi-
tates about very much is money. (To struggle for money,
if you do not have it—or to manipulate money, if you do—
is not the same thing as meditating about it.) There is an
enormous supply of American books and pamphlets designed to help parents explain sex to their children; but
aside from a few superficial notes on weekly allowances,
very little has been written for mothers and fathers on
what should be their conscious attitude about money, business and homo sapiens. I have mentioned certain prevailing falsities in our money society which I should like to
see my daughter side-step—notably the careless assumption
that money is the Great Simplifier—but it would perhaps
be more scientifically accurate to describe these beliefs, not
as falsities, but as folklore.

Folklore is a collection of ridiculous notions held by
other people, but not by you and me. Actually—although
it seems hard to believe at first glance—the business-dominated country in which we live is a teeming hive of folklore about money; and this folklore, dispassionately considered, is just as quaint as anything Scots Highlanders

believe about ghosts. Take, for example, the American legend of the Cosy Corporations. No literate American can get very far away from full-page ads and planted magazine articles in which one or another of our giant industrial empires is described as a great, lumbering, affectionate Newfoundland dog panting to lick the face of the beloved American consumer. Friendly General Motors. Likable G.E. Serious-minded U.S. Steel. Jolly good fellows, all of them.

The superstition is firmly established, in the United States, that the American citizen lives like a fluffy chick under the brooding, maternal wing of billion-dollar corporations. The chill and nonmythical reality, however, is that our Big Businesses have no personalities of their own, but are simply random collections of human beings who have been informally but very thoroughly trained to be—between the hours of nine and five—aggressive, competitive and skeptical in the pursuit of money. No such collection of human beings is, or ever could be, any cosier than a hanging judge.

Another well-established bit of American financial folk-lore is the idea that the small, independent businessman has what comes close to being the ideal way of life. In reality, the small, independent businessman is disappearing from the economic scene, except for a worried few whom the Cosy Corporations have not yet, in sheer impersonal momentum, got around to bankrupting. And were the American human being to acquire a small, independent business, could he—product of the Upward Step as he is—

be content to keep it small? Or, were he himself content, would not his wife, his parents, his children, his neighbors, his relatives, his friends, his customers and his bankers regard him as lazy? Two factors make the small, independent businessman increasingly a folk myth instead of a reality. One is external—the trend of our business enterprises to be organized in ever fewer and ever larger empires. The other is internal—the fear of being punished for not "getting ahead."

It is nevertheless easy to see why the idea of the small, independent businessman has such appeal. He seems to represent a healing of the split society. He seems to combine, in his single person, both the admirable mercilessness of business and the compassion and unstudied friendliness of the Judeo-Christian ethic. However, the advertisers and opinion-makers who keep the small, independent businessman so constantly in our mind's eye are not really doing us a service. It is not good for people to have perpetually before them, as a possible reality, a dream which has fewer and fewer chances of ever coming true. We have, to be sure, plenty of small businessmen—as the Cosy Corporations frequently point out in their advertising. But they are not independent. They are in hock. A man's home may be his castle, but his liquor store or his filling station is not. A sub-contractor is not, by any stretch of the imagination, a small, independent businessman.

At first blush, it is hard to grasp the fact that anything so infinitely complex, both financially and mechanically, as our movie industry, our advertising industry, our public-relations industry, our newspapers and our radio-television chains should be engaged in the simple, tribal operation of disseminating myths—differing only in the size of their audience from a medicine man in central Brazil. But reduced to their basic function, that is what they do. The fundamental myth, of course—the one on which all the others depend—is the primitive, pathetic American belief in the magical power of money. Not that one ever finds an average, decent American who actually says he believes money and the things it can buy make people feel better. He actually says just the opposite. But we have all become sufficiently expert in parlor psychoanalysis to know that when you want to find out what people believe, you look at what they do instead of listening to what they say. If Americans did not believe in the healing power of money, they would not spend so much of it. They would stuff it away in an old sock, like the French peasants—sturdy materialists, too, but in their own way.

Since we all have—at least, to a certain extent—this belief in money as God's Trouble-shooter, we all know how deeply ingrained the feeling is in our personalities and how hard it is to shake off, except in momentary flashes of insight. The truth, however, actually does set people free —in so far as they can lay hold of it. Ours is a money society, as everyone freely admits, and a money society inevitably raises, but does not answer, certain haunting and spectral questions. How much money is enough? How much money does a person need? Or, to phrase the questions so that there will be some chance of arriving at an answer, How much money does a person need, considered simply as protoplasm which must be fed, sheltered and clothed? How much money, on the other hand, does a person need as a "successful" member of the dominant, conspicuous, inescapable and constantly expanding business society? The two questions do not, obviously, have the same answer.

Night and day and around the clock, the communications industry pours out its ceaseless message that people can be made "happier" by money and the things that money can buy. The word "folklore"—with its connotation of childlike credulousness—may seem an odd one to use in connection with a business society which prides itself on its practicality. It is, however, clear to all but the dullest intellect that one cannot increase the caloric content of an egg by eating it from an expensive eggcup. And yet in the world as we know it—and as our children must come to know it—"hardheaded reality" is supposed to be represented by the price tag on the eggcup and not by the relationship between nourishing egg and eager, appreciative stomach.

In a previous chapter, mention has been made of the fact that there are certain widely held American beliefs about money which her father and I would like to see our daughter take with a grain of salt. One of the most generally accepted of these beliefs is the notion that the American business society, revolving on its axis of money, is "realistic." Actually, in terms of human flesh and human contentment, "realistic" is just exactly what the American business society is *not*. If there is any sort of answer to the problem of American chronic unhappiness, that answer begins with a firm, unshakable grasp of the fact that the American business society is based upon an illusion.

This illusion is the belief that money and the things it can buy will make people feel better—that money enables people to escape pain, insures them against criticism, makes them more self-confident and authoritative and less prone to self-mistrust and feelings of inferiority. The business society's illusion about the power of money takes tangible form in the Bath of Perfection in which we are all unavoidably immersed—in the perfect teeth, perfect bosoms, perfect young women, perfect romances, perfect clothes, perfect automobiles, perfect medicines, perfect food and perfect furniture which assault our eyes and ears all day and every day and to which we have become so accustomed as not to recognize the inherent menace of their unnaturalness.

It is easy enough to spot an hallucination in a single person. If a man tells us he is Napoleon, we have no trouble in classifying him as demented. But a mass illusion, accepted unthinkingly and without question by millions and millions of people, appears at first glance to have authority and not to be an illusion at all. And, as a matter of fact, all tribes, groups, societies and commonwealths are based to a certain extent on mass illusions—whether those illusions are concerned with totem poles, the spirits of the dead, dryads or dressing for dinner in the jungle. It is therefore no particular discredit to our or the other business societies to say that they are based on an illusion about money. What counts, rather, is whether the mass illusion is practical and workable in terms of human flesh and the human need for a measure of contentment now and then.

The illusion upon which our dominating business society is based—the illusion that money and the things it can buy will make people feel better—is not practical and not workable. If it were, the people in the upper income brackets would be distinguished for being much more contented, fearless, self-respecting and emotionally well-balanced than their less fortunate brethren. But they are not. American chronic unhappiness is no respecter of incomes.

It is hard for Americans to think of themselves as living in a society, since the American business society is never referred to as a society, but simply as Business, with a capital B, as if it were some sort of unusually good-looking and remarkably powerful Greek goddess. Business-with-a-capital-B, however, is nothing more than the unthinking activity of specially conditioned human beings who are doing what they have been told to do. Americans live in a society, a predominantly business society, and What Every Parent Should Know About Business can be telescoped into a remarkably small space. What Every Parent Should Know About Business is that the American business society —for all its unique contribution toward freedom from drudgery—is not "practical" and not "hardheaded" and not "realistic," but illusionary. And unworkably illusionary, at that.

The "reality" is the egg. The "reality" is Nature's di-

113

vine and comforting miracle of the human alimentary system. The eggcup, to which our attention is so persistently and unremittingly directed, is the fantasy. It is, to be sure, a magnificently well-organized fantasy. In fact, American business—with its torrents of advertising and of entertainment which is really no more than implied advertising *—could quite accurately be described as an Eggcup Civilization. But in terms of children, who are not in business and who need love, the eggcup is nevertheless not the reality. The eggcup is the fantasy.

In trying to work out a philosophy which might remove some of the groping and bewilderment from the task of parenthood, it must be accepted as a First Principle—and never for a moment forgotten—that a thing is not necessarily true just because a great many people think it is. Fifty million Frenchmen may, conceivably, err. And when they do, they pay for it. Nothing is more comfortably intimate, temporarily, than to go along with the crowd and to accept as truth what everybody agrees is the truth. But such good-natured compliance cannot always be relied upon to pay off.

The present writer is a suburban housewife with no claim to intellectual distinction beyond the fact of having predicted, four weeks before the 1948 election, that Harry S. Truman would win. Only my legal matrimonial mate was kind enough not to laugh. Before the election, I was

---

* Neither the movies nor the comics carry a line of advertising, but both of them function as a sort of permanent advertising for uplift brassières.

regarded as a promising candidate for a pre-frontal lobot-omy; afterwards, the prediction was described as "femi-nine intuition." But it was quite clearly observable—in fact, several political pundits commented on it at the time —that the President was campaigning with his whole per-sonality, whereas his opponent was offering the electorate only a parched segment of himself.

American voters being as humanly emotional and re-sponsive as any other set of people in the world, it is a fairly safe bet that in an American election, you can beat a total personality with a stronger total personality—Senator Taft, for instance, also campaigned with his whole person-ality in 1950—but you cannot beat a total personality with a half-personality. There was an additional factor, too, in the President's victory, about which your correspondent may very well have been intuitive rather than intelligent. That factor is that the American population—harassed, be-sieged, clamored at, exhorted, guided, directed and in-truded upon by the communications industry—can be relied on just in the nature of things to have occasional shuddering, convulsive rebellions against it.

It is a First Principle of parenthood, then, not to accept things as true just because a great many people think they are true. Nevertheless, the widely held American belief that money means "happiness" has a certain surface ap-pearance of truth; and there is every excuse in the world for the most intelligent American to feel that when he has got hold of money, he has got hold of "reality." Americans actually can be made to feel better by acquiring money.

They can purchase immunity to criticism. They can buy, along with the Cadillac and the deep freeze, the respect, admiration and half-throttled envy of their fellow citizens. They can duck out from under the unnerving responsibilities of parenthood and leave those responsibilities in the hands of well-trained hirelings. They can run away from themselves in travel. They can evade the laws which crash punitively down on the financially defenseless. They can even, if they are sufficiently in command of this world's goods, make laws. It is a fact beyond dispute that in the United States as it is currently organized, the acquisition of money does, momentarily, make people feel better.

But the deadly parallel is that it is equally indisputable that an alcoholic is made to feel better by his first drink. Alcohol is a food, and a celestially quick-acting food, at that. It is not the food to which the human body responds most gratefully or most gracefully; but that it is nourishment of a sort, no moderately well-informed person is prepared to deny. In a split society, dominated outwardly by its business half, money is nourishing to the spirit in the same way alcohol is to the body. In fact, as some of our novelists have already pointed out, we have developed what might be called the business alcoholic—the man who in his heart does not like business and what it does to him any more than the alcoholic likes liquor and what it does to him, but who is caught in the same kind of trap. For that matter, it is an even worse trap. The drinking alcoholic can at least count upon an occasional sympathetic magazine article describing him as the victim of a disease. The business alcoholic must try to regard himself as a conqueror, however inaccurate he knows the term to be, and he must keep his troubles to himself.

If further evidence is needed that a split society inevitably produces split personalities, one has only to consider that most American businessmen are also American parents—and are thus, although nobody ever tells them so, the innocent architects of some of their own parental dilemmas. The books on child-rearing tell us in a mighty chorus that the good parent relaxes and enjoys his children. But what do the businessmen say when they are talking to each other?

ONE THING NO EXECUTIVE CAN AFFORD TO DO

No executive can afford to stand still.

That is the unpardonable sin in American business. The pace is too fast, competition too keen, to permit any lagging. The man who falls behind is out of the race.

To get ahead and stay ahead, today's executive must keep abreast of the times. He must be informed of the modern management methods employed by successful, progressive companies.

Every alert executive realizes this.

That is why so many top management men are according so prompt and enthusiastic a reception to the new Funk & Wagnalls Reading Course in Executive Technique.*

* Adv.—New York Times Book Review.

The books on child-rearing do not tell us how the good parent is to cope with the fact that, in the business society, it is against the law to relax. To relax is to have your job snatched out from under you by some clambering upstart who is tense as a strung bow.

The split personality is always unconsciously trying to heal itself—trying to close the gap. Protection of the weak being inseparable from parenthood, and the United States being predominantly a money society, it is natural for many American parents to assume without thinking about it that they need money for their children, and to mention their children as the reason why they take part in what everybody agrees is a rat race. Making money for one's children—in the strenuous world of aggression, competitiveness and skepticism—is generally referred to as "giving them advantages." Children, however, do not need "advantages." Children need love, and people do not strain after "success" for the sake of their children. The children are just an excuse—albeit an unconscious one. People strain after "success" because they have been taught to make the Upward Step. They strain after "success," not because they have children, but because they have had parents. Childless people are not distinguished, as a group, for being less keen on getting ahead than parents.

No consideration of present-day American children can be very helpful which leaves out of the picture the people who once were children in the United States. We must not let the Upward Step mislead us. What happens to our children is very closely linked up to what happened to us, the adults, when we were children. The disastrous weakness of a business society is that children cannot move in the business world, so that there is always a fence between the child and the functioning adult. What is even worse, there is always a fence between the functioning adult and the child within him—which is another way of describing the American split personality.

Children are indifferent to the profit motive. Grownups are not. Or, at least, we have the word of the American press that grownups, so far from being indifferent to the profit motive, are inspired by it to all their most admirable behavior. Without at all conceding that the profit motive is as universal as the newspapers claim, it is nevertheless true that many Americans are the victims of a blind, compulsive need for money which exceeds by many hundreds or thousands of times their simple protoplasmic requirements for food and shelter. The word "victims" is an important one. All the stock, familiar phrases about individual initiative and free enterprise do not successfully conceal—although they are meant to—the fact that the enterprising American is not usually free to make a deliberate choice between being enterprising or not enterprising about money. He is pressured into his initiative by the threat of punishment and the promise of reward. Enterprise it certainly is, but it would not look like freedom to the Prisoner of Chillon.

American babies, kicking and squirming in their bassinets, have no thoughts or feelings at all about money. Twenty years later—often in a much shorter time—they have acquired, most of them, a very clearly defined attitude about money. This attitude can be summed up in three words. They trust it. They respect—without being aware of the respect—the people who have either inherited or earned it in large quantities. They are inclined to be contemptuous—again unconsciously—of the people who have not been able to earn it. For the people who could have earned it, but chose to do something else, they have a feeling akin to horror. If any doubting Thomas is skeptical about the fact that the American population is both frightened and angered by people who turn their backs on a money-making potential, he has only to try it and see.

Between the American baby's indifference to money and the American adult's reliance on it, what intervenes? In teaching a young person to drive a car, it is necessary to be specific. Similarly, children do not learn arithmetic by hearing the grownups talking about it. But what American children learn about money—what we ourselves learned about it, when we were children—is not the result of specific instruction. Nobody, now or formerly, takes American children by their infant lapels and tells them to go out after the fast buck. Nobody teaches them to make just-barely-legal "deals" the way Fagin taught his charges to pick pockets.

Children, as everyone knows from having been a child, are much more sensitive to inflections and much more perceptive about behavior than their dulled and battle-weary seniors. American children, past and present, learn to have faith in money from hearing the grownups talking about it to each other and from observing the behavior of grownups toward people who have money (or the prospect of it) and toward people who have not. American children learn about money from hearing the grownups pardon the unpardonable and forgive the unforgivable by saying, "But you've got to admit, he makes money." Children learn about money both from the grownups they know and from the grownups with whom they are not personally acquainted—notably, today, the grownups who shape policy in the communications industry. They learn, also, as much from omission as from commission. They learn as much from what is not on radio or television as from what is there. If there is one thing in the world about which children are experts, it is sincerity. The occasional isolated—and castrated—exhortations to virtue from the communications industry are correctly assessed by children as not having been torn raw and bleeding from the hearts of the exhorters.

A specific training can be successfully rebelled against and shaken off. Children can, and often do, promptly and completely forget all their arithmetic the moment the last exam is passed. But the training American children receive about money is nonspecific, atmospheric, subtle, intangible and pervasive. It is therefore supremely difficult for the adult American to free himself of it. We can all of us remember without too much difficulty when and under what circumstances we learned arithmetic. Very few of us can point to the day and the hour when we first began to learn that Americans get punished for not having money. Very few of us can remember the exact moment when we began to be afraid of not having money. Afraid in terms of our physical wants. Afraid of being old and ill and alone in a nonwelfare state. And equally afraid—every bit as much afraid—in terms of our need for recognition and for belonging.

A split society is a complex society. Wearisomely complex. The complexity of life in the United States stems from the complexity of the people in the United States and not, as is often suggested, from the complexity of the machines. The American business society is owned and operated by businessmen who spent a good many years being children before they got to be businessmen. In that prebusiness period, they had a specific training in the Judeo-Christian ethic and an atmospheric training in business behavior. The business society does not, therefore, come right out and say in so many words that money is everything. In fact, every year at commencement time, when the pillars of the business society get honorary degrees, they make a special point of telling the fledgling graduates that money is not everything. What the business society actually says to the young people is that, while money is not everything, money comes first. First you make your pile, and after that sacred obligation has been discharged, you are at liberty to go in for hobbies, leisure, philanthropy, psychoanalysis, politics, religion, art or getting to know your children.

The only trouble with this arrangement is that, in terms

122

of peace of mind, it will not work. When money comes first, it stays first—all good intentions notwithstanding. The business society pays unfailing lip service to the official ethic. It has to, because the customers were brought up on it. The business society even permits the businessman to throw an occasional sop to that morality, provided he does not let the sop-throwing interfere with the serious business of financial advancement. But—and here is the very crux and kernel of American chronic unhappiness—the Judeo-Christian ethic is, like the law, a jealous mistress. One can no more pay mere lip service to it, and get results, than one can pay mere lip service to business, and get results. Both of our two societies demand all or nothing.

Everyone knows what is meant by getting results in the business world. But what is meant by getting results in terms of the Judeo-Christian ethic? This question can best be answered by pointing out that the purpose of that ethic is to support people. This makes it exactly the opposite of the business society, whose purpose is to make money out of people. The purpose of the American ethic is to give help—to comfort people when they are alone, to support them against uncomprehending criticism, and to give meaning to their lives. The great disadvantage of being in a rat race is that it is humiliating. The competitors in a rat race are, by definition, rodents. It is the purpose of Christian morality to keep people out of rat races, and to give them the feeling of being dignified human beings with a personal responsibility for choosing between good and evil.

We may all certainly be excused for thinking of the Judeo-Christian ethic as a fancy accessory, like the overdrive on an automobile, to the "realistic" pursuit of money. That is the way it is always presented to us. But there is absolutely no way out of our present confusion save by accepting the fact that our traditional national morality is not an overdrive on the business society, but a way of life in itself. A way of life has to be lived. It does, at any rate, if it is going to pay off in terms of being a human being and not a badgered animal. Such a way of life has to be lived, furthermore, during the best years of one's earthly span, and not during the tag end left over after the annuities have been corralled. The purpose of our ethic is to protect people, but there is one form of protection which it adamantly withholds. It does not protect the strivers after money, successful or unsuccessful, from the consequences of striving after money. There are certain groups of people in the American population for whom American ethics actually do pay off, but as they do not make much money, they will be discussed in a subsequent chapter. They do not belong in this one.

Every human being has his own particular way of showing off. My particular way is to set up a bridge table and a typewriter in the engaging privacy of my bedroom, and see what I can do with the lessons in paragraph structure which intermittently starred my well-spent youth. The stage, the lecture platform or even the commanding position by the fireplace in a Sir Frederick Lonsdale drawing room have never constituted my particular outlet for what can be called either exhibitionism or self-expression. However, after I had on the record a published work on race relations, I taught myself—or rather, my husband taught me—to give a passable lecture on the thorny subject of Negroes and Caucasians in the United States of America. It was the Deity's obvious and visible intention that I should communicate with my fellow men through the written rather than the spoken word; but there exists among white Americans a great craving for affirmation and reassurance in their tentative efforts to set things right vis-à-vis the Negro Americans.

At these lectures, there was almost always some well-meaning soul who had brought along a rich old uncle—the uncle being rich by virtue of owning Negro tenements in Miami. The well-meaning souls always hoped that Uncle —having been given the straight dope on race relations by the speaker of the evening—would see the error of his ways and go in for slum clearance. So far as I know, Uncle never did, although I met him often. But in the question-and-answer periods which usually followed these lectures, the inevitable Uncle always made a point which is germane to the whole subject of parenthood. He always made the point that segregation of Negroes does not need our attention, since the coming generation—who will be much more enlightened and advanced than we are—can be relied upon to straighten out the matter with far less trouble than it would be for us.

This, of course, is cold comfort to the people who are being Jim-Crowed at the present moment. It is also nonsense. Our children will be as courageous as we are—

neither much more nor much less—because we are the only people from whom they can learn courage. If young people learn to be courageous, they learn it from associating with courageous grownups. Providence, in its wisdom, does not select one generation rather than another to be especially kind to. If the next generation of American children escapes the rat-race destiny and knows enough to look at the egg instead of the eggcup, it will only be because we, the adults, set their feet in that path and help to keep them there.

All normal human parents have the wish to do something kind and fruitful and constructive for their children. In our country, this wish has, up to now, taken the form of the Upward Step—of launching the children into American life on a higher rung of the financial ladder than the one the parents started on. But we are beginning to have the painful fact borne in on us that the Upward Step is not the answer to life. It undeniably produces an ever higher standard of living, physically, but it separates parent from child. It deprives children of that understanding of their parents as human beings which the children need to have if they are to arrive at self-knowledge and contentment. The Upward Step makes people lonely. It cuts them off, to a certain extent, from the most comforting and stabilizing of all sensations—the feeling of the continuity of life as it flows through the generations.

The kindest, most fruitful and most constructive thing which can be done for American children is to refrain from passing on to them, uncritically and unquestioningly, the tribal superstitions of the money society—the illusion that the American business society is "realistic," and the conviction that the more money people have, the better they will feel. More than any amount of "advantages," the American child needs parents who have correctly appraised the real situation in the United States—the real situation being that in our country, money, while not everything, comes first. That is to say, the businessman in his role of businessman is more important than the businessman in his role of parent. A more ridiculous setup it would be hard to imagine, since the human race can get along without business, and often does, but it cannot get along without parents and children. Having recognized, then, that American life is not so much complex as upside down, it is time to return to the disturbing question which a money society raises, but does not answer—to wit, How much money is enough?

VI

Money Is a Bandage

IT WAS with something of a start that I realized—a couple of months ago—that for the last ten years, my standard of living has been steadily declining. At least, that is one way of putting it. Another way would be to say that, although I was not aware of the process, I have been for the past decade consistently shedding material possessions and social entanglements and reverting to the austerity of my childhood. Ten years ago, I was a great girl for having things nice. In the United States, having things nice is a national pastime, like baseball, and I was devoted to it heart and soul. I had people in to dinner, and I had a maid to cook the dinner. The hostess may not have been a miracle of emotional stability, but the tablecloth blended with the carpet and the glassware was not infelicitous in design.

My Spartan upbringing has always prevented me from going really hog-wild about clothes; but ten years ago, the ones I had were good, and I took meticulous care of them. Nor did it occur to me at that time that I could attend a social gathering without pancake make-up, lipstick, rouge, eyebrow pencil, eye-shadow and mascara doing their humble best for my physiognomy. At the present time, my husband and my daughter and I occupy a six-room house; but as we moved into it from a three-room apartment, and as it took every penny we could raise just to make the down payment, the ménage does not suggest the Petit Trianon. The first floor has curtains and enough furniture so that visitors are not startled, but the second floor looks as if we were just getting ready for a barn dance. In the foreseeable future, there is no possibility that it will ever look otherwise. As for your correspondent, the gracious chatelaine of this moated grange, she wears cotton shirts and blue jeans to everything but weddings, christenings and funerals.

Of course, the advent of my daughter had a little something to do with my deserting from the bright banner of *Vogue* and *House Beautiful*. But actually, the process started before that, and my husband was an inadvertent contributor. My little girl's father has many beautiful and endearing qualities, but tidiness is not one of them. After a period of considerable strain, I reached a point in my life where I could see that I had to make an interesting choice. I would either have to give up the unfailing orderliness which I took over from my father, or I would have to give up being married. I could not have them both. By, paradoxically enough, the exercise of a great deal of self-control, I managed to shed some of my perfectionism. I will never, of course, reach the glorious heights of careless-ness upon which my spouse lives. While I am now able to drop a book or a coat on the floor, I will never—to my dy-ing day—be able to do what my husband does. I will never be able to tread on it on my way out of the room.

Since this chapter is to deal, in the fullness of time, with money and the question of how much money is enough, it might be added that another element of my retreat from having things nice was economic. There is a good deal of difference between my present frugality and the frugality my mother and father exercised when I was young. My parents were saving money to send their two daughters to college and to enable them—my folks, that is—to have an independent old age. My husband and I are, like many of our fellow countrymen, not saving any money at all. It takes all we can earn, in our honorable but unresplendent professions, to give our little girl approximately the amount of trees, space and fresh air we had when we were small—as well as access to a public-school system approxi-mately as good as the ones we attended.

Lest this sound like self-pity, it should quickly be added that circumstances have changed a good deal since my parents made their regular monthly deposits in the savings bank. A college education for our daughter is not quite the bright, definite and glorious goal for my husband and me that it was for both our sets of parents. For one thing—as has already been noted—the middle class is now pretty generally agreed that these present years of my daughter's life are more important to her character and happiness than the four years she spends between seventeen and twenty-one. These, therefore, are obviously the years on which to spend the money.

But how much money? How much money is enough? Perhaps the simplest approach to this query is to begin with human protoplasm. It is a fact beyond dispute that all Americans are made of protoplasm; and it is equally indisputable that human flesh is a rather tyrannical agency. There is a definite limit to how much food it can take in. It provides only a relatively small area upon which to drape even the most expensive clothes. It refuses to be any less sleepless or infirm in a twenty-room house than it is in a two-room apartment. And after an arbitrarily determined stay upon this planet, it disappears. If the needs of flesh and blood were all that had to be considered, a good many Americans who are now tense and strained about their incomes could afford to stop worrying. The money in a money society, therefore—the money so compulsively dreamed of, so tensely earned and so freely spent—must be serving some further purpose, for a great many people, than the mere maintenance of physical health.

This further purpose can be quickly enough described. In a business society, it is the function of money to take the place of affection. With the family on iron rations, human beings—a category which includes the businessman himself —cannot get from their parents, their children, their relatives, their neighbors, their friends, their co-workers or their fellow voters the warmth and security which all human beings absolutely must have. Once in a while, at any rate. Hence the people in a business society—for all the human dignity of their advanced medicine and their labor-saving devices—are under the painful necessity of trying to live in a prevailingly suspicious, cynical and unaffectionate atmosphere. In this withering situation, money—whether real, potential or only impotently dreamed of—is supposed to provide the protection and the emotional security which the beleaguered and discredited family cannot supply.

All writers are accustomed to being asked, once in a while, where they get the ideas for their work. The idea for this book—the little germ or kernel which started it off —came to me some years ago when I was writing about Negro-white relations and doing some reading on the subject to check my facts and figures. At that time it began to seem to me that discrimination against Negroes is only one part of a national pattern of underdeveloped affection; and that the punitive behavior of whites toward Negroes has its roots in the punitive behavior of whites toward other whites.

It should here be stated that this discussion of how much money is enough is not to be interpreted as an attack on the "haves" and a glorification of the "have-nots." I should be dismayed if this book were construed as a defense of the liberal tradition, since, in this writer's view, the liberal tradition does not need any defense. It just needs liberals. Rather, this is a conservative book, in the dictionary sense of the word "conservative"—meaning to save or preserve.

At this juncture, it would perhaps be wise to restate the purpose of the family. The family's job is to provide a clearly understood, workable relationship between the older people in a society and the younger ones who will eventually take their places. Children, however, are indifferent to profits and finance and they need affection, not money or "advantages." In a society based on profit-making, therefore, there can obviously be no clearly understood relationship between the older people and the younger ones. In such a society, the family must necessarily do its job superficially, intermittently, unsatisfactorily and with a great deal of strain, anxiety and tension.

Hence, the division of Americans into "haves" and "have-nots" is artificial and meaningless. The poor can be, and often are, just as effectively alienated from the Bankruptcy Qualities as the rich; and the mere absence of money is not in itself a sign of wholesome living. There is no basic difference between a man who is straining—for reasons he has never asked himself—to build a drygoods empire and a man who is straining to keep up the payments on a television set which he bought because everybody else has one. One man is a so-called producer and the other is a so-called consumer, but they are both helpless and uneasy drifters on the cold and uncongenial tide of American business.

Some Americans—through sheer good luck, not personal merit—happen to move more within the orbit of the Judeo-Christian ethic than within the orbit of American business.

Such people tend to choose, consciously or unconsciously, the kind of life work like schoolteaching, government service or motherhood where the only possibility of advancement is emotional and spiritual, not financial. I have spoken of such people as being fortunate, but it is a very modest kind of good fortune. The unbusinesslike Americans are always on the receiving end of the business society's hostility and contempt; and while their choice of jobs indicates that they do not aspire to more money than protoplasm needs, they must sometimes get along with a little bit less. They must also manage to get along with virtually no prestige, applause or recognition.

If one takes the customary path and divides Americans into "haves" and "have-nots," then it is easy to find pure types. If, on the other hand, one divides them more realistically into people who have been prevailingly influenced by business or prevailingly influenced by the American ethic, then it is impossible to find any pure types. A really pure type of the American businessman would have to be born at the age of eighteen. A really pure type of the American businessman would have to have no memory of a time when he was weak, helpless, dependent and in need of affection. On the other hand—ethic or no ethic—the piece of flesh and blood does not exist which can live in the middle of a business society and remain totally unaffected by its attitude toward money and toward the purchase of those charming or uncharming perishables which moth and rust do corrupt and thieves break in and steal.

Despite my own accession to unexpected cash—which

134

forced me to do a little laboratory work on money and its connection with the sense of well-being—I seldom have a fit of gloom or depression without feeling that if I could just go out and distribute some coin of the realm, my spirits would lighten. If I could buy a lamp for my little girl's room, or purchase, after exquisite deliberation, an ornament for the dining room whatnot, the sense of worthlessness would be replaced by a sense of worth and the sense of powerlessness by a sense of power. Since there is very little room in our budget—it being a characteristic of budgets not to have much room—for the Cure of Despondency by Expenditure, I must either sweat out my dejection or get it lightened, free of cost, by other human beings. (As we all know, this last is a risky procedure.) But the first impulsive, unreasoned (and socially conditioned) reaction is always there—that if I could just go out and acquire something, I would feel better.

This writer has been identified as conservative, in the dictionary sense of conservative as saving and preserving. Within the past few years, there have been several books —and they have enjoyed a good deal of popularity—pointing out that our natural resources of forest, soil and water are being recklessly wasted and destroyed owing to certain groups of human beings who are somewhat elusively identified as "the timber interests" and "the public-utility interests." By people who have looked into it and ought to know, we are told that the conservation of our natural resources calls for certain "socialistic" institutions like a Missouri Valley Authority and a Columbia River Author-

ity. The establishment of these preservative institutions
has been blocked by various influential stockholders who
do not want to go through the emotionally painful experience of taking less profit. Warmhearted but hot-tempered
liberals point out with considerable asperity that these influential, stockholding human beings and their managerial
grand viziers live considerably above the subsistence level;
and thus their motives can only be ascribed to plain greed.
But this is inaccurate. The inability to take less profit does
not come from greed. It comes from need. In a business
society, the emotional economy is an economy of scarcity.

Children need affection. Love, and not money, is what
children try to get. And since there is always continuity in
any person's life, no grownup ever reaches a point where
he ceases, utterly and completely, to be a child. In a business society, money, while not everything, comes first.
Money does not come first, however, in the life span of a
human being. Any given piece of protoplasm has to spend
at least a few years when he cannot put money first, because he is physiologically unable to do so. Unfortunately,
the kind of treatment he gets during those years of dependence sometimes turns him into an adult who has, not
a greed, but a need for money. I have been a parent long
enough to have gotten rather bored with the phrase about
the rejected child. But tedious or not, children do get rejected—all up and down the income scale. And when they
grow up, how it shows!

Periodically, in the American press, we have campaigns
to expose what is called corruption. Athletes, civil servants

and other fallible human beings are revealed in the papers to have taken money they should not have taken. And as most Americans are aware, the corruption which is exposed in the papers is only a fraction of the corruption which actually exists. The exposure of corruption by the newspapers is a mug's game, since this kind of behavior is routine in the high, the middle and the low places of American life.

And yet, curiously enough—though Americans have something of a reputation for unashamed candor—one never finds an American who says, "Yes, frankly, I have been corrupted by money." The reason Americans do not say they have been corrupted by money, even when the evidence is unmistakable, is that they do not feel corrupted by money. And they are right. Money does not corrupt people. What corrupts people is lack of affection. What corrupts people is being exploited, either emotionally or financially. What corrupts people is being treated with contempt or indifference. What corrupts people is the business society's intolerance of weak and helpless individuals.

What corrupts people is being brought up mechanically by parents who are obeying the injunction to get ahead. What corrupts people is the unstable family, besieged by a million entrepreneurs to whom the family—except one's own, of course—is a meaningless clump of potential customers. What corrupts people, very often, is being chivvied and pressured into the narrow mold of profit-making behavior when their real desires lie in other directions.

137

People are never corrupted by money, which is why the periodic campaigns to "clean up" corruption never accomplish anything and have to be endlessly repeated. Money does not corrupt people. Money is simply the bandage which wounded people put over their wounds.

Medicine heals wounds. Sometimes Nature heals wounds. Bandages do not. In our money society, we have a phrase which we use all the time without ever thinking of its implications. We say of this or that man that he is "worth" such-and-such an amount of money—fifty thousand dollars or half a million dollars or ten million dollars. But the phrase is a booby trap. To whom is a man worth this or that specific sum of money? To God? To his wife? To the American housewives for whom he produces extremely useful or practically valueless consumer goods? To the next generation? Above all, is a man worth this-or-that sum of money to himself? Does ten thousand dollars or ten million dollars represent—can it ever represent—what a man thinks about himself?

On this subject, Abraham Lincoln once wrote with a good deal of relevance. Some years before he became President, a New York firm applied to him for information about the financial standing of one of his neighbors.

"Yours of the 10th received," he wrote. "First of all, he has a wife and baby; together they ought to be worth $500,000 to any man. Secondly, he has an office in which there is a table worth $1.50 and three chairs worth, say, $1. Last of all, there is in one corner a large rat-hole, which will bear looking into."

The fabulously rich, the most brutalized and degraded poor, and the people in between must all arrive on this earth via the uterine process; and they must all spend a much longer time being weak and helpless than the progeny of other mammals. How much money, then, is enough to take the place of the family? Obviously, no conceivable amount. Money, over and above the needs of protoplasm, will not stabilize and fortify the family one is currently engaged in raising. Neither—and this is the saddest part of all—will it heal the wounds left by a family upbringing which was lacking in compassion and generosity.

This is a bitter truth, but a little bit more is gained by facing up to it than is gained by a life of permanent and fruitless flight. There is no more painful experience in the world—it is possibly just as grim as death itself—than the realization that one has not been loved. If American adults concentrate on the present and the future, and seldom spend much time mulling over and trying to appraise their own pasts, it may be because—for many of them—being a child in an expanding business society was in essence a cruelly lonely experience.

How much money is enough? How much money is enough for bodily needs? The people who live on the subsistence level could answer this question quickly enough. And grimly enough, too. But in trying to figure out how much money protoplasm needs, I do not mean how much it needs to drag out a wretched and greatly impaired existence. Wealthy alcoholics also suffer from malnutrition. In fact, that is what often kills them. Nothing is gained by

139

finding out how little people *can* live on. The question is how much money do people, considered as flesh and blood, *need*? The two things are not the same. The question should perhaps be revised to read: How much money is enough for protoplasm, if the protoplasm is to function with a maximum of satisfaction to the owner?

It is not a question which can be answered simply or quickly. Merely taking pencil and paper and writing down, "So much for food . . . so much for rent. . . ." will not bring us to an answer. There is a complicating factor which has to be allowed for. This complicating factor has recently been exhaustively explored by Dr. David Riesman in a book about Americans whose title I always think of when I go to my supermarket in the Saturday morning rush. The title of Dr. Riesman's book is *The Lonely Crowd*. In it, Dr. Riesman makes a point which has to be kept constantly in mind when trying to calculate how much money is enough for protoplasm. Dr. Riesman points out that—with the dizzying speed of movement which is a feature of societies based on getting ahead—the United States has changed from a "producing" nation to a "consuming" nation.

The United States is still discussed, in the public prints, as if it were a country with an open frontier and a primary concern with producing. It was my little girl, however, who brought it home to me that Dr. Riesman is right— that in the comparatively short time between my childhood and my daughter's, the business society has ceased urging people to produce and is now exerting its very considerable influence to get them to consume. When my daughter grew old enough to walk and talk, I was dismayed to realize that she was perpetually asking me to buy her toys. At first I had that dismal and unnerving thought which periodically visits all the conscientious parents who have read the books—the thought being, "Perhaps the child acts this way because her mother doesn't love her enough."

On further reflection, however, I realized that her chronic plea for toys is by no means peculiar to her. The other children seem to behave in a somewhat similar fashion. I also realized something which has already been mentioned in Chapter I of this book—that when my contemporaries and I were small, it was not possible to make very much money out of children. Now, however—what with Hopalong Cassidy suits, detonating cereals, comic books and an endless succession of incredibly flimsy toys —children are a gold mine to American business. When my mother took my sister and me into a grocery store, there was nothing in it but groceries. But when I take my little girl to buy groceries, she cannot get three feet inside the door before confronting a large rack filled with comic books, storybooks, coloring books and children's victrola records. If she is always asking me to buy her things, it is certainly due in part to the fact that American business is always trying to sell her things.

Like most people my age and older, I have a vivid memory of the United States when it was still a "producing" society. When my sister and I were small, we got presents

at Christmas and on our birthdays, and those two occasions stood out from the rest of the year with a wonderful
luminosity. When we were small, one doll a year was par
for the course. In the present-day consuming society, however, it is literally only a matter of months before the wet-
ting doll is succeeded by the doll that says, "Coo-coo"; and
this in turn is succeeded by a doll whose hair can be given
a permanent wave; and this is again succeeded by a doll
whose hair can be dyed. The next step, obviously, is going
to be the doll that can get pregnant.

At the period of American history when I was growing
up, thrift was a virtue which was by all means to be in-
stilled into the children. We also had, in our neighborhood, a phrase which has now gone completely out of use.
It was a phrase about "teaching children the value of a
dollar." The children of my generation were trained—
more or less unthinkingly, but nevertheless thoroughly—
to be hard-working little producers. Consuming was something which respectable people approached in a cautious
and gingerly fashion.

The spender, in earlier days, functioned as an individual. He made a choice of what to buy and what to refrain
from buying, and the choice meant something. Currently,
however, the spender—even little teeny ones, like my
daughter—does not make a choice. He just buys everything. Everything he can pay for, and possibly a few things
he cannot. This does not mean that my little girl was born
a wastrel. She is responding to pressure—pressure that is
superlatively well organized and that never lets up.

My principal objection to the business society's seduction of my daughter is not that the toys are shoddy and overpriced—though this is true. My principal objection is not that the twenty-nine-centses mount up, over the period of a year, into a formidable sum—though this is true, too. My principal objection to the seduction of my daughter by American business is that, being by nature a conservative, I am a firm believer in the joy of ownership and the pleasure of possession; and I should very much like to have my little girl learn to experience those delightful sensations. But as Mr. Charles Lamb pointed out a good many years ago, in his *Essay On Old China,* you cannot get the true heft and savor and exquisiteness of owning, if you own very much.

Thorstein Veblen, writing about American business when it was still in its producing stage, alluded in a famous phrase to the "conspicuous consumption" of the well-to-do. What characterizes American business in its subsequent development, however, is the inconspicuous consumption of my little girl with her reiterated plea for gimcrack toys. When it comes to answering the question, therefore, of how much money is enough for protoplasm, what must be kept in mind is that we have split personalities and therefore live in a state of chronic unease. This chronic unease makes us particularly vulnerable to the unceasing sales pressure of American business. The business half of our society has finished with its producing stage, when people were urged to work hard, spend cautiously and put money in the bank which could be used to con-

quer the frontier and build up American industry. The
frontier is gone, and American industry has been built
up to a point which is unparalleled in human history. The
business society, therefore, now wants us to be professional
consumers—thoughtlessly but wholeheartedly dedicated to
buying things, wearing them out, using them up (or possibly just getting bored with them) and then buying more
things to replace them. It gets us to do this by promising
us happiness, in addition to the merchandise. So we buy.

This kind of behavior is good for business, but bad for
protoplasm. Business societies come and go, but protoplasm, like Tennyson's brook, goes on forever. It is protoplasm—and not the advertisements, or even the editorials
and think-pieces—which furnishes the only truly reliable
yardstick by which we can measure our behavior. Protoplasm needs food, shelter, affection and intervals of relaxation. When it does not get these things, it kicks back.
The question of how much money is enough for protoplasm is, obviously, a question which the business society
does not want us even to ask, much less try to answer. But
while it is true that we are all the creatures of our society
—and to a much larger extent than we usually recognize—
it is also true that a society does not necessarily have to be
taken lying down.

The answer to a consuming society is to dig one's toes
in and resist the pressures. The answer to a consuming
society is to make one's purchases—not "instinctively" and
in unthinking response to sales stimulus—but slowly, reflectively and in the full awareness of what one is doing.

Protoplasm does not need its hair curled or its fingernails tinted, and it does not need a new dress because everybody has seen the old ones. In a consuming society, all buying is considered good; but the fact of the matter is, that there are several different kinds of buying, and not all of them are good.

The curls, the fingernail polish and the new dress are what might be called defensive buying—designed to avert criticism, to make one pleasantly inconspicuous and to evoke at least a fugitive sense of belonging. Then there is escape buying. Escape buying includes all the things purchased in order to give one a temporary sense of power in a life situation—i.e., the business-dominated United States —where one feels permanently powerless. (Of the permanent sense of powerlessness, more will be said in the next chapter.) Protoplasmic buying is most obviously illustrated by the purchase of food, and here the ability to consume— in comparison to defensive and escape buying—is very sharply limited.

One of my own ways of rebelling against the consuming society was to stop taking the Sunday paper. There was a time—and it was not so very long ago—when I read punctiliously and with devotion all the advertisements which are so conspicuous a feature of our Sabbath journals. I did not read these advertisements because I had any money to spend. It was merely that I felt "hep" and "adjusted" and au courant if I knew what was being offered for sale. But I am a working mother, and I can only maintain that two-headed status by a sort of niggardly attitude about the expenditure of time and energy. I discovered that Sunday seems a much longer day, if one does not take in the Sunday paper. Not only much longer, but much nicer. He knew what He was doing when He rested on the seventh day.

Seasoned parents will want to know what, if I do not approve of my daughter's torrents of toys, I do about it. It must long have been apparent that this book is not being written because the author is happily conscious of being a good mother and eager to share the secret. On the contrary, this writer is full of shattering qualms about the performance of maternal duties, and being the methodical daughter of a methodical father, wants to know the reason why. So far as my little girl's continual request for toys is concerned, I have a quota for her and I try to stick to it.

However, my husband and I are like most parents in that we have wonderful theories about parenthood, but when actually confronted by our screaming or sobbing child, we often give a fairly good imitation of that imperishable Saxon, Ethelred the Unready. I maintain a consistent attitude of disapproval toward non-protoplasmic spending; but my featherweight consumer does not pay much attention to it. If it is actually true, as we are told, that example is better than precept, then she may in the end come around to her folks' point of view—since with frankfurters at $.83 a pound, we are pretty much held down to protoplasmic spending through sheer force of circumstance. As to the quota, I cling to it with a certain amount of tenacity, but the little woman has been known to get the better of me. By unscrupulous methods, of course. Nevertheless, it is something of a comfort to have a definite policy; although a definite policy always gives you a sense of guilt when you do not live up to it.

How much money is enough for protoplasm? The question can only be answered by a long and careful scrutiny of one's buying habits; and by a breaking down of purchases into their basic categories of defensive buying, escape buying and buying for protoplasm. Defensive buying and escape buying are spending which is done in the hope —a hope doomed to disappointment—of stabilizing one's relations with other people. It is not, for example, defensive or escape buying to purchase a ticket to a play. It is both defensive and escape buying to pay $20 for a seat in order to see the play—and be seen at it—on the opening night.

The question of how much money is enough for protoplasm can, of course, be of interest only to people who are living above the subsistence level. In this discussion of money, not much has been said about the people who live on the subsistence level. This is partly because I have myself never lived on it; although I am like most middle-class people in that the mere passing fancy that I might be reduced to such a strait is enough to bring out the sweat on my forehead.

However, save as producers of guilt feelings in luckier human beings, the people on the subsistence level are not influential. If they were, they would not be on the subsistence level. Obviously, the Americans whose thinking about money is going to be the most influential are the

Americans who have got some to think about. But in a consuming society, with its constant sales pressure on chronically tense human beings, it is easy to feel that one is on the subsistence level when one is actually somewhat above it. Emotionally, of course, we are all on the subsistence level. But the answer to that chilly situation does not lie in the steady disbursal of funds.

The idea of using the needs of protoplasm as at least a partial answer to the Eggcup Civilization is not, I am sure, going to pass without challenge. The first and most spontaneous objection is likely to be, "But my protoplasm is rather special. It needs more money than other people's." This argument can safely be shelved until such time as it cuts some ice with an undertaker. A more respectable objection is likely to be, "But my need for beautiful pictures and beautiful fabrics and beautiful rooms is so basic and so chemical that it could certainly be described as a protoplasmic need."

However, the aesthete can justify his existence only by being artistic about the process of living itself. To be artistic about the process of living means that one's life, when it is over, should add up to something. To paint great pictures adds up to something. To buy great pictures—in preference to looking at them in museums—does not. It is impossible to express personality by spending money, even when the money is spent on the most priceless and beautiful objets d'art. To paint a picture one's self, even if it is execrable, is an expression of personality. But purchasing is not, and never can be, a form of self-expression; and the purchase of Beauty Itself is just as much escape buying as spending fifteen cents for a comic book.

Another objection to using the needs of protoplasm as a key to buying is likely to be made on a humbler, but much more important level. By women, it may be argued that the curls, the fingernail polish and the new dress—characterized here as defensive spending—are really protoplasmic spending, since without them, a woman could not either get married or stay married. This, to be sure, is what it says in the advertisements; but is it really true? Is there any way of wearing either a rhinestone pin from Woolworth's or a square-cut emerald so as to suggest that the wearer is tenderhearted, sympathetic, sensible, maternal, sexually undamaged, responsible and intelligent?

The pressure on American women to spend their way into womanliness is so enormous and unremitting and inescapable that it almost takes a decompression chamber to get away from it. Two thousand times a day, literally, the American woman is assured (a) that any woman who is not young and pretty is not a woman at all and (b) that any American woman can be young and pretty if she just buys this-or-that. In view of the pressure involved, it seems a little harsh and demanding to classify the curls, the fingernail polish and the new dress as defensive spending. But not to classify them thus is to go along with the advertisers (and the businessmen who hire them) in saying that a woman—just in and of herself, and without a nickel in her pocketbook—is less than the dust beneath the chariot wheels.

In a business society, women are one of the unbusiness-like minorities; women are a depressed class. Thus the curls, the fingernail polish and the new dress are certainly the most defensible of all defensive spending. But it is well to keep in mind a certain weird but comforting truth. In despite of the movies, the advertisements and popular fiction, women are in a position from which they are unlikely to be dislodged—no matter how little they spend on personal adornment. They happen to be the only other opposite sex there is. And a woman continues to be a woman —since there is, after all, nothing else she *can* be—for several decades after she gets her first wrinkle.

In asking the question of how much money is enough, it must be conceded that Americans are not ideally situated for finding the answer. We have to resist, not only the formal and organized pressure of the advertisers, but also the informal pressure of the people we come in contact with. My husband and I are probably not vastly different from many Americans in that we have both acquaintances and kissing kin who are strongly of the opinion that we do not earn and spend enough money. (The spending is important. Just earning it would not be sufficient.)

This is not to say that these are not nice people. Some of them are extremely nice—witty, intelligent and markedly generous. But they agree with the manufacturing Brahmins that all buying is good. They themselves do a great deal of defensive and escape buying; and they cannot completely hide their belief that if we would just shake off our sloth and get to work—neither of our professions being considered to merit that stern and beautiful word —we could easily acquire enough money to furnish our barren and makeshift second floor. The business society does not have to be taken lying down; but standing up to it requires a conscious effort. It is not child's play.

How much money is enough? I have not answered this question specifically, in terms of dollars and cents—nor do I intend to. For any given American, it is a personal matter, and it has to be worked out by the individual in terms of his own life situation. Furthermore, since the question is an individual and a personal one, it goes without saying that it does not have to be answered on behalf of anybody but one's self. If the reader wants to know what to do about his pleasant, generous, charitable, likable friend who is rich as Croesus, the answer is simple. Nothing. Let him take care of his own dualism. Nobody else can.

For the unquestioning disciple of the business-money-success society, no conceivable amount of money is enough. A parent does ultimately reach the end of the road. The children inevitably and unpreventably grow up, and for better or worse, the job is finally over. But nobody ever gets to the top in the business society, because in the business society, there is no top. Not if the top is defined as a place where one can rest from his labors (as my father could) in the contented knowledge that there is no further to go.

In the upper echelons of the business society, the quest for money is usually transformed into the quest for power

—power to mold public opinion, power to sway one's own or other governments, power to manipulate the lives of millions of strangers. But the Unholy Grail of power is just as frustrating as trying to achieve peace and dignity through more money than protoplasm needs. Power, like charity, begins at home. There can be only one life, the manipulation of which affords any real and lasting sense of triumph. That is one's own.

VII

The Rising Tide of Helplessness

———

THERE IS SOMETHING which needs to be said in a hurry. I have mentioned using protoplasm, and its comparatively simple needs, as a guide to buying. (For people above the subsistence level.) This does not mean, however, that anything is gained by turning off the water at the main and getting the aqua pura in buckets from the nearest stream. This writer's attitude toward protoplasm is one of respect, not unmixed with awe. I believe in treating it generously, no matter to whom it belongs.

Because of the age group into which I was born, I have been able to reminisce about the United States when it was still a producing society. I do not think, however, that either I or any of the other parents would be benefited by a return to the horse-and-buggy days. Mothers of small children do not usually have much wish to go back to the time when frozen foods, vacuum cleaners and washing machines had not yet come into general use. I am not, therefore, looking for a way back. I am looking for a way forward. But the way forward involves a slight exploration of the defensive and escape buying which use up such a large amount of American energy—sometimes to the unintentional detriment of the children. It also involves taking issue with some of the folklore and mythology about business which comes between us and reality.

There are a great many people in the United States who are weary of the kind of behavior which stems from the profit motive. Some of these people are individuals who have themselves showed no inconsiderable talent for earning money or making profits. But we all, business people and anti-business people alike, cling to the profit motive—disillusioning as it has shown itself to be. We cling to it because, according to business folklore, it is inextricably tied up with something we should quite properly be loath to relinquish—advanced medicine and labor-saving devices. The American business society, being the dominant one of our two societies, is in a positon to make its official contentions stick. And it is the official contention of the business society that if we dispense with profit-making attitudes, we automatically revert to the Stone Age—to operations without anesthesia, to early deaths and infant mortality and making soap in a caldron over a wood fire.

The fact that this belief is almost universally held in the United States—even by people who have no particular

154

love for American business—does not necessarily make it valid. In the past forty years, the business society has benevolently lightened the burden of homemaking to an almost unbelievable degree. What it took my mother hours to do, dusting and scrubbing on bended knee, I can do —with my vacuum cleaner and its attachments—in half an hour and standing nobly erect. But I am asured—all American housewives are assured—that we may only have our vacuum cleaners on the condition that souped-up junior executives give themselves ulcers trying to make more profit for their company than is being made by the vacuum cleaner company down the street.

This is taking a very limited view of junior executives. These junior executives go home to their wives and families, at the end of the business day, and try to be as kind and wise and full of vision as their state of fatigue permits. (We may safely assume that the junior executives have children, as the business society is considerably imperiled if they do not.) These junior executives go to P.T.A. meetings. They conscientiously endeavor to spend some time with the children. They have the children's teachers to dinner. If the children are in difficulties, they talk to a child psychologist or go to lectures on parenthood. For the sake of their own and other people's children, they sometimes take an active part in community activities.

The junior executives have, in short, two kinds of behavior: daytime behavior and evening behavior. It is the business society's inflexible contention that their daytime behavior represents the way they really want to behave.

155

It is the business society's contention that nobody in the vacuum cleaner company—employer or employees—could be induced to produce good vacuum cleaners except under the circumstance of grueling competition for money and financial advancement. But this has never been proved. And, indeed, it is a lower and more unflattering estimate of the American male than your correspondent is disposed to make.

If the junior executives' daytime behavior represents "human nature," their evening behavior represents "human nature," too. So far as anybody knows, it is perfectly possible for human beings to produce good vacuum cleaners without being flogged on from the rear by the wish for financial gain. The placid conviction that it is a fine thing for babies to have clean floors to play on and for mothers to have time to play with them could, quite conceivably, be a sufficient impetus for producing good vacuum cleaners. No one has ever succeeded in establishing any intrinsic connection between advanced medicine and labor-saving devices, on the one hand, and profit-making, on the other. The connection has been made. It has been made in the minds of practically everybody. But it has never been proved—any more than it has ever been proved that the Pueblo Indians' rain dances actually make it rain.

Ten or twelve years ago, when I was a feverishly gay divorcée, I spent more on myself alone than is now spent on my little brood of three. The gradual retreat from comparative luxury which has characterized the last decade of my life was not, as might be imagined, humiliating or degrading. On the contrary, it brought with it a certain feeling of freedom. For this feeling of freedom, I am somewhat indebted to the anthropologists. When I began reading in the social sciences, I took it for granted—as do most Americans—that the United States, with its liberating and humanitarian machines, represents the highest type of civilization yet developed by the race of man. But this apparently cheerful assumption raises, for a good many people, a disturbing question. "If the United States is the finest flowering so far of the human race, then why am I not happier in it?" Despite the advertisements and the Bath of Perfection, human beings know themselves to be incurably imperfect. Hence they are often driven to answer the question despairingly. "Well, there must be something wrong with me."

The anthropologists do not back themselves into any such dismal corner. To them, the United States is simply one of many societies, past and present, which resemble each other in having both advantages and disadvantages for the people who live in them. This point of view is rather a jolt at first; but upon getting accustomed to it, it is remarkably emancipating. The social scientists do not say that the United States is the best civilization yet developed. Instead, they ask, "Best for whom? For the children, perhaps?" We have the report of Margaret Mead that Samoan society, for instance, is much easier on children and young people than the American business society.

I am an amateurish and undisciplined dabbler in the

social sciences, but they have nevertheless had a considerable effect on the way I run my house and spend the family funds. Reading about people in non-business societies—or even in business societies other than ours—made some of my previous rituals in pursuit of having things nice seem rather unnecessary and, indeed, a bit tribal and primitive. I save a good deal of time and energy by reason of the fact that to me, the Duchess of Windsor is just another aborigine—though no doubt a very pleasant woman.

This does not mean that I know how to live serenely in a money society. I do not. As has already been noted, nobody—literally nobody—rises above the society which bred and trained him. One of the sources of tension between me and my little girl is the fact that she does not know how to hurry; whereas I am so much the creature of my time and place, that I can seldom make myself stop hurrying. In theory, I believe in leisure; but I can only act slowly and deliberately when my teeth are clenched. Nor have I been able to achieve, with my best efforts, any more than a partial and tentative freedom from that atmospheric training about money which all Americans receive.

I worry about money, as my publishers can testify. I rebel against it by not keeping my checkbook balanced. I am inclined to be sour and uncharitable about people whose old age seems in a fair way to be nicely cushioned. And when it comes to being the captive of materialism and empty show, it must be admitted that this volume would have been published a month sooner, had I not been tempted beyond my strength to paint the kitchen.

In making the statement that in a divided society, there are no pure types, I know whereof I speak. However, by no longer having the money to spend which I once had, I more or less accidentally achieved a little free time in which to speculate upon the nature of spending.

A good deal of what Americans buy, beyond the needs of their human flesh, is bought either as a defense against or an escape from an environment which is intuitively felt to be harsh and unfriendly. As described by one who has done a great deal of it, defensive spending is spending which is done to avoid being considered odd and peculiar and in order to have something to talk about with other people. Most of the purchases of television sets come under the head of defensive spending. So does a good deal of the money laid out in the United States for clothing and cosmetics. Defensive spending is peculiar to the United States, and is not nearly so characteristic of the Western European business societies as it is of ours.

In order to understand the necessity for defensive spending—and it actually is necessary—a few comparisons must be made with the other business societies. If the people in the Western European business societies do not go in as much for defensive spending as we do, it is not simply because they do not have the money, and we do. The answer lies further back in time than that. Among the other business societies, the United States is unique. It is the most highly developed of all the business societies. It is the one in which business activity is the most far-flung, all-pervasive, intensive and extensive.

The United States is also the business society in which, at the present time, radicals, crackpots, left-wingers, intellectuals, Utopians, eccentrics and various other sound and unsound critics of the social order get the roughest and most intolerant treatment. The Western European business societies are in considerably more danger of Russian invasion than we are, but they have not been characterized by the hysteria, smear tactics, witch hunting and merciless punishment of nonconformists which have blotted our escutcheon. England, France, Holland and Belgium have not even produced—much less elevated to a position of prestige—any such quirksome and erratic moralists as Elizabeth Bentley and Whittaker Chambers. When it comes to eccentrics, deviants, saints and sinners, the other business societies ride the punches.

This is not to say that the English business society, to take one example, is made up of nobler people than ours is. The English fell just as hard as we did for the illusion that money, over and above the needs of protoplasm, makes people happier and that making money therefore comes first. H. G. Wells and D. H. Lawrence were among many English writers who discoursed with biting eloquence about the disastrous effect of British business on British life and character. And when it comes to grinding in the faces of the poor, the early British industrialists of the nineteenth century hung up something pretty close to the world's record. The gin-sodden misery of the British working classes, in the opening years of the Industrial Revolution, has not been paralleled in the United States.

The English business society, however, has evolved more slowly than the American business society. The reason for this comparative slowness of pace lies in the fact that England, like the other business societies of Western Europe, is a small, long-settled country with a great many years of English history behind it. Much of the prosperity of these other business societies—while they were prosperous —was based on the fact that they had colonial empires. The point worthy of especial note is that these colonial empires lay overseas. The populations thereof did not have to be absorbed by the folks at home. The United States, on the other hand, was in a manner of speaking its own colonial empire. Unlike the other business societies, when the United States expanded, it had to absorb, too. Or try to.

The English, like the other Western European nationals, have lived together for a long time. They know each other well. The English do not speak of Scandinavian-Englishmen, Spanish-Englishmen or Irish-Englishmen as we speak of Scandinavian-Americans, Spanish-Americans or Irish-Americans. The Americans have not lived together for a long time and they do not know each other well. The United States, compared to the other business societies, is a nation of strangers in a bulky and variegated homeland. The United States is still on its shakedown cruise.

It was probably inevitable that in the United States, the Eggcup Civilization should reach a peak of development unequaled in the other money societies. American business is not generally regarded by scholars and classicists as a thing of beauty and a joy forever, but it has nevertheless performed an amazing job. It has done something which the businessmen in the other business societies did not have to do. It has welded together into a social unit a huge and heterogeneous population with no uniform history behind it and not even a uniform climate in common. The welding job was accomplished by inducing everybody—from the Atlantic to the Pacific and from the Great Lakes to the Gulf of Mexico—to buy the same things at the same time.

But although the job was amazing, it was fruitless. American buying cannot do for the Americans what English history has done for the English. By making people ashamed and afraid to wear old clothes and drive old cars, it is possible to give them a certain superficial resemblance to one another. But it is not possible to give them much comfort in their hearts, or the kind of unity that will stand up under pressures like the Battle of Britain and twelve years of scanty, rationed food. American business and American buying have not been able to give the American something he needs very badly.

That something is the sense of belonging—the sense of being a part of something larger, older and better established than any single individual could be. The other business societies are smaller, poorer and less efficient than ours; but history and geography have conspired to make them more homogeneous. Between one Frenchman and another, there are two thousand years of France. The people in the other business societies, therefore, do not have to look for brotherhood through buying things to the same extent that we do. What is significant about American purchasing is not its volume—although that is the only thing we ever hear about it. What is significant about American purchasing is the unconscious search for unity and kinship which lies behind a good deal of it.

It is important to recognize defensive spending for what it is—money down a rathole. Defensive spending is money laid out for a momentary respite from a harsh and narrowly critical environment—i.e., the business-dominated United States. Defensive spending is money laid out for protective coloration. It is money spent both to keep from being talked about and to have something to talk about. But its effects, though temporarily benevolent and relaxing, are not permanent. It does not permanently alter for the better the impossible relationship between the warmth-seeking human being and the most highly developed business society in the world.

Another form of American spending, escape buying, is also money down a rathole. Escape buying has already been mentioned as having its roots in the feeling of personal powerlessness. All human beings want and need intervals of feeling personally powerful. They want and need power over their heavenly garment of protoplasm so that it will digest peacefully, sleep restfully, respond sexually and in general perform to the gratification of the tenant. They also want and need power over their environment— power to make the environment produce food and shelter, power to make their votes felt in the government, power

163

to make their opinions felt with the local School Board, power to develop their talents in whatever direction those talents want to go. But for all his society's magnificent conquests of Nature, the one thing the mid-century American has not got is the feeling of personal power.

One reason for this aching void is that, economically, we actually are powerless. Only the merest handful of mid-century Americans, compared to the total population, is in a position to throw its weight around economically.* This is not anybody's fault. What happens when a business society moves is that, in a manner of speaking, the money drifts to the top and the people drift to the bottom. *All* the people drift to the bottom—the ones who appear to be riding herd, as well as the ones who appear to be ridden.

The congregation of producers and employers grows continually smaller (and lonelier and more frightened) and the congregation of consumers and employees grows continually larger (and lonelier and more frightened). The phrase "labor and capital" goes out of use and is supplanted by the phrase "labor and management." But "management" is simply a collection of employees whose salaries will buy them anything in the world except a chance to take the bit in their teeth. With the natural evolution of American business, we are becoming a nation of hired hands. And not, unfortunately, the kind of hired hands who sit down at the table with the family.

The drift of a business society is toward impersonality.

---

* To be sure, the American can make himself felt as part of a pressure group, but this is not *personal* power.

In human terms, this means everyone suffers, in his role as a person. As has already been noted, American chronic unhappiness is no respecter of incomes. Because of the underdevelopment of affection and the overemphasis on aggression, competitiveness and skepticism, personalness—like privacy—is going out of our society. When that happens, the personal human being—no matter where he stands on the income scale—suffers increasingly from the feeling of having no personal power. Only by purchasing—whether it be a pair of kitchen curtains, a baronial estate, an extra pair of play shoes, or somebody else's long-established business—can he have a momentary sensation of having some avoirdupois to heave about. The point to be emphasized is that the sensation is momentary. It does not last. The buying has to be done over and over and over again.

Another element which is responsible for the feeling of personal powerlessness lies in a simple but drastically important fact. Although the United States is dominated by its business society, most of the people in the United States are not businesslike. The children are not businesslike. The women are not businesslike. The people who educate the children are not businesslike. The people who work for the government are not businesslike. The artists are not businesslike, and neither are the aged, the ill or the unemployed. Even the businessmen themselves are not businesslike after five o'clock. At least, they hope they are not, and they try not to be.

If the question is put—What is escape buying an escape *from*?—the answer is that it is an escape from a situation which, to Americans, is well-nigh intolerable. That situation can be summed up as follows: That with the automatic and unplanned evolution of the business society, American business is coming increasingly to dominate the unbusinesslike American population in a fashion which is painfully similar—in operation if not in intent —to the way the Communist Party dominates the Russian population.

The merest nodding acquaintance with Russian history, however, indicates that the Russians have been accustomed for a great many centuries to having no personal power. They are not brought up to expect it. Americans, on the other hand, have had—up to now—the liveliest expectation of feeling personally powerful. When, in some apparently mysterious way, that feeling does not materialize, they feel baffled, frustrated and cheated, and they take the only way out which seems to be open. Either with resplendent cash or on the installment plan, they buy things over and above the needs of protoplasm—seeking, even though it is only for the moment, the enhancing and entrancing sensation of being dominant, of being responsible and of having things under control.

It is the feeling of having no personal power which lies at the bottom of many of the quarrels Americans have with each other. When a person is haunted by the feeling of having no personal power, he always assumes that although he does not have it, somebody else does. The banker thinks that the union leader must have it. The union leader thinks that the Chairman of the Board must have it. Actually, of course, nobody has it. The drift of money to the top and people to the bottom, characteristic of an uncontrolled and swiftly evolving business society, cannot be laid at the door of single human beings. It is simply the natural, unsurprising and inevitable result of applauding profit-making characteristics and of rejecting the Bankruptcy Qualities as weak and unmanly.

Two things are primarily associated with the name of the United States. Money and machines. Both American machinery and American corporate finance are so awesomely intricate that no single human being can hope to master either of them, in their entirety. But Americans have the reputation of being the fellows who know what makes things tick. The fact that they cannot construct or operate a calculating machine which can remember a million separate items, or that they do not know what you do when you want to sell the Empire State Building, gives them—once again—a horrifying feeling that the environment is out of control.

Americans accept the obligation to know how things work, and when they cannot meet the obligation, they feel depressed and helpless. But perhaps the environment is not out of control. Perhaps it merely seems out of control because our approach to it is wrong. The important question about American machinery and American finance is not, "How do they work?" The important question is, "What is their purpose?" If one understands their purpose, it is not necessary to know how they work

To the question, "What is their purpose?" the answer is not complex, but exceedingly simple. The purpose of American machinery and American corporate finance is to make money. And the purpose of the money is to compensate for the underdevelopment of affection. The purpose of the money is to provide the security and stability which can only properly be supplied by the family, past or present. The purpose of the money is to provide a defense in depth against the rigors and uncertainties of existence which, in actuality, can only be supplied by the Bankruptcy Qualities. The purpose of the money, on all economic levels except the subsistence one, is to serve as a sort of emotional Scotch tape for holding together people who, through no fault of their own, might come unstuck without it.

This purpose is, of course, foredoomed to failure. But although the picture seems a cheerless one, it should be recollected that the business society is not our only society. If there is an answer to the question of how much money is enough—and there is—that answer comes to us, not from the business society, but from the anti-business America. If there are better methods of defense and escape than relying on money for magical results—and there are—those methods must be looked for in the anti-business society. If there is a place in American life where one may expect to find simplicity, instead of numbing complexity, that place is in our official national morality—the Judeo-Christian ethic. It would now seem to be time, therefore, to give a little study and attention to the other side of the coin.

VIII

The Successful Failures

WHEN I was a child, the householders in our neighborhood used to lean on their rakes, on Saturday afternoons, and "talk politics" across the privet or barberry hedges. Politics, however, was not the province of women and children, and what the political complexion of our community was, I could not say. I do recall that my father was president of the local Civic Association for several years when it was at its most active and efficient. And my mother—though astronomically shy and completely allergic to the platform and the dais—accepted, out of a sense of duty, the presidency of the P.T.A. for one year.

No particular emphasis was placed on these activities, and I recall, in addition, that my mother did not join the Red Cross during World War I. The Red Cross women rolled bandages in the basement of the public school every

Wednesday night, and I remember hearing my parents say that the good ladies were inefficient bandage-rollers, were too gossipy and were more concerned with the becomingness of the white coifs they wore than with the staunching of blood. In our household, not much allowance was made for human weakness—the unstated philosophy being that the Deity had put us on this planet for the express purpose of overcoming it.

What my parents stressed verbally, in bringing me up, was "proper" behavior and "being a little lady." What they actually handed down to me was the idea of participating in some way in community life, and the further idea that one could afford to be a little thoughtful about this participation. I should like to pass on to my daughter at least as much as was handed down to me, and I think it would be convenient for her if I could do it a little less blindly. Children need love, as everyone is prepared to admit. But they need something more than that—and this is a point which is too often overlooked in the books on child care. They need a clear definition of what constitutes personal virtue.

All human beings have a deep craving to be "moral" or "good." "Goodness," of course, means different things in different parts of the world and at different periods of history, but the important question for the compassionate American parent is what it means here and now in the United States. To trace the outlines of the American business society is easy enough. It is the dominant one of our two societies; it is literally never silent; and it invades in

some way or other every single one of our waking hours.
But to define and understand the anti-business society is
a much harder job.

It will readily be understood that this chapter is going
to be more difficult for both reader and writer than the
preceding ones. It involves what is known to the trade as
a change of pace. Any cheerful and self-confident house-
wrecker can point to where people are doing the wrong
thing. The results tell the story; and destructive criticism
is downhill work. But to discover (a) what is the right
thing to do and (b) how to go about doing it is slow, painful, tedious, unpopular and generally uninviting. It has
nothing to recommend it except that the children need to
have it done.

Furthermore, "goodness" and doing the right thing always involve intangibles. The business society has given
all of us One Hundred and Ten Easy Lessons in putting
the tangibles first—the house, the car, the furniture, the
clothes, the television set, the Rembrandt original or the
week end at the Waldorf. Even with the best will in the
world, it is hard to shake off the semi-hypnotic influence
of American business. And it is the view of American business that the tangibles come first, and the intangibles exist
only to be snatched up at the last minute—just in case
there should, after all, be a God and we should be lucky
enough for Him to be a half-wit.

Here is perhaps as good a place as any to make an explanation. A great deal is being said in this book about
the Judeo-Christian ethic. The present writer is not, how-

ever, trying to prove anything about whether that ethic is, or is not, of divine origin. The whole point about it is that it was meant to be used. It may have come down from Heaven, or it may have been worked out by a pastoral and by-no-means-wholly-Caucasian society at the eastern end of the Mediterranean. Its function, however, not its origin, is the important thing about it. And its function is to give meaning and purpose to life. Its function is to guide people's behavior so that they will do the minimum of harm either to themselves or to other people.

By this time it is perhaps also unnecessary to add that morality does not mean only sexual morality. A good many Americans have been alienated from the Judeo-Christian ethic by the circumstance that, in the hands of our forebears, it often seemed to stand for rigid sexual repression and for very little else. But punitive sexual codes are a misuse—not a use—of ethics, which are designed to embrace all human activities and not just one.

Hence, although the admission is probably disastrous, not much attention is being paid to sex in these pages. In a business society, the role of sex can be summed up in five pitiful little words. There is money in it. In a business society, where everything else, from diapers to death, is commercialized, sex is obviously going to be commercialized, too. Although a great deal of anxious attention is paid to American sexual problems, they seem to this writer to be a symptom—a surface phenomenon—and not a first cause. In a society where tenderness is a Bankruptcy Quality and the province of nincompoops, sex is obviously going to be baffling and unsatisfactory to a great many people.

I am one of those not-very-highly-regarded little house-wives who is bathed in sex all day long by American advertisers. They disguise it by calling it "glamour." I am inclined to think, however, that the process of making tidy profits by pandering to the poor old housewife's dreams of glamour sometimes ends up with the biter bit. At least, I deduce from reading the newspapers and the novels on the best-seller list that the satraps and pro-consuls of the business society are as much victimized by cast-iron notions of Perfect Love, Perfect Romance, Perfect Beauty and Perfect Mates as are we hewers of wood and drawers of water. One gets the impression that the exploiters differ from the exploited only in having a little more mobility. The advertisers and the public-relations gentlemen are sometimes free to wear themselves out running after the dream, whereas the housewife does not usually get much chance to drag her anchor.

It does not occur to us often enough that this substitution of glamour for sex—and other equally dubious substitutions—is the work of the communications industry. This writer is aware that in discussing the American communications industry, she is practically begging to have her ears pinned back. There is a belief in the United States—as firmly clung to as a canon of sacred law—that only newspapermen, ex-newspapermen, publishers and cinema tycoons can speak with intelligence and authority about the communications industry. But I am endeavoring to hack out a little clearing, in the wilderness of money and myths, for my daughter to grow up in. Speaking simply as a parent, I cannot afford to recognize anybody —however illustrious or well-seasoned—as an authority on the communications industry whose experience of that industry does not include frequent pressure from a tiny consumer to buy Howdy-Doody Cookies.

Hacking out the clearing means trying to identify and recognize the other of our two American societies—the anti-business America. In this search, there are two preliminary jobs to be done; and the first of these is to assign the American communications industry—the movies, the popular magazines, the comics, the newspapers and radio-television—to its proper place in the scheme of things.

One of the major tenets of this book is that American life, in reality, is not nearly so complex as most people think it is. And the relationship of the American population to the communications industry is extremely simple. We are dependent on it. The dependence is not a healthy one; but as I will not do my daughter much good by chasing rainbows, it may as well be frankly admitted that very little can be done about this dependence—except to recognize and understand it.

We are not dependent on the output of the communications industry because that output is prevailingly wise, creative, challenging, inspiring and spiritually nourishing. It is admitted by all thoughtful persons that this output— at least, as far as advertising and entertainment are concerned—is for the most part shabby and tawdry. Compared, at any rate, with what it could be. We are nevertheless dependent on that output because, being Americans, we are tortured by conflicting goals and we therefore cannot afford to spend much time alone with our thoughts. Those thoughts, followed to their logical conclusions, would be too dismaying. The enormous influence and great prosperity of the communications industry, consequently, are not due solely to the virtue and intelligence of the communicators. They are based in part on the uncertainty, tension and fatigue of the communicants.

My little girl's father is in the field of adult education, and that means evening classes. When I am working alone around the kitchen, after my daughter has gone to bed, I usually turn on the radio. Since I am totally unmusical, symphonies are not my cup of tea; and for us tone-deaf clods, the evening radio fare is depressing and mechanical to a degree. I am, however, an American and a product of the American environment; and my tolerance for silence is therefore not very high. Forced to choose between an inferior distraction or no distraction at all, I choose the inferior distraction.

As has already been mentioned, in our household we do not take in the Sunday paper. Every seventh day, the United States—no matter what desperate straits it is in—has to get along without any attention from my husband and me. To date, the neglected commonwealth has always managed to squeak through anyway. But the first few Lord's Days this regime was in operation, my helpmeet had to ask—like Odysseus going past the sirens—to be tied to the mast.

Tense people—trying to live decently in the cynical, competitive and unaffectionate business climate—need distraction, even if it is only the unsatisfying distraction of reading what other tense people have to say about Korea, Indo-China or the Russians. Similarly, the fact that a great many Americans turn the knob and light up the dial does not actually *prove* that they do it with a pleasant feeling of anticipation. A great many prisoners pick oakum, but not usually after they are sprung.

To say that the bond between communicators and communicants is not a uniformly noble one is not, however, to condemn the communicators out of hand. The American communications industry is the most visible (and audible) of all American businesses. It is the mouthpiece of all the others, who, without it, would have no way of reaching the consumer except through contagious enthusiasm about the merit of their products. The communications industry is not only the most conspicuous of all American businesses, but it is also the one in which the division between the two American societies is most painfully apparent. It is an outward projection—an externalization, as the psychologists would say—of that uncomfortable and exhausting indecisiveness which, to a greater or lesser degree, afflicts all American-trained human beings.

Of all American businesses, the communications industry is the one most in need—from the point of view of the human beings involved—of compassionate appraisal. The steel industry does not have much trouble keeping the wolf from the door, and it is not without influence on American life. But most Americans are not vividly conscious of the girders and I-beams which hold up their stores, office buildings or apartments. The communications industry, on the other hand, makes a great deal—though not all—of its money out of banality, clichés, hackneyed old stereotypes and safely uninspired points of view. The banality and clichés are not decently hidden behind cement blocks or brick facing. They are right out there in the open for the customers to feel—consciously or unconsciously—dejected and frustrated about. Or angry and openly critical.

Nor is it only the customers. The communications industry suffers from a hideous and terrifying disability. It has to hire sensitive, well-educated people. Within its seething bosom, communications probably contains more disappointed, disillusioned and unhappy individuals than any other outfit in the bright hierarchy of the market place. Young Americans go into heavy steel with no further notion than that they will make money by participating in the production and distribution of that commodity. Toward communications, however, young people are frequently drawn by the idea that they will have a chance to set down an honest and fruitful reaction or two to life as they find it. (And perhaps also make money.) Expecting to be primarily communicators, and only secondarily businessmen, they discover that, in any business, it has to be the other way around.

But once having tasted the heady wine of communicating—even watered-down, as it is in a money-and-success
Republic—it is virtually impossible to change course and
resign one's self to selling steel. Unlike the people on the
other side of the fence, communicators are born, not made.
In our country, however, they are not born under a lucky
star. The ghosts of Shakespeare and Tacitus do not pay
much attention to heavy steel, but those mocking and derisive shades are always picking bouquets of nettles for the
crossed-up people in the word business.

The American communications industry produces three
things—advertising, entertainment and information. To
the charge that its advertising is frequently vulgar and its
entertainment more often than not pitiable, the industry
does not customarily react with very much heat and spirit.
But in its role as a news-gathering agency—in its function
as a collector and distributor of "the news" or "the facts"
or "the truth"—it is a red-hot champion of itself. And, indeed, even among the communicants, a good many honest
and intelligent people believe that communications does
penance for its sins and justifies its existence by its role in
distributing the news. Where the news is concerned, even
fairly sophisticated Americans generally take it for granted
that the press and its sister institutions operate—at least in
a rough sort of way—as a vessel of truth.

As has already been noted, however, we recognize truth
by the fact that insofar as we can lay hold of it, it sets us
free. It is liberating. It clears away superstitions and crippling misapprehensions. It dissolves tension. We recognize

truth-seekers through the fortunate circumstance that in five thousand years of recorded history, the human race has produced quite a few of them. Euclid and Sigmund Freud were in pursuit of truth, and both of them succeeded in capturing a segment of it. Between Euclid and Sigmund Freud on the one hand, however, and the American news-gatherers on the other, there is an important distinction. Euclid and Sigmund Freud were not also in business.

The news-gatherers cannot give us all the facts. There are too many of them. The news has to be edited—there is no way around that. And since the news-gatherers are in business, and bound by business convention to make the maximum possible amount of profit, what they give us is not "the facts," but the *salable* facts. A fact, of course, can be true in the Euclidean sense and still be salable. On the other hand, the circumstance of its being true in the Euclidean sense sometimes makes it completely unsalable— at least, in the view of a success-minded management which believes that even the news must entertain and which is in a position to operate on this somewhat peculiar theory.

The claim of the press and radio-television that—where the news is concerned—they serve at least approximately as a vessel of truth can by no means be entirely disallowed. On the other hand, it cannot be accepted without a certain amount of scrutiny. The matter boils down to a fairly simple question: How much emancipating truth can you collect, put together and distribute when your first and primary obligation—or even your secondary obligation—is to show a profit and keep the banks and the stockholders happy?

The answer is not long and wearisome. Some, but not enough. Some, but not enough to quiet the troubled conscience. Some, but not enough to satisfy the creative instinct and leave the creative person feeling contented and fulfilled. Some, but not enough to be wholeheartedly accepted as an authority and a leader of men. Some, but not enough to keep the communicants from going off by themselves every four years and electing their own boy to the Presidency.

In our time, the news-gatherers—and especially well-known columnists, political reporters and foreign correspondents—are regarded with respect, attention and reverence because they are supposed to have the "inside dope." But this suggests a query. Why should there *be* any "inside dope"? If a man writes a column or a newspaper story, and tells all the facts, then the reader of that piece is just as well informed as the writer. The dope—that is to say—is outside. If the man writes the piece and does not tell all the facts—if the dope remains inside—then the reader is entitled to ask why some of the facts were withheld.

Was the writer afraid of losing his job? And if so, what may be inferred about the purity and integrity of his employers? Or did the writer think it would not be good for the reader to know all the facts? And in that case, where did he—or his employers—derive the authority to act as an arbiter of what is good for the reader?

Access to the wire services does not heal the painful split in the American personality. It merely gives the people who have it a great deal of information. It does not teach them how to use the information. It is not a North Star by which they can navigate. The American communicators probably suffer more from the rift in American life than any other group of employers and employees in the country. It must be said to their credit that, in spite of the difficulty, they appear to handle the split personality about as well as anybody else. *But they do not handle it any better*. If there *is* any "inside dope"—that is it.

In examining the claim of the news-gatherers that they serve as a truth-disseminating agency, a distinction must be made between truth and information. It is often said of Americans—indeed, we often say it of ourselves—that we are a pragmatic and practical race of people and that we like "the facts." A fact, however, has no life of its own. It is mere deadwood until it is put together with other facts to make a structure which has usefulness, significance and purpose. It is not quite accurate to say that Americans like "the facts." There is a certain kind of fact which we like—the isolated fact. The enormous success of "Information, Please" and similar sorts of quiz shows is evidence that we like the truth—but only when it is an orphan.

Karl Marx once said that religion is the opiate of the people. In our country, however, it is not religion but information which is the opiate of the people. One New York radio station concludes all its news broadcasts with the announcement that an informed America is a free

America. Actually, America is in the process of being smothered by information—of a certain type. Along some lines, America is not only informed. It is overinformed.

If a well-known movie star travels in Europe with a man not her husband, no expense is spared to make the folks at home aware of the situation. But having gotten the information, what are we supposed to do with it? Write the girl a letter and tell her to come home? This is only one, all-too-easily duplicated example of how communications—trying desperately to live up to its two self-imposed obligations of purveying the truth and fattening up the exchequer—gets off the Euclidean beam. Information we have in abundance, but a good deal of it is pointless, useless and extremely difficult to be practical or pragmatic about. And some of it—as the Lindbergh kidnaping so dreadfully illustrated—we are just simply not entitled to. "Human interest" slides by the easiest of gradations (and degradations) into subhuman interest.

In the last analysis, what counts, in communications, is content—not noise or volume or infinite repetition. It is often said that the late President Roosevelt owed a great deal of his popularity to radio. One may regard Franklin Delano Roosevelt's impact on the American social structure as good or bad, but the social structure would have felt that impact, even if radio had not been invented until after Mr. Roosevelt died. Radio simply hastened a process that would have taken place anyway.

President Roosevelt had something to say to his grateful electorate—or beggarly adherents, however one chooses to describe them—which, at the time, they wanted to hear. Had radio (or the newspapers) not been in existence, people would have written each other letters about it or passed it on by word of mouth. It was the content of the Fireside Chats, not the fact that they were on the radio, which accounted for their great influence. Had the content been unacceptable, not all the money or "promotion" in the world could have forced the American public to listen to them. The business society conditions and influences us because we cannot get away from it. The Chief Executive, however, we can get away from.

Radio cannot take the credit for having "made" President Roosevelt without also taking the blame for having "made" Hitler. Actually, of course, machines are unselective and do not discriminate between one sort of user and another. What counts, in communication, is content; and what also counts—although not enough attention is paid to the fact—is the communicants. The communicators, defending themselves against the charge that so much of their output is utterly ordinary, sometimes say that the masses of the American people have the mind of a twelve-year-old child. The indictment is not as damning as it is intended to be. An affectionately treated twelve-year-old child has more on the ball than a warped, despairing cynic of forty-two. And history has already demonstrated that there is a highly significant difference—in terms of mass behavior—between the twelve-year-old American communicants and the twelve-year-old Germans.

If one is trying to trace the outlines of the anti-business

America, the communications industry is the last place in the world to look. The reason for this is simply that these outlines are not what is called newsworthy. The anti-business America is based on Christian morality, and the goal of Christian morality is for people to get along well together *outside the framework of making money.*

Some of our giant corporations go in rather heavily, in their personnel programs, for what they refer to as "human relations." In fact, "human relations" is the new twist in modern management. Wistful management yearns to get off the cross of gold. But since management's "human relations" must always be conducted within the suffocating confines of profit-making, they are jinxed from the start.

To the extent that non-money-making human relations are successful—as Negro-white relations were successful at the Stage Door Canteen, for instance—they are not messy, bloody, lurid, dramatic, provocative or exciting. They are not, in the communicators' view, salable. It is possible, of course, that the communicators may be making a mistake about the salability. Some pre-industrial observers came up with just the opposite opinion. "How beautiful upon the mountains," they said, "are the feet of him who bringeth glad tidings, who publisheth peace."

The American communications industry is a business. Save for the one particular of being more shot through with personal anguish, it differs in no respect from any other American business. Therefore it cannot speak for the anti-business America. In its output, occasional transient inklings and fugitive glimmerings of the Judeo-Christian ethic can be discerned. But not the mother lode.

The business society makes the secondary mistake of treating both its enemies—Communism and the Judeo-Christian ethic—as one and the same thing. But it does not make the primary mistake of failing to recognize an enemy when it sees one. When the American ethic goes into action—when, that is, American human beings put it into action—those Americans are almost invariably treated by communications as the enemies of business. And therefore of itself. In this, the communications industry is quite right. Such Americans actually are the enemies of business. Business has a great many enemies. It also has a great many captives, not all of them willing.

The place to look for the Bankruptcy Qualities is, so to speak, among the bankrupts. Parents cannot hope to accomplish their job—much less enjoy it—unless they are able to pass on to their children some fairly workable idea of what constitutes personal virtue. In this responsibility, the movies, the popular magazines, the comics, the newspapers and radio-television are not of much use to American fathers and mothers. Those flourishing institutions have little to offer parents except the somewhat quavering assertion that they have found out how to serve both God and Mammon. On the subject of personal virtue, the source and the authority is the anti-business America.

If the anti-business America is to be grasped and made to yield up some of its riches, the communications industry must first be seen for what it truly is. And there is yet another job which has to be done. This second job is to retrieve the phrase "do-gooder" from the ignominy which currently surrounds it. If further proof is needed that communications speaks for the business, and not for the anti-business, society, one has only to consider that the American press is responsible for the fact that the phrase "do-gooder" has a highly uncomplimentary connotation to Americans.

This connotation, the communications industry has succeeded in selling to everybody. Probably the only point upon which American liberals and American conservatives are in complete agreement is the belief that the phrase "do-gooder" should be surrounded by quotation marks, when written, and inflected condescendingly, when spoken. My little girl, if she is alive fifty years from now, will not be able to hear the inflections. But the quotation marks will still be on the record. And I think she and her contemporaries may find it extremely puzzling that "doing good" should have been regarded, by mid-century Americans of every conceivable type, as a bad thing.

In the United States, in the middle of the twentieth century, the best the do-gooders * can expect is to be apologized for. "He's a do-gooder, but he's a swell guy anyway." Only do-gooders of exceptional personal charm rate this accolade. True, it seems like a rather grudging plaudit; but compared to the way do-gooders are usually men-

---

* From here on, I shall omit the quotation marks. They are too much trouble.

tioned, it is positively doting. That a do-gooder is an unattractive person is, in our day and age, taken for granted.
But perhaps it should be explained, for the benefit of future generations, that not everyone is agreed as to why
do-gooders are unattractive.

Sometimes they are considered unattractive because it is
assumed that they are simply disguised cynics. It is assumed, that is, that they have cooked up some ingenious
little racket which pays off very well and have chosen to
conceal it behind a sickening display of virtue. Of course,
the people who take this view of do-gooders are more unconsciously self-revealing than they would consciously
choose to be. A second reason why do-gooders are considered unattractive is that they are believed to be meddling,
interfering busybodies. "Meddling," however, is a meaningless word unless one also states what the meddler is
meddling with. A surgeon who removes a tumor could be
described, in the strictest accuracy, as meddling and interfering with the course of Nature. And as a matter of fact,
there have been times in the history of medicine when
certain physicians were referred to, with considerable heat,
in just this way. My little girl, too—if she were old enough
to use the words—could certainly point to occasions when
she considered my behavior both meddlesome and revolt-
ingly intrusive.

For the benefit, once again, of a future generation, it
should be explained that nobody is antagonistic toward do-
gooders because they have high ideals. In the United
States, everybody has high ideals. What makes the do-good-

ers unattractive is that they act upon these ideals and more often than not, the action is rather fumbling. If there is one thing the American people cannot stand, it is a fumbler. The American, steeped to the eyebrows in precision machines, feels more relaxed and at home with a competent, skillful evil-doer than with a good man who is all thumbs.

Another reason why do-gooders are considered unattractive is that they are always on the defensive. This permanent defensiveness is usually explained as neuroticism. But while it is quite true that do-gooders are always on the defensive, this behavior is not neurotic, but completely rational. The do-gooders are always on the defensive because they are always in danger of attack. To do good in a money-and-success society—even fumblingly, even amateurishly, even part time—is to thumb one's nose at the tribal totem pole of personal advancement and financial prowess.

The last, and possibly the most telling, argument against the do-gooders is that they are so often overearnest and humorless. Against this charge, they cannot be defended—except possibly by suggesting that it is not so much that they are overearnest and humorless as that they are overearnest and humorless about the wrong things. In their long and active careers, neither Governor Dewey nor Senator Taft has ever been taxed with being a muddleheaded do-gooder; but their very own lieutenants are reported in the public prints as sighing a little sadly over the fact that Presidential timber is sometimes just that.

In trying to grasp, define and put to better use the other
America—the anti-business society—it is of the utmost importance to salvage the phrase "do-gooder" and relieve it
of its present connotation of knavery and idiocy. The
words "do-gooder" mean exactly what they say. A do-gooder
is someone who does good. A do-gooder is someone who
either preserves or improves life. The most illuminating
way to define a do-gooder is to describe him in terms of his
opposite. The opposite of a do-gooder is not, as might be
supposed, a do-badder. The confirmed do-badders are almost all confined in institutions. In the normal walks of
life, the opposite of a do-gooder is a talk-gooder.

A society split the way ours is split produces, under-
standably enough, a bumper crop of talk-gooders. A
talk-gooder, however, is interested in virtue; whereas a do-
gooder is interested in his own personal virtue. The difference between the two is roughly commensurate with the
difference between being dead or being alive. The talk-
gooder applauds generously (and breathes a sigh of relief)
when some person or persons two thousand miles away
gets a Caucasian church opened to Negro communicants.
The do-gooder says shakily, "Bring me my bow of lukewarm gold," and tackles his own "hardheaded," "realistic"
vestrymen.

Do-gooders, in the United States, are in such undeserv-
edly ill repute that very little has been said or written
about them—in the communications industry, at any rate
—except in the way of uneasy condescension or contemptu-

ous dismissal.* There are, nevertheless, enough of them so that they can be divided into two kinds. Usually, the phrase is employed in a socio-political sense; but the words have a basic, philosophical meaning which needs to be understood before they are whittled down to the narrower political meaning. To use "do-gooder" in this basic, philosophical sense—meaning someone who preserves or improves life—is to see immediately that there are millions and millions of do-gooders in the United States. Mothers, for instance. Or housewives. Or schoolteachers. Or civil servants. Or musicians. Or research scientists. To mention only a few examples from a list which could be considerably extended.

This is only another way of saying what has already been said: That although the business society dominates the United States, most of the people in the United States are not businesslike. The business society, with its communications industry, is the dominant one; but the anti-business society has the broader base. And despite the unpleasant aroma which is attached to the word, if there were not millions and millions of do-gooders in the United States, we should, long before this, have been at one with Nineveh and Tyre. The crucial point, however—and the one which is of most interest to parents—is that most of these do-gooders are not drawing down the dividends of prestige and self-respect to which their behavior entitles them.

---

* One minor exception must be noted. Do-gooders are sometimes very kindly spoken of when they are far, far away. Father Damien and Dr. Schweitzer get a wonderful press.

They are being cheated. They are being cheated because American business, while it does not frown on helping the human race, frowns on people who start right in helping the human race without first proving that they can sell things to it.

The philosophical do-gooders—as, for the sake of convenience, they might be called—are not usually conscious of being do-gooders. They preserve and improve life, but not always in the full awareness of what they are doing. They are conscious, though—at least, in a dim sort of way —of being regarded by American business as pretty poor sticks. Of course, in their role of consumers, they receive a great deal of attention. As long as some part of the weekly pay check remains in their pockets, the business society courts them like an enterprising call girl. But as fully rounded individuals, as people who have a job to do and who do it—the job of preserving or improving life—they are either ignored or actually abused on the grounds that they are slothful and do not "work."

In the business society, to "work" means to make money, and it follows as the night the day, that the less money made, the less "work" involved. As Margaret Mead has already pointed out, in *Male and Female,* a woman who earns $50 a week as a stenographer is spoken of as "working"; but when the same woman brings up three children on the $75 a week earned by her husband, she is spoken of as "doing nothing." Similarly, a woman who works in a factory or office, as well as taking care of her family, is referred to as a "working" mother. The phrase suggests that

191

there is such a thing as a nonworking mother. But among the matrons who take care of their own offspring, no such thing exists.

On the so-called audience-participation shows, a woman who does not earn money always refers to herself as, "Just a housewife." Upon questioning, it usually turns out that this woman has somehow managed to steer a family through depressions, inflations and wars with no further resource than the wages of a pharmacist or a garage mechanic or a mailman. She nevertheless takes over, without question, the business society's idea of "work." She would have to be a genius, not to. Schoolteachers, of course, are painfully familiar with the American fiction that teachers, while admittedly not well paid, are recompensed by having an infinity of leisure.

Among my own souvenirs, I have a priceless sample of the fiction that people who do not have a great deal of money to show for it do not "work." During the war, while my husband was overseas, I wanted to dull the rigors of separation by fatigue. I wanted to find a job that would get me thoroughly tired out; and I discovered one that met the specifications perfectly. In the winter of 1944-45, I worked as a teacher's assistant with the six-year-olds in a small school in Brooklyn. One rainy day, when the children had not been able to get out to play, I went for dinner in the evening to the home of a businessman who, though unqualifiedly successful, is perhaps a little less subtle and knowledgeable than most. By the assembled guests it was observed that I looked pale and tired. My host turned to me in genuine astonishment. "But how could you be tired?" he said. "You get out at three o'clock, and besides, it's only children."

The broad base of the anti-business society is formed by the philosophical or unconscious do-gooders. By the business society, these unwitting Samaritans are regarded, not as do-gooders, but as no-gooders. They are parasites. They do not "work." But if one is to see life steadily and see it whole, it is not always safe to assume that the voice of business is the voice of God. The standard defense of the business society—back in the good old days, when people outside the Kremlin were allowed to criticize it—used to be that the businessman is born businesslike and that his pursuit of money is "human nature." In the last seventy or eighty years, however, we have learned—we have learned it as parents, if not in any other way—that "human nature" is whatever human beings feel like making it, and that "human nature" varies considerably from place to place and era to era. In fact, it is the responsibility for shaping "human nature" which weighs so heavily on the conscientious mothers and fathers.

In the mid-century United States, we seem to have two kinds of "human nature." The pressure of business-minded people on young and malleable American males has produced what is recognized the world over as a type —the successful American businessman. In the bright lexicon of business, this type has its opposite number. Opposite, and inferior. The opposite of the successful American businessman is The Type That Fails To Make Money. All the huge minorities in the business society—women, children, Negroes, artists, schoolteachers, sick people, bookkeepers, stenographers, and so on—are lumped together under the convenient but misleading label of The Type That Fails To Make Money.

Once a human being * has been identified as belonging in this category, he has been taped as an undesirable and you have said all that needs to be said about him. There is an ideal American type—the money-maker—and he either could not or would not live up to it. He is a drag on the wheels of progress, and it sometimes requires a portion of the taxpayer's luscious, hard-earned money to keep him alive. Or well. Or working (no quotes) at some job which does not produce much money. Money means "results." One of the sad effects of this equation is that the schools of the country are chronically behind the eight ball, since they do not, and cannot, produce "results."

The successful American businessman has been trained to exercise one narrow and particular talent, and he exercises it. He has been trained to make money, and at the same time to make dutiful noises about "serving the public," and he does just that. To say that a human being is a successful American businessman is to describe him

---

* Or a group of human beings, like a tenants' association, or a share-croppers' league, or a defensive alliance of consumers, or the dingy brotherhood of the Okies and the "wetbacks," or clumps of pigheaded professors who will not sign loyalty oaths.

fairly accurately—at least for eight of the sixteen hours he is (presumably) awake. In the United States, there is only one way of making money, and that is by being aggressive, competitive and skeptical.

There are, however, dozens of ways of failing to make money. It is one thing to fail to make money because your single talent happens to be a flair amounting to genius for translating the plays of Aristophanes. It is quite another thing to fail to make money because you are a Negro. Or a child. Or a woman. Or because you want to run a small farm. Or because you want to be a nurse. Or because you have religious convictions against making money. Or because you went to West Point. Or because you do not enjoy the society of people who think too much about making and spending money. To say that a human being has failed to make money in the United States of America, is to say nothing about him at all. The description covers sexual degenerates, Abraham Lincoln and everything in between.

In refusing to accept as a reality the ignominy which attaches to The Type That Fails To Make Money—in asserting the crucial importance of the philosophical or unconscious do-gooders who preserve or improve life—I should not like to be taxed with a sentimental overevaluation of the American people. I am not disposed to grow saccharine about "the little man" or "the common man" without first asking what is meant by "little" or "common." But the single fact of having failed to make an impressive amount of money does not, in itself, prove anything. It does not establish incompetence. Neither does it establish virtue. I therefore go no further along the road of sentimentality than the unarguable fact that human life is still going on in the United States.

Very few people die in our streets. Rioting, though not unknown to us, is sporadic. Somehow or other American children do learn to read and write. The position of the Negro has improved, and if, as Mr. Gunnar Myrdal says, this is 70 per cent due to the efforts of the Negroes themselves, it only goes to show that "doing good" is not limited to the Caucasian race. If human life is still going on in the United States, it can only be because a goodly part of the population is more interested in—and better at—the job of preserving and improving life than in the job of making money. If human life is still going on in the United States, it is not because we have a business society. It is because, fortunately, we also have an anti-business society.

Children belong to the anti-business society; and so do all the people who think that taking care of children is a serious and important job. (Some of these people, especially if they are males, also belong to the business society —which is only further evidence that a split society means a split in the single human being who has got to live in it.) The anti-business society has no communications industry. It operates for the most part by personal contact, force of example and word of mouth. But—with the distinguished exception of Lord Chesterfield—personal contact, force of example and word of mouth is the way parents operate with their children. (Or where they fail with their children, when they do fail.)

The most important question of our time and place is, "What constitutes a good human being?" Nobody tries harder to answer this question than some of the businessmen themselves. But they do not succeed in answering the question because they do not ask it at the right time in their own lives. They ask it when they are fifteen or sixteen—which, practically speaking, is too early. Then they do not ask it again until they are forty-five or fifty—which is too late. Among the more articulate businessmen—the ones who participate in forums, symposiums, and seminars and who write thoughtful pieces for the magazines—the good human being is defined, by implication, as the proven success in business who then turns to "serving the community."

This is what might be called, not so much the "noblesse oblige" as the "richesse oblige" theory of the good human being. Of its several weaknesses, there is one so completely fatal that no others need be discussed. It leaves mothers out of the picture. Were women to accept wholeheartedly the "richesse oblige" theory of the good human being, the business society would commit suicide quite neatly but effectively by simply not producing enough children to keep going.

During the 1930's, it was fashionable to glorify the underdog. Today, merely to speak of him kindly is considered proof positive that the mentioner is a card-carrying

member of the Communist Party. Neither of these attitudes is particularly sensible. The underdog exists; but his
subordinate position does not, in and of itself, ennoble
him. Nor does the position of the upperdog prove anything in particular about his superiority, although he is
certainly America's Dream Boy.

It is a fact beyond challenge that both the underdog and
the upperdog finally end up in the grave. And well before
they reach that terminal point, they are both under the
urgent necessity of asking, and of answering, the question
of what constitutes a good human being. If a good human
being is a person who preserves or improves life, then,
clearly, there are millions of good human beings in the
United States. But we are prevented from seeing the clear,
true outlines of the anti-business society by reason of the fact
that the business society and the communications industry
have tacked a lethal rider on to the notion of the good human being.

The business society does not object to people who preserve or improve life. It merely says that they cannot be
considered good human beings unless they have also got the
ability to attract money out of other people's pockets and
into their own. Some few of the philosophical or unconscious do-gooders who keep human life going in the
United States do happen to have, in addition, the talent
for making money—usually by some unique skill or creative gift. But compared to the total number, they are an
infinitesimal minority. And when the concept of the good
human being is so narrowly limited that only a very few

special people can lay claim to it, the society which supports that concept is in trouble.

The trouble is not, however, hopeless or incurable. We do not suffer from a shortage of good human beings. But the fact must be faced—bizarre as it may seem—that the great majority of them are, and always will be, unbusinesslike and basically indifferent to business. The anti-business society exists. It operates. Its broad base is the philosophical or unconscious do-gooders. And while the business society is the dominant one of our two societies, the anti-business society is the indispensable one.

This chapter can be no more decisively concluded than by quoting from the section on Religion in a book by two British sociologists entitled *English Life and Leisure*:

"But even among people who are indifferent to the Church, and find that it has no answers to their problems, there is not infrequently a spiritual hunger, a wish that there was something in which to believe. It was put well in one of our case histories by an elderly man of the lower middle-class who said,

" 'Is there nothing for me to believe? It's no good going to church where people read out prayers they don't really believe themselves. But there must be something. There is so much love and unselfishness in the world among all the evil things. And just look at those (pointing to a row of sweet peas in full bloom). You can't tell me that's all just accident. After all, people know the difference between right and wrong, and what's beautiful and what's ugly. I'm old now, and I'm not afraid to die, but I wish I

199

could understand more clearly what this "good" is that we can feel and see. It would be a help to people to get it organized a bit. . . .' "

It is now time to turn to the human beings who do organize it a bit—the socio-political do-gooders.

How to Be Happy,
though American

I F THE DISTINCTION between the talk-gooder and the do-
gooder seems to this writer an important one, it is
partly because I have been both myself. When I went to
college, I picked up what were referred to as "liberal"
views; and when I was in my twenties, I defended these
views with heat and spirit in whatever drawing room or
front parlor I found myself—one of these front parlors
being my father's. I did not, however, do anything about
my opinions, except verbally. Once in a great while the notion would go through me like a dagger that after all, talk
is pretty cheap; but like Scarlett O'Hara, I said I would
think about it tomorrow. Personal problems preoccupied
me—getting married, being married, going to Europe,

writing a book and trying to figure out how to behave after the book made money.

Nor did I go to the Stage Door Canteen because I knew that, unlike most of its sister institutions, it did not bar Negroes. I went to work at the Stage Door Canteen only because everyone was doing some kind of war work and I was too squeamish to be a Nurse's Aide. But once there, I found myself in the company of a group of people who were going to considerable trouble to put, and to keep, their liberal views in action. I stumbled into the situation by accident, but it seemed like a golden (if slightly unmerited) opportunity to quiet the conscience which I had picked up during my American childhood.

I am not looking backward at the past through rose-colored spectacles. The do-gooders at the Stage Door Canteen were fallible human beings. They had, by the end of the war, thousands of letters from Negro servicemen—and a few from white servicemen—as testimony that the racial equality they believed in and practiced had not been a failure. But the administration of that policy involved the usual clashes of temperament. There was the usual internecine warfare. There was the usual nubbin of really mature individuals; the usual nubbin of unreliable self-dramatizers; and the usual collection of indispensable, half-and-half people in between. It was nevertheless a group with a firm foundation in the American ethic; and belonging to it taught me something which was to come in handy later on, when I had a child to bring up.

There are fashions in children, just as there are fashions

in necklines and hats. The child who is currently at the height of the mode is the child who can get along well with the group. The parents who suffer the most anxiety —sometimes, I think, unnecessarily—are the parents whose child elects to stay on the sidelines. Because it is considered so extremely desirable to have a child who gets along with the group, a great many American children are sent to nursery school at the age of two-and-a-half or three. To be sure, the nursery school is a necessity for "working" mothers and for families who live in cramped quarters. But it has a position of its own, quite apart from necessity, and that position is based on the fact that it is the first of the organizations which teaches the child the all-important knack of adjusting to the group.

I am disposed to be a little skeptical of this enthusiasm for the group just because it is a group. The group with which I worked at the Stage Door Canteen had a goal which could be respected and it achieved that goal, in spite of various difficulties in the way. But none of the people in it had been intensively trained—as children nowadays are intensively trained—to get along with the group. There are, after all, a great many crucial areas of life where group training is completely irrelevant. In death and birth and bereavement—in eating, illness and elimination—and in that celebrated protoplasmic activity where three is a crowd—it is not of the slightest consequence to be able to get along with the group.

And as far as the group itself is concerned, a chain cannot be any stronger than its weakest link. The important thing about a group is not to be able to get along with it, but to have something, however modest, to contribute to it. My daughter's parents are not actually opposed to her getting along with the group, but we do think she ought to have learned, by the time she has grown up, to ask some sensible questions about any given group—such as, What kind of group is it? What is it doing? What holds it together? What is the caliber of the single human beings who make it up? If a group is only a collection of frightened people, desperately holding hands in an anguish of confusion—a description which fits a good many American groups, formal and informal—that group is certainly entitled to mercy and compassion, but one scarcely need go to a great deal of trouble to get along with it.

The emphasis on having a child who can get along with the group is only one aspect of the larger question of what constitutes a good human being. Who may lay claim to that title? To mention the good human being is to reach, by the most natural of transitions, the subject of the socio-political do-gooder. The socio-political do-gooders are the people for whom the phrase "do-gooder" was originally—and derisively—coined. They are the conscious do-gooders, and they are hereinafter referred to with capital letters to distinguish them from the philosophical or unconscious do-gooders.

The Do-Gooders are the people who welded the trade-union movement out of the misery and degradation of early British industrialism. They are the people who got the vote for women. They are the people who "interfered"

with the right of the manufacturer to employ small children for twelve hours a day. They are the people who
"meddle" with the segregators of Negroes. They are the
"fuzzy-minded idealists" who try, both at home and
abroad, to get the nourishing egg into the empty stomach
—while the "realistic" business society keeps its eye firmly
glued to the price tag on the eggcup.

A customary way of brushing off the Do-Gooders and
of getting their worthlessness firmly established is to charge
them with never having met a payroll. In a divided society, however, there are bound to be some Do-Gooders
who can, and do, meet payrolls. Not many, but some. From
the business point of view, the dangerous and infuriating
thing about the Do-Gooders is not that they have never
met a payroll. The dangerous and infuriating thing about
them is that they regard payroll-meeting as a necessity, but
not an ideal.

The Do-Gooders are not exempt from the split personality which is the common disease of us all. Each of our
two societies is bound to have *some* effect on the thinking,
feeling and behavior of any given American. The number
of possible combinations is, of course, as high as the number of Americans. But the Do-Gooders have grasped the
fact that an ethic is not an ethic unless and until it goes
into action. True, they sometimes accept the business society's definition of "work," and suffer hideous qualms because they have failed to make money. And they sometimes
—owing to clouded vision or failing strength—make com-
promises with business behavior which, ideally, they ought

not to make. Similarly—on the other side of the street—the ardent disciple of business sometimes gives generously to "good causes," in the secret, wistful and impossible hope that he can somehow get back to the ethic of his childhood and at the same time manage not to anger and frighten his colleagues in the business world. The dualism in American life—it must be constantly borne in mind—is a dualism in the character of the single American.

There is no pure type of the Do-Gooder, any more than there is a pure type of the American businessman. But the Do-Gooders have been sufficiently active to have incurred the official enmity of the dominant society—an enmity which is unhesitatingly expressed by the newspapers, radio-television, the movies and the popular magazines. They have been sufficiently effective to have been publicly labeled—"branded" is perhaps the better word—as people who do good. The interesting question is, Where do they come from? In a country candidly geared to money and self-advancement, what accounts for the behavior of the Do-Gooders? What makes them spend the precious years of the human life span swimming against the stream?

The explanation is easy. In each generation of young Americans, a certain number of emergent men and women stubbornly resist the dominant side of the society and base their lives, as far as they can, on the American ethic. In the popular phrase, they've bought it. These are the people who speak for—and, more importantly, act for—the vast unbusinesslike minorities. These are the people who

206

fight for civil rights. These are the people who organize share-croppers. These are the people who moved heaven and earth trying to save Sacco and Vanzetti from the chair. These are the people who close up tax loopholes. These are the people who resisted the hysteria about West Coast Japanese-Americans after Pearl Harbor. These are the people who try to block the ruthless exploitation of natural resources. These are the people who labor unceasingly to the end that American jurisprudence should not descend to the notion that to be unbusinesslike is to be subhuman. The list could be extended—although not indefinitely.

This chapter, like the preceding one, is bound to be hard going. The difficulty stems from the fact that it is impossible to solve any of the problems of American parenthood unless one is willing to examine some extremely unfamiliar ideas. The idea that a Do-Gooder is not necessarily a ridiculous and embarrassing nuisance (and probably pro-Communist) is as distressingly novel, in American life, as it would be to see the sun rise over what our British cousins rather poetically call the western approaches. But an idea can be dismayingly unfamiliar and still be entirely correct—a point established, beyond any possible, probable shadow of doubt, by Christopher Columbus.

Besides, an idea can always be relied upon to grow familiar, if one stays with it long enough. That is why Do-Gooders are often very highly spoken of after they are dead. The most conservative apostles of American business now take it for granted that we should have public schools for American children and pure food and drug laws to protect American health. But when the American Do-Gooders first launched these proposals, the business society affirmed violently that they would bring us to the brink of ruin. They were the "creeping socialism" of their day.

One of the distinguishing characteristics of the Do-Gooders is that they are intuitive sociologists. They respond to their society as a society, and not as a free-for-all and a rat race. That is to say, they treat the United States as a still-unfinished social organization which needs to struggle toward a more positive unity. The Do-Gooders may not all of them be able to put this reaction into so many words—although for the most part they are an articulate class of people—but their general behavior, and the results they get, tell the story.

A second distinguishing characteristic of the Do-Gooders is that they commit themselves. They cut off their own retreat. They take a stand. Openly and in their own names, they embrace the idea—so offensive to the business society— that people are responsible for other people's welfare. They take risks. They are publicly identified with movements, groups, ideas, professions, organizations or institutions which put people ahead of property. That these groups, ideas, etc., are likely to be unpopular, goes without saying. The way to identify a Do-Gooder quickly—supposing one should wish to do so—is to look behind him and see whether his bridges are burned.

"Doing good" is therefore (it is perhaps hardly necessary to add) not to be confused with charity. To take responsibility for other people's welfare—in the Do-Gooder's sense —does not suggest the kind of responsibility assumed by women who give dances to raise money for a favorite settlement house. This is by no means to impugn the good intentions of such women, but only to explain that the Do-Gooders work in a much larger frame of reference than Christmas trees for tenement children or contributions to the Hundred Neediest Cases.

The Do-Gooders work on the basic assumption that the United States cannot function rewardingly and satisfyingly unless, *as a society,* it takes a measure of responsibility for the dignity of all the people in it. The Do-Gooders, therefore, do not write checks for fifty or a hundred underprivileged children. They take a personal responsibility for putting a crimp in the tribal folklore which leads to rural and urban slums. Charity, seen from this viewpoint, is not an acceptance of responsibility, but an evasion of it. Charitable acts do spring from good intentions. But the point needs to be particularly emphasized that charity does not mean change, and the Judeo-Christian ethic does.

On this score, it will readily be seen that what is called "benevolent paternalism" is not the answer to the split in our society. Notably paternalistic organizations like the Hershey Company and Johnson & Johnson are sometimes pointed to, by businessmen, as examples of business and ethics dwelling side by side in happy unity. But while it is certainly true that benevolent corporations are better than exploitative corporations, the striking fact about benevolent paternalism in the United States is that there is so little of it. And this is hardly surprising. Urgent, imperious pressure is put on young American males to establish their manhood and their grasp of "reality" by getting in there and taking care of Number One. With this kind of training, it is scarcely likely that many of them will emerge, in middle age, with an incurably fatherly attitude toward the people who work for them.

However, the most telling argument against benevolent paternalism is the fact that fatherhood is supposed to be self-terminating. The child grows up. The father dies. A permanent father-child relationship—which is the core of benevolent paternalism—is, as every enlightened parent knows, a horror by all means to be avoided. The baby changes into an adult. The adult changes into a dead person. Societies change. The more determinedly a society struggles not to change—to maintain what is called the status quo—the more likely it is to come popping out in a series of social hernias.

My daughter is not being reared with an idea of "adjusting" her to the business society. By the time she is twenty-five or thirty years old, the business society as we know it today may no longer exist. Change is the law of life. That being so, the way to deal with change is first to acknowledge its inevitability and then to control or direct it in terms of a clear idea of what constitutes a good human being and a good society for human beings. It takes a bit of discipline to acknowledge the inevitability of change; for while human beings like and enjoy growing up (when they are given the chance to), they do not generally like to die. But, on the other hand, to control and direct changes which are courageously acknowledged to be unpreventable is to lay hold of the one thing the mid-century American yearns for and has not got—the sense of personal power.

If American business were truly "realistic," it would acknowledge with becoming candor that it does not take care of its own. American business puts the American businessman in a position where he is more or less forced to be a talk-gooder. And when a person knows enough about goodness to talk about it, he is bound to be unhappy, discontented and disillusioned when he is constrained by fear of condign punishment to limit himself to mere talk. When the American businessman reaches what Dante calls the middle of the journey of his life, he has to make a choice. He has to choose whether he will spend the balance of his time on earth being viciously cynical, quietly heartbroken or just plain numb. A society which does that kind of thing to its favorite sons is approaching the end of the road. If American business were truly "realistic," it would acknowledge the imminence of its departure—in the form in which we know it today—and would set about making that departure a neat, orderly and nicely modulated demise. The business society underwent some rather radical transformations, under the influence of Franklin D. Roosevelt, and it has by no means suffered its last sea change.

In the meantime, however, there are children to be taken care of. For parents (and others) who are charged with the upbringing of children, the key society, the indispensable society, the society with survival value is the anti-business America—the invisible Republic of the conscious and unconscious do-gooders. This Republic is kept going by unpopular people. It is kept going by "crusaders," "reformers," clubwomen, schoolteachers, labor organizers, social workers, ministers, nonconformists, a very few Congressmen and Senators and by energetic moralists and practicing idealists in other walks of life—up to, and of recent years including, the Presidency. The position of the Do-Gooders in American life is richly ironic; for while the business community fears and despises them, that business community is nevertheless dependent for its very existence on the tempering idealism they put into circulation. No society which officially encourages ruthless self-seeking could expect to perpetuate itself for a single generation if there were not some opposing pattern of human gentleness and human hope.

The anti-business America is silent, but it is by no means ineffective. The Do-Gooders have only the loosest kind of organization—when, indeed, they have any at all. They have nevertheless exerted a traceable influence on the social structure of the United States, and that we no longer have a nineteenth-century, laissez-faire economy is owing to the fact that the Do-Gooders were able to prevent the business society from developing itself right out of existence. In the hotly resented "government interference"

with business—which not all businessmen resent—the interference always results in the businessman's making less
rather than more money. (When the interference takes the
form of subsidies or high tariffs, it is not described as
interference.) "Government interference" with business
represents the influence of the Do-Gooders, acting to limit
the full and free development of profit-making qualities,
and to assert the value and worth of The Type That Fails
To Make Money.

The basic philosophy of the Do-Gooders is the belief in
man's humanity to man (not to mention women and
children). This philosophy has found outward expression
in such projects as F.E.P.C., social security, unemployment
insurance, TVA, minimum wage laws, child labor amend-
ments, school lunch programs, federal aid to education,
low-cost housing, the Federal theater, socialized medicine
and the "welfare state"—to mention some of the favorite
targets of the business society's ill will. To a great many
Americans, of course, the above are loaded phrases. To a
great many Americans—carefully coached by the communications industry—the above-mentioned institutions suggest nothing nobler than undeserved benefits showered on
lazy, self-indulgent people who have no talent for anything
but parasitism. The dominant society construes the Do-
Gooders' philosophy to mean that hard-earned money
should be taken away from successful businessmen and
dazzlingly solvent corporations and bestowed on human
trash.

But there is an implied comparison here which needs

213

to be more fully expressed. American business, like all societies, sets up an ideal type for its citizens to model themselves upon. This ideal type is the person who can make money, preferably against odds. The beneficiaries of the Do-Gooder projects are—it must be admitted—too old, too young, too sick, too artistic or too maternal to measure up to this ideal. But how good is the ideal? Is the ideal money-maker also the ideal husband and parent—relaxed, contented and self-confident in those relationships with wife and children where all the money in the world will not make up for inexperience? And if not, how long can the woman-and-child-rejecting business society look forward to renewing itself?

The job of the Do-Gooders as a social force in American life can be summed up in a single sentence. It has been their function to pressure American business into spending money on people the business society does not consider valuable. That the Do-Gooders are now, and always have been, confronted with a huge task, is obvious. But some of our contemporary institutions exist as evidence that they have not been wholly unsuccessful. Moreover, where the Do-Gooders have actually succeeded in wresting concessions from that iron-jawed goddess, Business-with-a-capital-B, the triumph is all the more to their credit in that it has been consistently uphill work.

The Do-Gooders have no organization and no communications industry. The general body of the citizenry has been carefully trained to fear and despise them, and that training is growing more intensive with every passing week. Also, while it is true that the Do-Gooders have certain sanctions—at least, until such time as the Judeo-Christian ethic is heaved bodily out of the window—those sanctions are shadowy and spiritual. They are nothing like as generally agreed upon as the businessman's sanction to take advantage of tax loopholes, to bribe government employees or to take questionable short cuts with the law of the land. The Do-Gooders are nevertheless, so far as our two societies are concerned, on the winning side—the only side, that is, which can win.

I can scarcely claim to be a socio-political Do-Gooder, but if my daughter were looking for a pigeonhole in which to put me, she could perhaps say that I was a socio-do-gooder. At least, I have occasionally been referred to as a "reformer," a "crusader" and a "do-gooder"—and these nouns did not arrive, surrounded by hearts and flowers, on St. Valentine's Day. So far as my own experience of "doing good" is concerned, I can sum it up fairly succinctly. I hated every minute of it (pretty nearly); and if I had it all to do over again, I would do exactly the same thing.

My mother was brought up in the very heart and core of the Victorian convention about female genteelness—which makes it unsurprising that this writer should have been imbued, in the formative years of childhood, with a considerable fear of being conspicuous. But although my upbringing gave me a certain amount of social timidity, I do not have one of the virtues which often goes with timidity. I am not temperamentally patient. The long and often wearisome committee meetings which are an unavoidable part of co-operative endeavor, and the un-brilliant slowness of progress which characterizes any attempt to put our national morality into action were, to me, more than a little taxing.

But quite aside from my own personal disqualifications, the role of the Do-Gooder is not what actors call a fat part. It is haunted by that most gruesome of all specters—the fear that one is making a fool of one's self. Besides, the audience sits on its hands. Americans have a great distaste for what they call "controversial" issues. This distaste is natural enough. The American has a built-in controversy raging within his skeletal boundaries. He does not want the Do-Gooders hanging about, serving as painful reminders and reactivating the internal conflict he hoped to be able to forget. The Do-Gooders are sometimes accorded, by other individuals, a sort of nervous respect; but that is not quite as comforting and reassuring as being warmly liked and genuinely welcomed.

Furthermore, the frequent failure of the American family—combined with our national pattern of underdeveloped affection—has produced, here and there in the United States, some very ugly customers. It is possible to accomplish a substantial amount in the way of "doing good" without crossing the path of an ugly customer. But the ugly customers are always there, lurking in the background and generating tension. The job of the Do-Gooder is always at least faintly overshadowed with the threat of violence, either physical, economic or spiritual; and for some

216

Do-Gooders—Negro Do-Gooders, for instance—the threat of violence is considerably more pronounced than faint.

When I was writing a book about the people at the Stage Door Canteen who launched and carried off a successful experiment in race relations, I used to stand at the window—standing at the window is the way writers get most of their work done—and wonder morbidly whether the book would get a bad press ("crusader," "reformer," "meddler," "fuzzy-minded idealist") or whether it would get no press at all and just sink like a plummet into an ocean of silence. I had had a little first-hand experience of American skittishness about "good causes," and while I knew it was humanly possible to persuade my fellow countrymen of the practicality of righteousness, I also knew that the job was not unlike maneuvering a high-strung horse past a clotheslineful of flapping laundry.

It turned out that I was unduly pessimistic, although this is not a failing to which I am usually prone. I received as much mail on the race relations book as I did on my first and more "famous" one, and the letters were much more gratifyingly thoughtful and provocative. About my first book, a great many people wrote to me because the book was, at the moment, fashionable. About my third book, people wrote to me because they had read it. It is a basic principle of mine to answer all the letters I receive about my publications, since in this era of mass communications, I am committed to the theory of personal contact as the only way to get very much enjoyment out of life. But the race relations letters could not be answered with a mere flap of the wrist. They required care and study, and sometimes even a little research.

At this point, my editor—a woman from whom practical problems slink away, diminished and with their tails between their legs—pointed out that all the letters asked, in essence, the same question. They all asked, "What can I do about race relations right here and now, in this place in which I happen to be living?" My editor then rounded up some money from the gentlemen who work at my publishing house, and some young women who could type from the distaff side of that corporate enterprise, and between the collection of us, we published a monthly Race Relations Bulletin. This bulletin was exclusively concerned with specific and practical measures for according the necessary ration of prestige to Americans of color. In a modest way, the Race Relations Bulletin was not unsuccessful. It was in demand by schools and various religious organizations, as well as by individuals.

We did not ask people to pay for the Bulletin. We sent it to them free. And after a while, the project developed to a point where it needed to be put on a professional basis. We needed to ask people to pay for it, and to get a paid worker to keep it going. At this juncture, I made a rather odd decision. I decided to give it up. The decision was not as freakish and perverse as it sounds. I believe in improving race relations; but I also believe that people cut down their potential value if they do not live a balanced life. My husband had by that time come home from

the wars, and we wanted to have a family. In taking care
of this family, I did not want to be pressed for time,
drained of energy or absent-minded. That was not, however, the fundamental reason for saying good-by to something that all of us who worked on it were rather proud
of. The fundamental reason was that I had at length concluded that the greatest service which could be performed
for race relations would be to explore the whole national
pattern of the inability to love, of which discrimination
against Negroes is only one conspicuous part. I had, that
is to say, come upon what seemed to me like the key to
what is generally called "the minority problem." That key
consisted in giving a little much-needed attention to what
American business regards as the Mongol hordes of the
unbusinesslike.

When I was working on the Race Relations Committee
at the Stage Door Canteen, and subsequently when I was
writing and lecturing on race relations, my heart was
rather accustomed to spend a good deal of time in my
mouth. Part of this apprehension was neurotic—I use the
word, even though I distrust it—but part of it was firmly
grounded in reality. There is no way to be of genuine service to one set of people without making another set of
people regard one as their least favorite character in fact
or fiction.

Peculiarly enough, the job which I remember as being
the most distasteful was a minor one and, as it turned out,
empty of results. After *Color Blind* came out, I was invited
to join a great many organizations concerned, either di-

219

rectly or indirectly, with improving the status of Negro Americans. But save for a nominal yearly membership in the N.A.A.C.P. and the Urban League, I joined only one. For this choosiness, there was a reason.

If the Do-Gooders and the Do-Gooder organizations in the United States have a fault, it is that they sometimes make the mistake of trying to spread themselves too thin. The temptation is understandable. For my own part, it always gives me an extremely uncomfortable feeling of nervousness and guilt when I decline to contribute to or work for some organization which is doing a job that needs to be done and of which I heartily approve. But the First Law of "doing good" is to recognize one's limitations as an individual and not to bite off more than one can chew.

Similarly, and with the same drift toward overexpansion, the Do-Gooder organizations sometimes unconsciously take over the business society's belief in gigantic markets. They sometimes unwittingly fall in with the idea that if a thing is not "nation-wide," it is useless and futile. "Good causes," however—or rather, the attitude toward human beings on which they are based—cannot be sold like aluminum saucepans. The Judeo-Christian ethic is kept going, in the United States, in the same way it has been kept going for two thousand years. It is kept going by personal contact, force of example and word of mouth. Hence, making a vivid and lasting impression on a few people is much more important than collecting a dollar apiece from half a million people. The day may come when the business society is administered so as to give us advanced medicine and labor-saving devices in terms of Christian morality. In that case, of course, the business society will be totally unrecognizable to those of us who know it today. But Christian morality will never be operated in terms of business customs, because it is concerned, not merely with virtue, but with *personal* virtue.

The solitary Do-Gooder organization upon whose Board of Directors I said I would serve is called The National Scholarship Service and Fund for Negro Students. It was founded by a young woman perceptive enough to notice that there are $11,000,000 worth of scholarships to white colleges in the United States and that most of these scholarships are open to Negroes. However, Negro high-school students—whose families rarely have the money to send them to college—either do not know about the scholarships or else assume that they would not be welcome at white colleges. But a great many colleges in the North and West would be glad to welcome Negro students, if only they knew how to secure any. Briefly stated, it is the purpose of this organization to act as the middleman between the Negro high-school students and the scholarship-offering white colleges which would welcome them. Its introduction of Negro students into well-known preparatory schools has proved to be the most salable fact about it, but it also adds money to the frequently inadequate scholarships, and it is currently engaged in a program of breaking down old barriers in the Southern states by placing numbers of white students in colleges which have hitherto been predominantly Negro, and vice versa. Slowly but surely, it is making a dent in an educational setup which only fairly recently was usually considered hopeless.

I was impressed by this line of endeavor because it was very sensibly and economically utilizing two items which happened to be in ample supply—Negro high-school students and scholarship-offering white colleges. As money is conceived of by the big heart and cancer and polio funds, this organization does not need much. But it does need some. Part of its funds comes from the Campus Chests of interested colleges, but the rest has to be secured from foundations. The only possible use a Board Member can be is to help in meeting the modest budget. So I agreed —this was before I started writing these pages—to do my quota of going around to foundations and soliciting their financial aid.

About foundations, my feelings are mixed, since I suspect they can never, however wisely administered, make up for the damage which was done by collecting the money in the first place. However, like most women, I seldom experience much difficulty in choosing between two evils. (This shady dexterity may account for the fact that the female sex has never produced any great philosophers—a charge which has always seemed to me inconclusive, to say the least.) At any rate, the Negro high-school students were there, and I was enthusiastic about their going on to college.

I did not loathe soliciting foundations because I am ambivalent about foundations. I loathed it because a feature of my youth—only oldsters will remember this—was something called "refinement." "Refined" people are supposed to be utterly above anything coarse and mundane like money—at least, if they are women. Especially, they are not supposed to go around with their hats in their hands, begging for it. Logically considered, this is nonsense; but it is nonsense I learned when I was rather young for logic.

I was completely unnerved by the prospect of approaching the foundations. But I did it, and I failed at it. The organization did get money from foundations; but not from any of the ones solicited—in a manner not noticeably suggestive of Richard Coeur d'Lion—by me. Nevertheless, in terms of the moral effort involved, I am quite sure that if St. Peter ever gives me a starry crown, it will say on the front, "She asked for money." If St. Peter is truly an angel, he will not add, "P.S. She did not get it."

The Do-Gooders do not enjoy their job, but the significant thing—and this is very important—is that they did not expect to enjoy it. About the pleasures of virtuous conduct, they were "disillusioned" when they were little toddlers attending Sunday School. And therein lies a difference between our two societies which it is of paramount importance to grasp. The Judeo-Christian ethic does not promise people freedom from pain. American business, however, does. And, obviously, that is a promise it cannot keep. The business society promises the businessman—the promise is implicit in practically every line uttered by the communications industry—that if he will just follow the club rules, he will either arrive at emotional maturity by magic, or he will be so happy and powerful in buying things and pushing people around that he will enjoy having his boyhood extend to the brink of the grave.

It is because of this false promise that I do not look to see the American business society last as long as Ancient Egypt or dynastic China. If one puts aside, for the moment, all the tribal myths and legends about American business—if one looks at American business with the eye of a visitor from another planet—the most conspicuous thing about it is that nobody likes it. "Everybody's out for the fast buck," says the man in the street, and his manner does not convey that he thinks this is a good thing. It is unlikely, though, that the business society as we know it today will be destroyed by the insurgent peasantry. People without risk capital do not care enough about business to destroy it. People with no prospect of being successful American businessmen—and this includes the majority of employees, as well as women and artists— would be happy if business would pick up its marbles and go away. But their underlying attitude toward business is less one of hostility than of indifference.

There are only two possible future developments for the American business society. It can either destroy itself in blood and flame—dropping atom bombs on Chinese cities would be a handy way to start this process—or it can modulate into a "welfare state" with a philosophy of government sufficiently well-rounded to exorcise the much—and rightly —dreaded specter of regimentation. (Of the philosophy of government, in terms of the anti-business America, more

will be said later.) However, if the American business society is destroyed, it will be destroyed from the top and not
from the bottom. It will not be destroyed by schoolchil-
dren who have been subverted by collectivist textbooks. It
will be destroyed by angry businessmen who—promised
freedom from pain and not getting it—put their arms
around the pillars of the temple, like Samson, and avenge
themselves the hard way.

My own experience of being a do-gooder was lonely,
dismal and frightening; but I would nevertheless make
the same choices over again without a moment's hesita-
tion. Whatever their drawbacks, those decisions gave me
a sense of there being some continuity between my father's
life and mine. They gave me a feeling of having roots in
the past—the distant past as well as the immediate past.
To try to get through life without that feeling, especially
if one has children, is to suffer a much deeper and more
permanent anxiety than anything a do-gooder has to experience. I have not made anything like the amount of
money that, with my lucky start, I could have made; and
for that reason I am considered, by some few of my acquaintances and relatives, a disappointing failure. But my
daughter does not currently share this view, and I have a
cheerful suspicion that she never will.

X

Men, Women, and Children Last

———

THE *hearts of small children are delicate organs. A cruel beginning in this world can twist them into curious shapes. The heart of a child can shrink so that forever afterward it is hard and pitted as the seed of a peach. Or again, the heart of such a child may fester and swell until it is a misery to carry within the body, easily chafed and hurt by the most ordinary things.*

These words were not culled from a book on child care, though they might well have been. They are from the pen of the gifted novelist, Carson McCullers. But they certainly express—although more poetically and powerfully than is usually the case—something that all conscientious parents have had drilled into them.

A business society is embarrassingly well supplied with peach-pit hearts. But before condemning out of hand the mothers and fathers who produced the peach-pit hearts, the point must be made—again and again—that responsible, compassionate parenthood in an Upward Step commonwealth is an astonishingly difficult job. There is small reason to wonder that it is sometimes done badly. A cruel beginning in this world need not mean anything as obvious as being beaten up by a drunken father. A cruel beginning in this world is not incompatible with the best of care. The best of care can be given mechanically, and can serve as a screen—to everyone but the child—for a basic preoccupation, as per instructions, with getting ahead. The best of care can be nothing more than an elaborate system of defensive and escape buying.

All parents are familiar with the small child's command, "Pay attention to me!" But to pay *real* attention to children, in a business-dominated society, is sometimes just not humanly possible. Children's demands for affection and attention are vigorous and unremitting—at least, until they learn better—but these demands often land with a screech on parental nerves tightened apprehensively against the heartless atmosphere of profit-making. The new and compelling doctrine of child-raising is that we should be permissive with our children. But who is going to be permissive with the parents? Certainly not American business.

The tightened nerves of American parents are going to have a very considerable bearing on the future destiny of the United States. Since there is no possibility of persuading the children to demand less, the only way to make the

American destiny fruitful and life-giving, instead of destructive and death-dealing, is to cope with the problem of relaxing the parental nerves. If one listens to Official Dogma, this job is hopeless. According to Official Dogma, the parental nerves are being frayed and rubbed raw by people over whom we have no control—to wit, the undeniably hostile Russians.

But there is ground for the suspicion that in some of the contemporary expertizing about Russia, we are not so much looking at the Russians, as we are looking away from ourselves. The great disadvantage of looking away from ourselves is that it turns parenthood into one long series of instrument landings. In pursuit of a little more visibility for American fathers and mothers, it might be a constructive notion to give the Russians a rest for a moment and to study with a meditative eye the three primary character traits which American business has set up as the hallmark of the good human being—aggression, competitiveness and skepticism.

Of the three, competitiveness needs the most extended treatment. Speaking simply as a parent, I am not at all sure that I want to see my little girl develop a highly competitive personality. I am even less sure that she will have a good life if she marries someone with a highly competitive personality. But competitiveness is celebrated by American business as a desirable and socially creative quality. Men striving against each other, the theory goes, get more things done, and do them better, than men who are working simply because the job itself gives them self-respect.

But if competitiveness is socially creative, what does it create? The answer that it creates money and machines—the two great commodities most closely linked with the name of the United States—will probably not be open to much dispute. The machines are a real achievement. They are our great national contribution to human welfare, and we have a right to be proud of them. But there is a possibility that we are not quite so much indebted to American competitiveness for these machines as we usually assume.

The great Greek plays which have come down to us through the ages were the result of a public competition among contemporary playwrights, so it may fairly be allowed that competitiveness plays a certain role in creative activity—whether it involves machinery or plays. But a competition is always *for* something. It always has a goal, and the most significant part of the competition is the nature of the goal. The goal of the Greek competitions was to inspire plays which would give the population a healthy emotional purge. The goal of American competitiveness is to make money. The machines—highly creditable as they are, in terms of human welfare—were a by-product. Machines make markets, and markets make money. The goal of American competitiveness is not machinery for other men's aching backs. The goal of American competitiveness is money for one's own aching heart.

The Greek competitions were designed to benefit a great many people. The goal of that competitiveness was religious, communal and social. The goal of American competitiveness is individualistic, personal, non-co-operative and self-seeking. It is "private" enterprise in every sense of the word—my foot on the other fellow's neck. If proof is needed that American competitors aim to make money for themselves rather than to produce machinery for the benefit of everyone, one has only to consider that TVA is the rather lonely example in the United States of the use of machinery—by itself, and divorced from profit-making —to mitigate human toil. There are half a dozen other areas in the country where similar projects could have a similarly magnificent effect in raising the standard of living, but TVA just barely squeaked past the hostility of American business, and it took the tragic, criminally wasteful and totally unnecessary floods of last spring to reactivate even the mention of a Missouri Valley Authority.

American machinery is not the conscious and deliberate expression of the national genius, as were the Greek plays. It is the inadvertent by-product of American competition for money. This circumstance accounts for the fact that although the machines are the glory of our society, we do not enjoy them very much. In their entirety, they make us nervous. Although the machines are supposed to belong to the Americans, they are often spoken of as if it were the other way around. Actually, we are not the slaves of our machines, since machines do not have the capacity for enslavement. We are the slaves of *what the machines are used for*. We are the prisoners of money.

Competitiveness is, in essence, a special way of looking at one's fellow human beings. One does not look at them carefully and interestedly, in order to see what they are really like. One merely keeps glancing at them nervously in order to make sure, if they are behind, that they stay behind, or, if they are ahead, that the gap is being closed up. The basis of competitiveness is permanent insecurity. And permanent insecurity—no matter how much it can, and sometimes does, produce in the way of expanded income—makes the job of rearing children a disguised little purgatory for all concerned.

The disadvantage of competitiveness, as a social force, is that it cannot be contained within the limits of office and factory. It spills out into non-business areas. Is your child more "secure" than mine? Does your daughter have more dates than my daughter? Do you keep a cleaner kitchen, do a whiter wash, play a better bridge game or carry your liquor better than I do? It does not matter whether we are liked; but we *must* be envied. Competitiveness is sanctified unrest; but upon unresting people —no matter how thrice-blessed they are by American business—the demands of children are a heavy drain.

American competitiveness, as fostered and encouraged by the business society, does actually serve a social function. But not a good one. In an industrial society, much of the work which has to be done is monotonous, boring and depersonalized. A housewife—if she wants to take the trouble, and if she is living above the subsistence level—can put the stamp of her personality upon her dwelling place. Upon her children, too, for that matter. But short of throwing sand into the machinery, there is nothing the worker on an assembly line can do to distinguish his work from that of the man next to him. A file clerk cannot personalize filing except by doing it badly.

Nor is this depersonalization of work limited solely to the lower echelons of industry. Frederick Wakeman in *The Hucksters* and Eric Hodgins in *Blandings' Way* have given us a graphic picture of sterile occupations among the top brass. Apropos of the question posed in Chapter I—What is the real nature of American life, as distinguished from the various popular legends?—it is extremely important to keep in mind that American business can sometimes be just as boring for those who are well paid as for those who are not.

In this situation, competitiveness—at all income levels—serves the purpose of displacing attention from the work itself and focusing it instead upon the other workers. This sounds as if it might be a good thing. But attention is not directed to the other workers for purposes of warmth, friendship and shared endeavor in a deeply felt cause. The other workers are not friends or co-idealists, but antagonists upon whom it is necessary to keep an Argus eye. By injecting this note of personal struggle into business activity, a certain amount of artificial excitement is created, in spite of the fact that some of that activity is quite the opposite of exciting. But the excitement is synthetic. It does not touch people's hearts. And after a while it leaves them empty, cheated, disillusioned and ready to drop atom bombs on other hemispheres just for the sake of having one single moment of feeling really alive.

Some of our bolder social thinkers have made the extremely sensible suggestion that since a certain amount of boring work is unavoidable in a highly mechanized society, people should be paid a living wage for doing it no more than three hours a day—leaving the rest of their time free for activities about which they are able to feel a little genuine enthusiasm. This suggestion, so far from being Utopian, is a much more practical approach to "human nature" than the feverish myth that in an industrial society, all the work is challenging. We are kept from putting such an approach into practice, not by the fact that our machines are unequal to it—they are more than equal to it—but by the fact that we have gotten so accustomed to being bored that it seems natural to us. We hug our chains. A bored population, however, is a potentially dangerous population.

The most damaging charge against competitiveness is that it wreaks havoc with the parent-child relationship. The child is his parents' "product." He is good or bad, accepted or rejected, in terms of how he stacks up with the other "products." Since there is no definite ideal of what constitutes a good human being—especially where children are concerned, for children do not have the escape hatch of being successful businessmen—the mothers and fathers have to keep looking, not only at their own child, but also at the child ahead and the child behind.

One of the things by which I was most struck, during the year when I was teaching, was how competitive the parents were and how thirstily grateful they would have been for some clear-cut and reasonably attainable standard of merit by which to set their compasses. The dominant society gives us a clear-cut standard—making a lot of money —but most of us cannot meet the standard, and it is impossible to use it with children.

What does American competitiveness mean, in terms of the child himself? It means that the child never knows when some other child will turn up whose performance he will be expected to beat. This can certainly be defined, within the meaning of the act, as a cruel beginning in this world. At best, life is an uncertain and intermittently tragic proposition, and men have never found any way of responding to it adequately except by trying to understand their fellow men. Competitiveness, however, reduces human companionship to a set of space relationships. How far ahead? How far behind? How cold and lonely!

The other two qualities which the business society nurtures and applauds—aggression and skepticism—are somewhat different in nature from competitiveness. They are not, in themselves, either good or bad. Their merit or lack of merit depends on the uses to which they are put. In business societies, the goal of aggression is money; but aggression is capable of being put to much broader use than that. To drive the money-changers out of the Temple was indisputably an aggressive act. In fact, it was accomplished with a whip.

Similarly, skepticism in a business society finds its usual expression in the belief that human beings are incapable of idealism—at least, until they have first established themselves as successful businessmen. But skepticism, although we are most familiar with it in the role of handmaiden to business, can with equal facility be turned against business. It can be used to set us free from the business myths and financial legends which are choking the life out of the American spirit.

That the American population has been intensively trained to be aggressive and skeptical is not in itself a disastrous state of affairs. The possibility of disaster does not lie in these characteristics themselves. Actually, they can be very useful and satisfying qualities to have, *provided they have a goal which is big enough to contain them.* But the making of money is not such a goal. It is too small a target to accommodate the aggression and skepticism of the American population and to leave that population healthily tired, relaxed and satisfied. Just as it is not our machines in themselves which are bad, but the fact that we use them for the basically trivial purpose of making sales—so it is not aggression and skepticism which are harmful, but the fact that money-making is not a big enough purpose to exhaust them. There is a dangerous residue left over. The decent people bottle up this residue and punish themselves. They suffer from insomnia and other forms of anxiety. The indecent people do not bottle it up. They punish others.

If the making of money is not a large enough goal to use up our national energy, what goal is large enough? At the risk of setting the obedient, unquestioning American somewhat back on his heels, the suggestion is advanced that the much-derided objective of "making the world a better place" will absorb all the aggression and skepticism anyone can put into it, and there will still be room left over. The aggressive man who drove the money-changers out of the Temple was not blighted by the Five O'Clock Shadow which casts its pall of pressure and suffering over so much of American life. The career of Christ shows periodic evidence of hostile behavior, but it was not *surplus* hostility. He used the hostility. It did not use Him. The people who clamor for a preventive war furnish a sad example of human beings who are not the managers of their own aggressiveness, but its victims.

"Making the world a better place" can take any one of a thousand forms. It may take the form of permanently improving children's bodies through Federal funds for hot school lunches. It may take the form of permanently increasing the productivity of men and meadowlands through projects like TVA. The list could be multiplied indefinitely, but the phrase speaks for itself. To the people who have had the experience, in however small a way, of leaving the world better than they found it, the idea will not be wholly unfamiliar or unrecognizable. The people who have never wished to have that experience are unlikely to see these pages. The supreme importance of "making the world a better place" is that—so far from being a laughable and "unrealistic" goal—it is the only objective broad enough to take the impact of the aggression and skepticism which have been implanted in the American character. To try to use the American personality, in the present stage of its development, for as flimsy a goal as money-making is like trying to put a Diesel engine into a baby carriage.

If children are to get the affection they need, the tightened nerves of American parents will have to be examined with a view to remedial measures, and not just accepted with a sigh as the cross we have to bear. American life is so energetic and so seething with activity that it is difficult to pierce through the agitated surface and see the unsatisfied cravings lying underneath. But unless those cravings can be acknowledged and—to a certain extent, at least—satisfied, it is a waste of time to talk about children needing love. Children need love, but they are by no means the only people who need it.

On the score of taut parental nerves, there is one circumstance which—though not generally recognized or very frequently discussed—is pivotal. The circumstance is that, except as a consumer, the child-bearing and child-rearing woman is of no use to the business society. To be sure, were I not a woman, I would not have the temerity to be writing this book. The business society is fundamentally indifferent to, and unaware of, women. Hence it permits the American female to display an interest in ethics and morality for which an American male would be razed to the ground like Carthage. The English anthropologist, Geoffrey Gorer, refers at some length—in his book, *The American People*—to American women as the carriers and transmitters of American morality. The "nihilistic progress" (of American business)—says Mr. Gorer—"is held back by the tightly corseted figure of Madame Chairman, by the pinched and overeager schoolmarm. They are the present embodiments of the Goddess of Liberty." *

In a business society, there are only two things the maternal woman can do, and both of them are bad. She can try to get closer to the male by taking on, to a certain extent, the supposedly male characteristics of aggressiveness, competitiveness and skepticism. A reminder should perhaps here be inserted of something already said. It is not necessary actually to be in business to have an aggressive, competitive and skeptical approach to other human beings. One can have a primitive, tribal and childlike belief in the magical power of money without actually earning money.

If the child-rearing woman in the business society is unable or unwilling to be a sort of echo of the business world, then her only other choice is to live out her life in a lonely trance. The American woman's day is customarily so full of activity and so crammed with duties and obligations that it may seem odd to speak of her as either lonely or tranced. But the very absence of leisure—the very absence of any time for laziness and meditation—suggests a flight

---

* Mr. Gorer is a somewhat waspish commentator, but the present writer is not in a very strong position to tax a British subject with lack of charity.

from pain. The source of the pain is that the maternal woman is rejected by the business society.

Activities she has in abundance, but they have no status and no prestige. The child-rearing woman in the business-dominated United States can keep busy until she drops in her tracks, but she is still "just a housewife." She does not "work"; she does not produce "results"; and she has never met a payroll. Fourteen thousand different ways will be invented to persuade her to buy Washing Machine A instead of Washing Machine B. The fact that it would be possible for her to have a washing machine without any wasteful and meaningless scuffle called "free competition" will be noted by nobody except her own subconscious.* She may rely with a good deal of certainty on receiving a gift on Mother's Day, but the one thing she may *not* have—she and all her ilk—is another TVA.

This is not sexual chauvinism, although it may sound like it at first blush. If it is chauvinism at all, it is human-race chauvinism. I am not angry because the Overbearing Males of the business society have denied maternal women the respect and prestige to which they are entitled. Rather, I am concerned because the Overbearing Males—insofar as they support and believe in a business society—are inad-

---

* It will, of course, be argued that owing to "free competition," the maternal woman can get Washing Machine A twenty dollars cheaper than Washing Machine B. It is the tiniest of blessings. The maternal woman does not pay merely for the cost of putting the washing machine together, plus a modest profit. She pays for the advertising, the public relations, the expense account and the house organ. Into each washing machine some Martinis must fall.

vertently robbing themselves. The counterpart of the maternal woman is the paternal man. But in our business-dominated Republic, the paternal man is not allowed to come into existence until the sunset gun. This is, to say the least, rather late in the day. What keeps the human race going—what guarantees its fullest and richest development—is not money and machines, but maternal women and paternal men. If American women are amateurish and ineffective in their concern with ethics and morality—and it must be honestly admitted that they are—the difficulty is that the job is too big for a single sex. The Ethics Department is understaffed.

The child-bearing and child-rearing woman can echo business attitudes and admire business goals—and to the extent that she does so, she is unfeminine and unmotherly. If she cannot echo and admire, she is isolated and immobilized. In either case, her ability to give her children real, and not mechanical attention is gravely impaired. Love, affection, tenderness, sympathy and compassion are not qualities which the individual, all by himself, *invents*. They are qualities that he *transmits*. The qualities which make a woman maternal are condemned by American business as "idealistic" and "impractical." The maternal woman in the contemporary United States is therefore in the position of trying to give her children something she is not receiving herself. It *can* be done—just barely—by extremely determined people. American middle-class parents are, for the most part, extremely determined people. They have to be. But a society which puts parents under this kind of strain has very little chance of lasting for a thousand years.

By the Freudian psychoanalysts, the unsatisfied cravings which lie beneath the hurried, unresting, hyperactive surface of American life are described as a yearning for physiological sex. But this is an oversimplification. The yearning —the unsatisfied craving—is there. But it is not a yearning for the act of sex. It is a yearning for an atmosphere—an unbusinesslike atmosphere of generosity and ease and sanctioned idealism and wide spiritual horizons. In such an atmosphere, physiological sex would be, for a great many people, both reliable and rewarding. This kind of atmosphere has, of course, one serious drawback. In that kind of emotional and moral climate, nobody could make a nickel out of sex.

The so-called "women's magazines"—in a sincere and genuine attempt to be helpful—devote a good deal of space to American marriage problems. But these well-intentioned articles are usually wide of the mark. The difficulty is not, as the magazine writers say, that American males and American females have had an inadequate training in how to get along with each other. The difficulty is that American males and American females have had an inadequate training in how to get along with *anybody*. They are competitive. Billions and billions of dollars have been spent to make them that way. They are money-oriented— for the extremely sensible reason that they have seen with their own eyes what happens to people in the United States who are not money-oriented.

To be fully male or fully female means to be paternal or maternal. Animals are capable of siring. Only human beings are capable of fatherhood. There is a curious paradox about mid-century American life which I think will be more apparent to my daughter and her contemporaries —when they grow up—than it is to us. Despite the romantic movies, the titillating advertisements, the bosomy comics and the concupiscent popular fiction, the American business society is sexless. It is not a male society. It is a neuter society. That is one of the principal reasons why so many people do not like it. That is why it cannot be relied upon to last very long.

Another factor which tightens the nerves of American parents is the emphasis placed on that ill-assorted cluster of attitudes known as American foreign policy. It is one of the fictions of American life that American foreign policy has a special and separate kind of importance. In the editorials and the think-pieces, foreign policy seems to be suspended, like Mohammed's coffin, between earth and heaven. However, American foreign policy is not, and never can be, anything more than domestic policy for export. It needs to be administered by specially talented, gifted or experienced people only to the extent that domestic policy also needs to be administered by such people.

The human beings on this planet are organized into various societies, and almost all these societies are currently in flux and in torment. It cannot be said that the American press—concerned, as it has to be, with salable facts—plays down this turbulence. Or knows how to in-

terpret it. But American behavior toward these other societies—"free" or not "free"—is not hard to explain.

Each of our two American societies would like to capture American foreign policy. Not only would each of
them like to. Each of them has. We have Point Four, and
we have the isolationists. We have the Marshall Plan, and
we have the bold spirits who want to reduce everything to
beautiful simplicity by dropping atom and hydrogen
bombs on Russia.

One thing may be said with certainty about American
foreign policy. It is honest. It reflects with mirrorlike ex-
actitude the split in the American personality. Our foreign
policy owes some of its seeming importance to the fact that
it provides—or seems to provide—a wonderful excuse for
not facing up to the headaches of domestic policy. But
those headaches somehow manage to wangle a visa and slip
past the Statue of Liberty anyway. The sustained note in
all the discussions of American foreign policy is the note
of exasperation. Americans are not really interested in foreign policy, for the quite understandable reason that they
have too many troubles at home. Literally at home—in
their dwelling places. When the maternal woman and the
paternal man must constantly apologize to business for existing, they can scarcely be expected to have much sympathy for the woes of peasants six thousand miles away.

The best remedy for the tightened nerves of American
parents is perspective. A good deal is said and written in
the United States about the Russians dropping atom
bombs on New York, and since my little girl's father works

in that metropolis, it is a topic to which I am disposed to pay serious attention. But while the Russians have been consistently abusive, arrogant, vituperative and dismayingly non-middle-class, they have never threatened to bomb us. If they had, we may be sure the American communications industry would have let us know. It would be *the* salable fact of the day.

In terms of perspective, it is of the utmost importance to realize that both American business and Russian Communism are materialistic societies based on the idea that man is primarily an economic animal. Where they differ is in their separate approaches to this economic-ness. The Judeo-Christian ethic, on the other hand, asserts that man is *not* primarily an economic animal. According to that ethic, man manipulates economics—not vice versa—and he manipulates them, moreover, with his eye fixed on non-economic, brotherly, co-operative and nonmaterialistic goals.

American business is hostile to Russia because the Russian state, though materialistic, is a non-money society. The anti-business America is hostile to Russia because it is a cruel, arbitrary and nonhumanitarian state. Could not the two American societies pool their interest and form a common front against Russia? The answer is no. American business asserts that money, while not everything, comes first. Christian morality avers that any conclusions based on this premise are false and essentially unworkable. The two American societies have their *separate* reasons for being opposed to Russia, and it is utterly impossible to combine these two separate reasons.

The Big Fight of our time is not going to come. It has come. The tightened nerves of American parents are partly due to the fact that we are all despairingly apprehensive of a planet-destroying conflict between the United States and the U.S.S.R. This apprehension, if justifiable, makes the job of trying to turn children into good human beings somewhat academic, to say the least. However, this Titanic struggle has not yet taken place. But under cover of the threat, an equally Titanic struggle actually is taking place, and that is the conflict between the quickly evolving American business society and our two-thousand-year-old morality. This internal struggle is infinitely and supremely the more important—if for no other reason than that it is not still in the future. It is occurring right now.

Most Americans are conscious of this desperate subterranean conflict only through the panicky awareness that old, familiar landmarks have disappeared. Mr. Whittaker Chambers—whose life has at no time suggested the reserved, self-reliant, self-disciplining Puritan—is enshrined as a responsible man and a reliable witness. Senator McCarthy is regarded by respectable Americans with horror, but if there is one thing in the world about which the Senator from Wisconsin is cheerful and undismayed, it is the wrath of respectable Americans.

In the supposedly sacred name of foreign policy—and to insure that the clinkers left over from the holocaust will

245

be American clinkers—a great many of our old, familiar landmarks of proper behavior and recognized decency have been done away with. But there is only one really significant aspect of American foreign policy at the present time, and that is how clearly it shows that it is time for us angels to look homeward. "I will not turn my back on Alger Hiss" was not "policy"; but to a great many middle-aged and/or middle-class Americans, it was not foreign, either.

The Consent of the Governed

TAFT TELLS GRADUATES
TO AVOID FEDERAL JOBS

ASHLAND, OHIO, June 9 (AP)—Senator Robert A. Taft, Republican, of Ohio, in a commencement address at Ashland College here today, advised the eighty-seven graduates to avoid government work as a career. Civil service jobs, he said, in his commencement address, offer little opportunity for advancement.

New York Herald-Tribune
June 10, 1950

* * *

GOVERNMENT ATTORNEYS

Editor
New York Herald-Tribune
New York, New York

Dear Sir:

In your editorial column you have posed the rhetorical question: "But when a businessman, a corporation or an

247

income-tax payer is involved, what government lawyer ever stops to worry about fairness?"

At first blush, such a question would appear to be libelous per se to any member of the bar who has chosen to make a career of public service rather than to represent the corporations, businessmen or income-tax payers for whom you are apparently so solicitous.

I have been a "government lawyer" for fifteen years, engaged in Admiralty and other aspects of the maritime law for the United States, both at home and abroad. I have always deemed it a privilege and honor to be so employed by the United States, although, I might add to you, as a "taxpayer," at considerable personal financial loss. You probably could not understand the motives which have prompted me to so serve my country, for your editorial indicates that you believe all government attorneys are unethical knaves. However, I sincerely believe that the government of the United States, of which you and I are a component part, vitally requires the services of experienced attorneys to insure that all of us receive equal protection under the law.

My return inquiry to you is: "Did you stop to think about fairness when you published such a canard about all government lawyers?"

> Frederick K. Arzt
> Member, National Republican Club
> Baltimore, Md.
> March 17, 1950

The two men quoted above are both Republicans and they are both government employees. But in their attitudes toward American government—and, indeed, toward life itself—they are poles apart.

American government is a topic very close to this writer's heart, since I was brought up in a Civil Service household. There is no part of my little girl's social heritage which is potentially more comforting or more fortifying than the American system of representative government; but there is also no part of that inheritance which is more sadly in need of having fact dug out from the obscuring fiction. The American child gets accustomed at a very early age to hearing government brushed off as "politics"—polluted, cynical and too unashamedly venal for decent people to be involved with. This popular and widely held notion is not so much inaccurate or untrue, as it is out of focus.

Few people would be prepared to quarrel with the statement that Senator Taft defends and champions the business society. In that role, he unwittingly—and with complete sincerity—reveals the basically anarchistic quality of the business community. If all the young people agreed with Senator Taft about the paramount importance of "advancement," who would teach the children to read and write? Who would deliver the mail? Who would administer justice in the courts?

This book has no villains, and the Senator's commencement speech has not been disinterred with the idea of making the gentleman from Ohio look like the Prince of Darkness. Senator Taft is non-regal, and does not figure in people's minds as any kind of prince at all. In both the Democratic and Republican parties, there are public figures whose actions and fairly consistent policies quite recognizably have their roots in a sense of morality. In both parties, there are equally identifiable, and infinitely more numerous, public figures who break lances on behalf of business as wholeheartedly as Senator Taft. Senator Taft is distinguished from the other business-minded legislators (of both parties) only by a certain stark and tundralike simplicity for which one must, in the last analysis, be grateful. He is not a talk-gooder.

In a split society, what happens to representative government? The embittered query of the *Herald-Tribune* editorial writer—Where business is concerned, what government official ever stops to be fair?—reflects a widely prevalent feeling in the business community that government is hostile to business. The question of fairness has been adequately disposed of by the correspondent from Maryland, but the feeling of the business community is quite correct. Representative government *is* hostile to business.

In our country, there is a basic clash between government and business. Government cannot be anarchistic and irresponsible, and still be government. Business, on the other hand—with its emphasis on private financial triumph as the first and most important job of any human being— cannot be anything except anarchistic and irresponsible, as Senator Taft so truly, if unintentionally discloses. The middle-aged businessman—his pile safely made—is sometimes prepared to relax and to take a genuine interest in the fortunes of unbusinesslike people. But what can he do about the younger men who are still remorselessly and ruthlessly on their way up? Or about older ones who never arrive at relaxation at all?

The desirability of co-operation between government and business is a favorite topic of American editorial writers. However, the nature of representative government and the nature of American business are such that there never has been any co-operation between them and there never will be. The business community sometimes permits the government to underwrite the losses on railroads, transatlantic liners or mail-carrying airlines. It never willingly cuts the government in on the profits from such enterprises. Such a policy falls a little short of co-operation.

In our time, it has become a function of government to take care of the unbusinesslike minorities in those areas where they cannot take care of themselves. It is the old frontier pattern of protection of the weak. For the purpose of protecting the weak, the government uses funds, a portion of which the American Do-Gooders have wrenched and pried loose from the business society. It is not possible for the government, if it is to remain a representative government, to yield to business' stern demand that the unbusinesslike minorities should be forced to become businesslike or be made to take the consequences.

Since American business is the dominant one of our two societies, it is sometimes able to capture government; but capture is not the same thing as co-operation. When the government succeeds in evading capture—as it did, to a large extent, under Franklin Roosevelt—its relationship

251

with the business community is, and has to be, one of in-curable struggle. In our torn-down-the-middle Republic, the same thing happens to government which happens to the Judeo-Christian ethic. Government is spoken of by the communications industry with the highest respect, until it goes into action on behalf of the unbusinesslike. When it goes into action to protect the weak, and thereby *becomes* a government, the respect is instantly transmuted into derision, contempt and hostility.

But American representative government is, by defini-tion, supposed to do one thing. It is supposed to represent. Most of the people in the United States are unbusinesslike —and will continue to be, until the Last Trump. Hence it is the unbusinesslike people who ought to have the most influence on the American government, and whose needs and potentialities that government should be most con-cerned with. In these pages, I have avoided like the plague any use of the word "democracy." That beat-up collection of sinned-against syllables has taken such a mauling that it is no longer possible for any two Americans to agree on what they mean by it. Everybody, however, knows what is meant by representative government.

Against the American representative government, two ac-cusations have been consistently and unceasingly leveled by the business community. These two accusations have been so staunchly reiterated that almost everybody be-lieves them—even, sometimes, government people them-selves. The first accusation is that our representative government is inefficient. The second accusation is that that government is inevitably and innately corrupt.

The idea that American business is efficient and American government is inefficient has been so relentlessly dinned into our ears that to question it verges on blasphemy. However, this year's blasphemy is next year's liberating truth; and the fact of the matter is that efficiency in itself is meaningless. Efficiency has no importance except in connection with what one is being efficient *about*. Indisputably, American business is efficient; but according to the findings of the Kefauver Committee, American crime is even more efficient than American business. At least, that is what it said in the papers.

It is a mistake to accept meekly and without query the legend that American representative government is a contemptible clump of dim-witted bureaucrats tied up like a Schrafft's Week-end Special in yards of red tape. The sacrilegious but not wholly unpalatable fact remains that never since it emerged in recognizable form—not even during the Civil War—has the American government cracked up, gone to pieces and failed in its job of governing the way the business society cracked up, went to pieces and failed in its job of being prosperous in 1929. This may be treason, but by all means let us make the most of it. It is one of the most stabilizing and reassuring facts in the whole of American life.

Historically, American government has been more efficient than American business, and for this demonstrable superiority, there is a sound reason. Our population has always, fortunately, included a certain number of Americans who wanted the working years of their lives to add up to something better than three or four decades of self-seeking. In terms of government employment, this kind of American antedates the New Deal by a good long time and can by no means be uniformly relied upon to approve of Franklin D. Roosevelt and his works. When this kind of public servant receives any attention at all, it is generally unfavorable. There is hardly a newspaper in the country which would not automatically allude to the government lawyer quoted above as a "bureaucrat." According to the dictionary, a bureaucrat is "an official who works by fixed routine without exercising intelligent judgement." The bureaucrat's letter, however, is almost embarrassingly superior in intelligence and discernment to Senator Taft's awkward little effort at vocational guidance.

The strength and staying power of American government are based on an idea. This idea the lawyer from Maryland has expressed with a certain amount of eloquence—to wit, that it is an honor and a privilege to serve the United States, even at the cost of a certain amount of "advancement." About this idea, there is one really superlative attribute. It does not have to be abandoned at five o'clock. The owner can—with complete propriety and utter safety—bring it home from the office. It does not do the children a bit of harm.

Behind the charge that American government is inefficient lies the tacit assumption that that government is a

money-making organization which has somehow disgrace-
fully failed to make money. Which has done even worse—
which has lost money. However, government in the United
States is not, and cannot be, a money-making institution.
Government renders a great many services to people who
cannot pay for them. Children, for example. (Indeed—in
the form of favorable legislation—it also renders services to
people who could pay for them, but do not want to. Stockholders, for instance, in luminously non-anemic indus-
tries.) In the United States, American business and representative government cannot *both* make money. It has to
be one or the other.

Government is not business. It is wholly different in motive and intent from business. Business is unashamedly individualistic and self-seeking. The social scientists have a
special word for it. They call it "privatist." Government,
on the other hand, is public, communal and concerned
with the welfare of all the citizens, and not just the ones
who are talented acquirers. Potentially, there is an enormous amount of satisfaction in being able to live out one's
life in a country with a representative government. But
the whole flavor and quality of the American representative government turn to ashes on the tongue, if one regards
that government as simply an inferior and rather second-
rate sort of corporation.

In this country, we have a phenomenon which is described by the conservative press and conservative businessmen as "government spending." The fires of hell do
not look more hideous and alarming to American business

255

than the disbursal of funds by the United States government. "Government spending," however—as the phrase is
used by the business society—has a very narrow and particular meaning. It does not refer to government moneys
which, through renegotiation contracts, find their way into
the businessman's pocket. It refers to the government
moneys which are used to benefit The Type That Fails To
Make Money. "Government spending" does not mean *all*
government spending. It means the expenditure of money
on children, veterans, farmers who cannot singlehandedly
cope with the Dust Bowl, Navajos, old people, the victims
of technological unemployment, drug addicts, Point Four
foreigners and housewives who use government bulletins
in doing their home canning and home nursing.

In business terms, it is "inefficient" to spend money for
the purpose of conferring benefits on unconscious do-gooders of The Type That Fails To Make Money. But in terms
of representative government, such spending is not only
efficient—it is the only claim the government has to call
itself representative. In our society, money is constantly
moving in a circle. It goes out of the consumer's pocket
and into the producer's. Then, via taxes, it goes out of the
producer's pocket and into the government's. From the
government, it flows back to the consumer in the form of
postal services, new roads, day nurseries for "working"
mothers, forest conservation and—when the unbusinesslike
people are having a lucky year—TVA.

In business terms, only one arc of this circle is "efficient." When the money flows out of the consumer's

pocket and into the producer's, the producer is "efficient." But when the producer is taxed, the taxing agency is de scribed as bungling, greedy, inept and punitive. And when the tax money is spent on people who have never met a payroll and who do not get "results," this is "government spending" and the communications industry assures us with passion and fervor that we must vote for the candidates who have sworn to put a stop to it.

If the American representative government ever reaches a point where American business is prepared to commend it as efficient, that government will have become tyran-nical and nonrepresentative. (Or American business will have changed so that its own mother would not know it.) There is comfort and reassurance to be derived from Amer-ican life in the middle of the twentieth century, but that comfort and reassurance are only available to people who are prepared to take business myths and financial legends with a very considerable grain of salt. Last year my hus-band and I bought—and paid cash for—a washing machine of a widely known and widely celebrated brand. The ma-chine which was delivered to us was defective. It took three months of letters, phone calls and stayings-at-home-for-re-pairmen-who-did-not-come before the illustrious gadget was finally put into working order.

The incident is tiny, but not untypical. If American business would do something completely unprecedented— if it would stop perpetually talking to the American housewife and spend ten minutes listening to her—it would find that under many a $7.98 seersucker wrap-around lies a mute but stubborn skepticism about the allegedly flawless efficiency of the business society. When the American representative government takes three months to fix something which is broken, the blame is placed on red tape and bureaucratic inefficiency. When the American entrepreneur takes three months to fix something which is broken, nothing is said about red tape or inefficiency. When American business leans on its shovel—in the fashion so widely attributed to W.P.A. workers—the businessman has a rather lyrical name for the dawdling and delay. He calls it "the human factor."

The second charge which is constantly made against government—the charge that it is just naturally and inevitably corrupt—is not wholly untrue, but it needs to be brought into perspective. Corruption is a general circumstance of American life, and American government is very much a part of American life. Government officials sometimes take bribes. So do college athletes. However, the businessmen who offer the bribes do not do it out of sheer, wanton deviltry. They do it because they expect to make money faster by offering bribes than they could by not offering bribes. Between the little fellow's bribe and the big fellow's "fast deal," there is no essential difference. The bribe-taker and the bribe-giver both suffer from the common American blind spot. They are both unaware that money, over and above the simple needs of the flesh, does not solve problems—it just permits them to get worse.

In this present day and age, any talk of American government appears to lead quite naturally into the much-canvassed topic of loyalty to that government. Actually, this easy transition from the topic of government to the topic of loyalty is something which—the writer suspects—is not going to stand the test of time. Two or three decades from now, the American government will still be here (one imagines). But the next generation may not agree with those of their parents who said, in the middle of the century, that what keeps the government's chin above water is the informal crucifixions which take place in the name of discovering and punishing anti-government sentiments. To some Americans, those crucifixions do not look very handsome, even now; and Time is going to be merciless with them.

Before touching on the tangled subject of loyalty, it must be admitted that your correspondent is fully conscious that some of the viewpoints expressed in these pages may seem, at first glance, startling and unfamiliar. (Actually, the point of view herein contained is very, very old; and this book was put together with a Resurrector Set.) But the startling and unfamiliar can sometimes be extremely comforting; whereas the familiar—as we know it today—is disturbing, confusing and bleak. We have "public relations," "public opinion," "the power of the press" and all the din and racket of the all-too-communicative communications industry. But we also have—like Mr. Wordsworth's violet by the mossy stone—the sober truth.

Even by dogged pursuers, the sober truth is not very easily arrived at. But a good handy device for getting a line on it is to try to project one's self into the future and to imagine how contemporary attitudes and contemporary behavior are going to look to our children and grandchildren—as they reach maturity. When my father declined to change his name from Reinhold to Reginald, there were not lacking substantial and respected citizens who said he was giving aid and comfort to the enemy and that "traitor" was not too strong a word for him. (Of course, in that undeveloped era, everything was miniature and non-gigantic —even treason.) As time passed, however, the old man's testy negative came to look less and less like treason and more and more like the intelligent and rational action of a self-respecting citizen.

For my own part—since I have quite a stake in securing the good opinion of at least one member of the rising generation—the transmuting touch of time is something on which I like to keep a wary eye. Devoted and conscientious public servants like Mr. Seth W. Richardson, former Chairman of the President's Loyalty Review Board, have given extremely careful and painstaking study to the question of loyalty—or rather, to the question of disloyalty. Not for a moment do I wish to impugn the serious-mindedness of those mid-century Americans who have sincerely tried to come to grips with the issue in non-hysterical terms.

But one cannot help suspecting that in twenty or thirty years' time, the current obsession with loyalty is going to have its comic aspects. It is quite likely that the next generation will laugh out loud upon being told that a commonwealth whose official morality states categorically, "Thou shalt not bear false witness," was defended from its

260

enemies (some people said) by Senator McCarthy. Over treason-by-letterhead and treachery-by-brother-in-law—otherwise known as guilt by association—our descendants will certainly chuckle. Was Christ a pickpocket because He was crucified between two thieves? The issue of loyalty or disloyalty to the United States can be considerably simplified by asking one brief question: Which United States? The American Way of Life can mean the anti-money, Jewish-Christian system of ethics which we have inherited from the distant past. Or it can mean the much-publicized and much-emphasized business philosophy that money, while not everything, comes first. *But it cannot mean both.*

The mid-century bacchanal about loyalty oaths and loyalty investigations and being "cleared" by this or that agency or smeared in a paroxysm of generalized spite has arisen out of a failure of understanding. What has not been understood is that to be anti-business does not ipso facto mean to be pro-Communist. Anti-business sentiments can stem from nothing more treacherous and unpatriotic than a thorough grounding in the principles of Christianity or Judaism. Presumably, libelers and self-servers can defend the American business society against Communism. At least, American business thinks they can. But libelers, self-servers and male and female hysterics cannot defend the American ethic against Russia—or even against Tierra del Fuego. It is a cardinal principle of the Judeo-Christian ethic that the end *never* justifies the means; and the evil-doer does not exist to whom either our morale or our morality is the slightest bit indebted.

Except among trained social scientists—and not always among them—there is no recognition in the United States of the fact that we have a split society. This ignorance produces, every now and then, some paradoxical situations. The year before last, a great deal of money was spent on investigating the loyalty of two or three million Federal employees. Although government money was spent, the disbursal was not described as "government spending." Nobody, however, asked the pertinent question of what the Federal employees were supposed to be loyal *to*—to American business, which consigns government employees to the outer darkness of The Type That Fails To Make Money? Or to American representative government which, if it does not represent the interests of the unbusinesslike, is not representative at all?

Nothing exists by itself. Everything has roots in the past. The "treason" and "disloyalty" by which we have all been so much disturbed and so much puzzled have antecedents. Our problem, however, is that the communications industry—in giving what it describes as "coverage" to disloyal people—has presented us with salable facts instead of with the sober truth. A half-antecedent is as dangerous and misleading as a half-truth. A great many young Americans —my husband, for example, when he was nineteen—belonged briefly to the Young Communist League. According to current folklore, the most charitable interpretation of this bit of personal history would be that it was a hideous and disastrous mistake for which only a thousand strenuously vocal "mea culpas" can atone. However, what sets people free from American chronic anxiety is not salable facts or popular folklore. What clears the air and lets people breathe freely and untimorously again is the sober truth. The sober truth is that the precise moment in history when the Great Russian Experiment looked at its best also happened to be the precise moment in history when the American business society looked at its worst.

A young man might have joined the Young Communist League because he was angry and distressed at the undeserved misery which the Great Depression brought in its train. From immediate practical experience, he discovered that it is no more possible to team up Communism with the American ethic than it is possible to team up American business with the American ethic. But in terms of our ancient national morality—and those are the only terms which merit attention and respect—no apology is necessary for having made the discovery. It is not necessary to be sorry for not having a peach-pit heart.

Seen against its proper background of the needless waste and undeserved humiliation produced by the Great Depression, joining the Young Communist League was—if not *the* thing to have done—at least *one* of the things to have done. Betrayal was involved in the Great Depression; but it was the betrayal of harmless and hard-working Americans by a few self-willed and astigmatic business-lovers. Perspective and sober truth are the nearest things we have to a remedy for American chronic unhappiness. But perspective cannot be achieved without admitting that the Hoovervilles, the bread lines and the apple-sellers really existed. Because of them, some people committed suicide. Some people put on gray uniforms and pledged themselves to technocracy. And some people (by no means the least sensitive and least intelligent) turned—not so much toward Communism, as away from American business. The suicides are beyond anyone's reach. Technocracy is not making much headway in Asia. But the depression-inspired fellow travelers of the thirties—the depression-induced Communists of the thirties—are salable in just about the same way and just about the same direction as Uncle Tom was salable.

In the emotional vacuum which followed upon the end of World War II—a vacuum which was made emptier, even for the business society, by the death of President Roosevelt—a few ex-Communists turned back to the alabaster arms of American business and performed, for its sweet sake, prodigies of profitable peaching and remunerative talebearing. But a distinction must be made—merely in the sacred name of the human nervous system—between third-decade left-wingers who do not believe in human sacrifice and the very tiny, but highly publicized group of third-decade left-wingers who bandaged their bleeding hearts with other people's reputations.

I have mentioned the matter of long-dead Communist affiliation with a more or less prefatory purpose. In itself not particularly significant, it nevertheless raises a very important question. That question is: Why was it that, after the depression, a certain number of stable, rational and well-brought-up people thought—for a while—that they could discern in Communism the mien and lineaments of the Judeo-Christian ethic? Why has it been so scandalously easy for American business to pin the label of Communism on any sort of decent, humanitarian behavior?

The only possible answer appears to be that Communism and our ancient and traditional system of ethics seem to have something in common. And they do. The business society directs the individual's attention to himself. Furthermore, it urges him to cultivate and develop only those parts of his personality which he can sell. Both Communism and Western-world ethics, on the other hand, direct the individual's attention outward and away from himself. They both invite him to be subservient—in the literal sense of giving service, and of giving it under an agency which is postulated as bigger and more important than any single person's life.

Here, however, the resemblance ends. And very sharply. Communism directs the individual's attention toward the state; but state-worship is just as false an idol as money, and just as unworkable a substitute for the family. The Judeo-Christian ethic says that the state exists to serve man —not vice versa. It directs the individual's attention to what the theologically-minded call the Kingdom of God and what non-ritualists might be content to describe as the Kingdom Where Money Doesn't Count. Western-world morality directs man's attention to other men. These other men are conceived of—not as consumers or customers or competitors or expendable slaves of a governmental Moloch—but as complex, significant and valuable human beings. Western-world morality, in short, directs man's attention to life itself.

The source of all our mid-century anxiety is supposed to be that we live in a two-piece world—the two pieces being Russian Communism and American democracy. But it is not a two-piece world; it is a three-piece world. For Americans, the three points of the triangle are Russian Communism, American business and American ethics. So far as the sober truth is concerned, there is nothing the Russians could do to us—or to anybody else, for that matter—which could not be parried by unashamed Judaism or entrenched Christianity, armed with our magnificent machines. A good many years ago, Franklin P. Adams summed up the American split society in one brilliant sentence—"Christmas is over, and business is business." When business is over and Christmas is Christmas, we shall have a good deal less reason to fear the Russians. What is even nicer, we shall have less reason to fear each other.

XII

Summary

SOMEWHERE in the United States a little boy is growing up who may some day ask for, and get, my daughter's hand in marriage. I think a good deal about that little boy. I wonder whether his mother is trying to escape from her essential loneliness, as a maternal woman in a business-dominated country, through an exhausting schedule of defensive and escape buying. I wonder whether his father is a successful businessman who—inarticulately oppressed by his job and baffled by his own character—cannot fully respond to the language of a child's face and body. Or perhaps his father is an unbusinesslike man whose courage and authority have been slowly but steadily eroded by the mechanical contempt of American business.

I wonder whether that little boy is going to school on part time, because a school board of "realistic" and "practical" men have concluded that it would be "government spending"—and unfair to the taxpayer—to construct new schools. I wonder whether the sensitive and intelligent schoolteachers who might have had a lasting and felicitous effect on his life—and therefore on my daughter's—have been driven out of the profession by distinctly lower-than-middle-class salaries. Or whether those teachers are constrained from giving him of their best because they know from harsh experience that their best will be described as "subversive."

In terms of Western-world morality, there is only one possible philosophy of parenthood, and that philosophy can be summed up fairly simply. It is impossible to betray another man's child—for whatever reason—without also betraying one's own. To do less than justice to another man's child, no matter who that man is, is to impair by that much the chances one's own children have for a life of meaning and purpose. This is the only—and the point should be emphasized, the *only*—rational, logical and realistic approach to "politics," to American government, to American business and, in short, to American life.

As these pages are being written, the American Congress has just voted down a proposal that the Federal government should command the income from tidelands oil and should use that revenue for the education of American children. "The halls of Congress"—in the words of one radio commentator—"are sweating and slippery with oil." It is the careless assumption of the business society that the only children who suffer from this kind of legislative behavior are the unimportant children of the un-businesslike. Actually, the oilmen's children, the lobbyists' children and the Congressional children were right in there taking the rap, too.

The mills of the gods grind slowly, but they grind exceeding small. A slippery inheritance is a disappointing inheritance and an unreliable inheritance. Thoughtless, myth-swallowing parents—no matter how well-heeled—produce anxious, unhappy children. And sometimes angry, defiant and rebellious children. Silk purses are made out of silk, and never out of porcine ears.

It is one of the most frequently reiterated fictions of American life that "private enterprise" is good for people and that everybody benefits from it, regardless of what his income is. Actually, "private enterprise" is not even good for the round pegs—the Dream Boys—the successful American businessmen. It amputates a section of the mind and heart which no human being really wants to relinquish. Furthermore, "private enterprise" leaks imperceptibly into the area of bringing up children. We bring up our children privately—as if, that is, there were no other children in the world. American children are as much personal adjuncts of the parent as the parent's bank account. Like the bank account, they must be fat and sassy, or the parent cannot be accounted "successful" as a parent. But "private enterprise" does not belong in the field of parenthood, and a society which springs this kind of leak is headed for something really drastic like death or reform.

American business—and the kind of legislation which

shields and protects it—is based on a theory which is never put into words, but which is often very successfully translated into action. That never-verbalized theory is that the American child has an obligation to the business society. His obligation consists of either (1) selecting for himself the kind of father who is able and willing to earn a good deal of money under circumstances which are frankly described as a rat race or (2) getting away from any other kind of father just as fast as a paper route can carry him.

Actually, of course, the grownups are responsible for the child—not vice-versa. Ideally—and in societies which survive and flourish, practically too—children learn to take responsibility in the same way they learn everything else which determines their cast of character and the kind of lives they ultimately live. Children learn to take responsibility by force of example. How much responsibility a child has learned to take—by the time he is grown up—depends on *the number of people who were able and willing to take responsibility for him.* Even if they did not know him personally. Even if he existed for them only as a statistic or a principle or a still-unrevealed son-in-law.

Children need love—not only from their own fathers and mothers—but also from all the other fathers and mothers in the society. Children need love, not only personally, but also *as a class.* Similarly, parents cannot do a good job in bringing up their children unless they, too, have status and prestige in their role of parents—regardless of whether they can or cannot make money. American children are the most important group of people, bar none, in the United States. The Americans who have been able to grasp that supremely decisive (if elusive) fact are identified in these pages as Do-Gooders. But they might with equal accuracy be described as the Children's Lobby.

The prevailing problem of the mid-century American is that he has a split personality. Whether he is a liberal or a conservative, he has had not one, but two educations. With a conscience acquired in childhood, he has to live as a grownup—and as a parent—in a business society which presses him unceasingly to betray that conscience. However—despite the agonizing split between our two American societies—not many Americans make the kind of spectacular bargain with evil that Faust made. Fallible most of us are, but not as a rule *that* fallible.

What usually happens is that, under the merciless crowding of the business society—sometimes also known as "progress"—the mid-century American surrenders his ethical birthright in little bits and pieces. A point yielded here. Something left unsaid there. We try to "adjust," as the psychologists say, to a situation where no adjustment is possible. And we do not usually find out—until it is too late, until too much has been given up—what has happened to us.

American chronic anxiety can be very easily explained. The Judeo-Christian ethic is the source of all our public and private morality, and that ethic has changed very little in the past two thousand years. The American business society, on the other hand, is one of the quickest-moving, most swiftly-developing and fastest-evolving of all human societies. Consequently, the faster the business society moves—the more real privacy gives way to the false intimacy of nation-wide publicity—the more money flows to the top, while the human beings (*all* human beings) sink to the bottom—the more barrenly impersonal and aimlessly mechanized our lives become—the more these things happen, the more the American people are faced with a truly grisly situation. That situation is just this: The American business society must either stop "progressing," or it must find some way of scuttling and getting rid of the money-rejecting Western ethic.

And this last is exactly what—since the end of World War II—American business has been trying to bring about. No deliberate evil-doing is involved. It is strictly a matter of "Father, forgive them, for they know not what they do." Not villainy, but social training is the point at issue. When human beings are educated and conditioned as a certain number of Americans are educated and conditioned by the business society, those human beings will continue automatically to act out that conditioning until the Grim Reaper stops the process. Unless, of course, the people who have been less strongly conditioned are able and willing to put the brake on.

The American business society is currently self-hypnotized. It has persuaded itself that in celebrating the importance of money and the superiority of the money-making personality, it is fighting Communism. What the business society is actually doing is engaging in a compulsive attempt to destroy our traditional national morality. That is why American parents have tightened nerves. In the United States, there is no way of having a good parent-child relationship except against the background of a generally acknowledged and generally practiced system of ethics. But the Hiss trials illumined with dreadful clarity what is really taking place upon our native heath.

The enormous amount of attention given by the newspapers to the Hiss trials is a fairly clear indication that something much more significant was involved than a mere technical adjudication on a perjury charge. And in reality, it was not the primary social purpose of the Hiss trials to disestablish Mr. Hiss. That was secondary. The meaning of the Hiss trials—as a social phenomenon—was that they were an unconscious attempt, on the part of the business society, to toss our official national morality overboard and to set up its own ethic instead—its own ethic being, of course, anti-Communism. In the Hiss trials, and in the person of Whittaker Chambers, the business society and the communications industry were trying to bring into general acknowledgment and good repute a kind of behavior which would have all the appearance of being an ethic—but which would not raise any awkward questions about the money-changers in the Temple.

But it is impossible to make an ethic out of anti-Communism. To be sure, there are countries in the world where it takes superlative courage to be an anti-Communist. But the United States is not one of them. An ethic implies discipline and effort. More importantly, an ethic directs people *toward* something, not merely *away from* something. Western-world morality directs people toward the good. Anti-Communism, as it is presently practiced and recognized in the United States, is a fussy, spinsterish, semi-hysterical flight from evil. But it is not, in itself, an approach to the good. To approach the good, you have to have muscles.

European observers are fond of saying that Americans are temperamentally optimistic; and personally, this writer does not deny the soft impeachment. American chronic anxiety is by no means completely incurable. That is to say, we do not have to *create* good human beings in the United States of America. We have millions and millions of them already extant. All we have to do is to stop scaring them to death—to cease spitting on their do-gooder gaberdines, and to desist from beating them over the head with the ten-cent-store morality of anti-Communism.

As Americans, all of us now mature are condemned to a certain amount of schizophrenia. (To talk about getting away from business attitudes is easy enough; but it is a long, slow process to weed them out of the habit-dominated mind.) We do not, however, have to pass on the split personality—in all its shattering completeness—to our children. There is still an Upward Step available to American parents, although that step is no longer the comparatively simple matter of earning the money for expensive schools or expensive skills.

As Americans, we have a heritage which is not only ancient and glorious, but which is also—what is more to the point—psychologically and emotionally suited to the

274

needs of warmth-seeking human beings. We do not have to invent, explore or pioneer. All we have to do is turn our backs on the cactus forest of Eggcups and put our heritage to work. There is conflict in all societies. At the very simplest, there is usually conflict between the young and the old. But no tribe or commonwealth in the world has ever demanded that people should be both young and old at the same time, the way Americans are expected to be both pious and acquisitive in one single breath. "When a society is perishing," said Pope Leo XIII, in his encyclical letter on the condition of labor, May 15, 1891, "the true advice to give to those who would restore it is to recall it to the principles from which it sprang."

A NOTE ABOUT THE AUTHOR

READERS *of this book will learn a great deal about Margaret Halsey in her own words. The publisher, therefore, is concerned only with statistics in this brief note.*

Miss Halsey was born in Yonkers, New York. She got her B.S. from Skidmore College, her M.A. from Teachers College, and then worked—in moderately rapid succession —for a bank, a real-estate company, a radio agent, and a publisher. In 1936 she married and went for a year's visit to England, during which time she wrote her first book, With Malice Toward Some. *Since then she has written* Some of My Best Friends Are Soldiers, Color Blind, *and* The Folks at Home.

LAZLO'S STRIKE

Also by T. V. Olsen
in Large Print:

Eye of the Wolf
Haven of the Hunted
The Lost Colony
McGivern
Rattlesnake
Run to the Mountain
Savage Sierra
The Stalking Moon
Treasures of the Sun
Arrow in the Sun
Blizzard Pass
Blood Rage
A Man Called Brazos
Man Without a Past

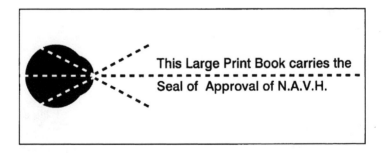

LAZLO'S STRIKE

T. V. OLSEN

Thorndike Press • Waterville, Maine

Published in 2005 by arrangement with
Golden West Literary Agency.

Thorndike Press® Large Print Western.

The tree indicium is a trademark of Thorndike Press.

The text of this Large Print edition is unabridged.
Other aspects of the book may vary from the original edition.

Set in 16 pt. Plantin by Ramona Watson.

Printed in the United States on permanent paper.

Library of Congress Cataloging-in-Publication Data

Olsen, Theodore V.
    Lazlo's strike / by T.V. Olsen.
        p. cm. — (Thorndike Press large print Western)
    ISBN 0-7862-7397-6 (lg. print : hc : alk. paper)
    1. Hungarian Americans — Fiction.   2. Gold mines and
mining — Fiction.   3. Sierra Nevada (Calif. and Nev.) —
Fiction.   4. Large type books.   I. Title.   II. Thorndike
Press large print Western series.
PS3565.L8L39 2005
    813'.54—dc22   2004028359

To Dorothy Guilday

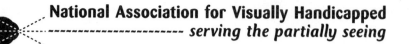
As the Founder/CEO of NAVH, the only national health agency solely devoted to those who, although not totally blind, have an eye disease which could lead to serious visual impairment, I am pleased to recognize Thorndike Press★ as one of the leading publishers in the large print field.

Founded in 1954 in San Francisco to prepare large print textbooks for partially seeing children, NAVH became the pioneer and standard setting agency in the preparation of large type.

Today, those publishers who meet our standards carry the prestigious "Seal of Approval" indicating high quality large print. We are delighted that Thorndike Press is one of the publishers whose titles meet these standards. We are also pleased to recognize the significant contribution Thorndike Press is making in this important and growing field.

Lorraine H. Marchi, L.H.D.
Founder/CEO
NAVH

★ Thorndike Press encompasses the following imprints: Thorndike, Wheeler, Walker and Large Print Press.

CHAPTER 1

The one-room stone jail was pierced by a single small high window. As the sun got higher, a narrow shaft of light crawled down the inside wall and touched the cheek of the sleeper sprawled on a straw pallet on the bare dirt floor.

Lazlo Kusik groaned. His bearded face twitched. He came by miserable and grudging degrees out of a deep well of sleep, shrugging away the frayed horse blanket under which he'd huddled through most of a freezing night he could hardly remember. Then he edged to a sitting position, holding his head and shuddering with agony.

Now he did begin to remember, and it made him groan again.

Over by the wall opposite him, Hutch Prouter was stirring on his own moldy pallet. He cocked open one eye and turned his shaggy head enough to give Lazlo a raffish wink.

"How do there, little pard?" said Hutch.

"Man, you do look like hell."

Lazlo planted a hand against the scarred wall and maneuvered gradually to his feet. When he'd made it, he teetered unsteadily. He knew exactly how Sisera would have felt if, by some unwelcome magic, he could have survived with that spike driven through his skull.

Nice thought. It drew a third tortured groan out of him.

Hutch Prouter yawned and patted his great tub of a belly. He sat upright on his heap of straw, combed a hamlike hand through his curly thatch of blond hair, and said agreeably, "God's own truth, ain't it? Know just how you feel. 'Bout now you be afraid you gonna die. One hour from now you will be afraid you ain't gonna."

Lazlo eyed him with a sick resentment. "You had as much to drink as me," he managed to croak. "That is, I think you had as much."

"Ain't that God's truth," Hutch said cheerfully. "I had more'n that, little pard, a whole heap more. But my plumbing is fixed for it, you see. It is used to taking on mebbe a half gallon o' tanglefoot ever' night. The godawful lizard pee they serve up in this camp do take some getting used to, what I mean."

8

Then too, maybe Hutch was just plain built for taking on a load of that kind and quantity. As he stood up now, scraping wisps of straw out of his hair, Hutch's head was an inch short of brushing a ceiling beam. It was a broad jug of a head that went perfectly with his huge, imposing frame. That, along with his sway-bellied front and the layers of tallowy fat over his massive musculature, reminded you of an overgrazed bull in a pasture. Even the bunch of crinkling curls over his forehead resembled a bull's poll. Hutch was about thirty.

Still holding both hands to his head, Lazlo Kusik shuffled shakily up and down the ten-by-fifteen-foot floor of the jailhouse and tried to collect his thoughts. Damn Hutch Prouter anyway.

How much did I say to him last night? Lazlo wondered dismally. How much did I tell him?

The battering hurt of his head made it impossible to sort out many details just yet. Memories of last night all flowed together in a fragmented mishmash.

Later. Maybe it would all come clear for him later.

How long had they been in this place? Lazlo couldn't even remember being hauled off to jail or the events that had led up to it. He patted his pockets. Amazingly, all their usual contents were in place. At least he hadn't been "rolled." His knife sheath was empty and his rifle was missing. But that was to be expected.

Pacing up and down, fighting not to retch, he tried to get up a painful interest in the gloomy interior of their cell. He had never seen the inside of Bozetown's little stone-walled jail before, and he decided it was about as interesting as slow death. It contained a single slop bucket and a few straw pallets for overnight inmates, and that was all. The stones were so poorly mortared together that probably a few husky men could set their shoulders and push out a wall, and one man could tunnel out under the same wall in a few hours. However, hardly anyone ever bothered to.

Who needed a secure jail for a flare-up, die-fast camp like Bozetown?

The gold-strike camp was barely a year old and might not last another year. The usual way of dealing with a felony such as stealing a mule or salting and selling a bad claim — murder and actual claim-jumping ranked somewhat behind those injustices — was at the big hanging tree on the edge of town. Minor transgressions of various kinds earned you a night in the pokey. The lines were pretty clear-cut; there was no reason to bother with the niceties of a judge or jury.

A key rattled in the padlock that secured the oak-slab door. It swung open. A stocky man with a traplike jaw stood in the sudden blaze of sunlight.

The two prisoners blinked at him owlishly.

"Abe Friendly," Hutch greeted him, "you look just awful this morning. Christ, do you ever!"

Marshal Friendly was not amused. He swung out of the doorway and jerked his head sideways. "Out," he said.

They picked up their hats and tramped out past him, the sun hurting their eyes.

"What the Christ time is it?" asked Hutch.

"Hard onto the hour of noon. You two was dead to the world when the sun come up, so I let you sleep. Here —"

Marshal Friendly was toting Lazlo's rifle under his arm. He gave it to him, and pulled Lazlo's Bowie knife from his belt and handed that over. Then he returned Hutch's pocket knife and his Whitneyville Walker Colt, a vintage weapon with most of the bluing worn off its long barrel.

11

Lazlo inspected the mechanism of his rifle, feeling a nudge of shame even in his physical misery. He remembered practically nothing of last night but was reasonably sure that some of his behavior hadn't been all wool and a yard wide.

"Marshal," he said tentatively, "I hope I did not —"

"Not much, you didn't. You had yourself quite a snootful. First time I ever seen you kick up a ruckus, Kusik."

Lazlo grunted, feeling a little more sickish.

"You shot off seven of them ornamental wood knobs on the sign Dick Slade has over his saloon. Eight shots, and you missed one." Marshal Friendly's voice held neither censure nor interest. "Fair shooting for a man who couldn't walk a straight line anymore."

"Oh, Laz is a seven-day wonder when he is good and likkered. Say there, Abe Friendly" — Hutch gave a broad wink as he rammed the pistol into the waistband of his greasy leather pants — "what's chances for the law giving us a good breakfast. Customary thing, ain't it?"

The marshal gave him a steely-eyed look. Abe Friendly was only a provisional official, hired by Bozetown's vigilante committee

12

to handle troublemakers in the camp proper. He had a long and varied background as a peace officer; now he was gray and getting a hint of paunch, but you never doubted he could still handle himself in the clutch.

"It's waiting for you over there." He pointed his thumb at a nearby horsetrough. "Fill up."

He turned on his heel and walked away.

"Now don't that beat all kinds of generosity four ways to hell!" Hutch let out a throaty roar of laughter, then smacked a massive palm between Lazlo's shoulders, staggering him. "Well, we can rinse our heads out anyways, hey, little pard? Then, I will allow you to buy me breakfast. What say?"

On wobbly legs Lazlo followed his hulking companion over to the horsetrough. They knelt down beside it and ducked their heads. The water was clear and icy-cold, being piped from a mountain stream above the camp and also having an outlet pipe from the trough. That made it all right to drink the water too.

At least Lazlo hoped so, for he had a burning thirst. He drank long and deep.

When he straightened up, he mopped his

face dry with a pocket bandanna and felt a little better. At least the fuzz was out of his brain as well as his mouth. He slid Hutch Prouter a wary glance as the latter heaved to his feet, spluttering like a walrus.

Again Lazlo thought worriedly: What did I tell him? How much?

He suspected that if he *had* spilled any of the beans, he might have good reason to worry. He didn't know Hutch very well and couldn't call him a friend. Last night they had joined forces for a monumental drunken tear — the first of its kind in a short and casual acquaintance.

What Lazlo did know, or had heard on pretty good authority, was that Hutch had a kind of unruly reputation. Nothing quite on the outright shady side, but more than a little rascally.

Hutch dressed with slovenly indifference. He wore dirty rawhide trousers and an equally dirty cowhide vest over dirty red flannel underwear — no shirt. He topped off the ensemble with a filthy battered hat. All of it went with the expression on his face, which was thick and stupid.

Except for the eyes. They were chill as ice, and for all his constant banter, they never lost that sly and searching look. You had the feeling that nothing much got by

14

Hutch Prouter. Nothing, that is, which could be turned to Hutch's advantage.

"How 'bout that breakfast now?" Hutch patted his great kettle gut. "Man, I could put away a whole steer off the hoof by my own self. But I'll split 'im down the middle with you iffen you can dig up the where-withal."

Lazlo's stomach gave a queasy lurch. He grimaced and shook his head.

"I know how you feel, little pard, and that's God's truth. But a mite o' grub will serve to settle your innards, take it from ole Hutch."

"I think I must get back to my claim," Lazlo protested. "I have work to do. Also, I came to town to buy a wagon and a team . . ."

"And not get full o' redeye, hey?" Hutch chuckled. "Hell, it done you good. Man is got to get loosed up oncet in a while. 'Nother hour or so 'fore you get back to your digs ain't gonna hurt none. That claim ain't gonna up and fly away on you meantime . . ."

As he spoke, Hutch took Lazlo's arm and effortlessly propelled him down Bozetown's single dirt street.

"Got a mite o' coin left in my own poke," Hutch went on, "and I will spend it

15

to settle your bad belly iffen you will do as much for my empty one. What say?"

There wasn't much Lazlo could say against the clamp of Hutch's powerful hand on his arm. Worry that he might arouse Hutch's curiosity by protesting too much overrode his uneasy wish to have no more to do with the man. Also, he was as sick as a dog. So he let himself be dragged along.

The morning was still brisk and even a touch chilly, although the sun was high above the ramshackle sprawl of Bozetown. A typical gold-strike camp, it had been laid out for expediency, not permanence. The whole town was built in gulches and on slopes, so that many of the shacks and buildings that composed it were set above or below others. A man couldn't stand on his own doorstep and take a healthy piss without putting out the fire in his neighbor's chimney, or so went the saying. Since the female population of Bozetown was almost nil, that was more than mere speculation; it was a downright possibility.

The muddy squalor of the camp was in contrast to the rise of timbered foothills above and around it and the soaring grandeur of the Elk Mountains against a clean blue sky beyond. The majestic sweep of nature dwarfed and swallowed man's little effacements.

Lazlo Kusik never contemplated the virgin vastness of this mountain country without feeling properly awed and humbled. There were mountains in Hungary, too, but they were faint in his memory. His parents had departed the old country when he was five or six . . . and for nearly twenty years afterward he had known only the swarming ghettoes of New York's Lower East Side. Then there was five years of following the wheat harvests on the flat plains of the Middle West.

Yes . . . this western land was still awesome country to a Hungarian immigrant. Lazlo Kusik had lived in its wilds for several years now, had come to know it a little, and had learned how to cope with its rough and savage ways. But it was still bigger than any man could hope to know, even in a lifetime.

Hutch headed straight for the Hoodoo Bar, tramping in ahead of Lazlo at his rolling swagger, elbowing apart the batwing doors.

"Hey there, Aussie!" Hutch's booming voice caromed around the stale confinement of the Hoodoo's log walls. "How's chances for a snort o' the dog's hair this early? What say?"

17

Aussie Stubbs was a sallow runt of a Sydney Duck who, like many of his countrymen, had come to work in the American gold fields. He'd decided almost at once that at gold-camp prices, there were easier ways to make a living. Aussie had set up a saloon and charged his own prices.

"Coming right up, gents." Aussie promptly left his task of sweeping the packed-dirt floor and stepped behind his plank bar. "Couple of 'Shawn O'Farrells,' will it be?"

"That'll do capital. Belly up, little pard."

The suggestion stirred Lazlo's churning stomach juices almost to eruption. "I do not think that would be a good idea . . ."

Hutch peered at him closely. "Why hell's bells, Laz. You are green to the gills, boy, and no mistake. Aussie, you got a can o' tomatoes handy? And maybe a raw egg?"

"Right on 'and, guv'nor. But the egg'll cost yer. They're fifty cents apiece, you know."

"I know, you little gouging Limey pipsqueak," Hutch said affably. He slapped some coins on the bar. "There's the color o' my goods. Let's see yourn."

Lazlo, his eyes glazed with internal anguish, watched without interest as Hutch razored open the can with his pocket knife,

18

fished out the tomatoes, and popped them one by one into his mouth, then broke the egg into the juice, and with a spoon provided by Aussie whipped them to a sickly seeming mixture.

"There now, little pard. You drink up. This will get you settled for somp'n better. God's own truth!"

Lazlo gazed at the proffered can in Hutch's paw. He shuddered, and decided quite abruptly that even if it made him sicker, the result might be therapeutic. He grabbed the can and drained its contents.

To his amazement, his internal churnings subsided a little. But this made him even more aware of his pounding headache.

As if having read his mind, Hutch said, "Aw right now, you take that 'Shawn O'Farrell.' Down the hatch with 'er."

Aussie had set out two shotglasses, a bottle of whiskey, and two glasses of beer. He poured whiskey into each shotglass, cocking a sympathetic eye at Lazlo. " 'Aven't 'ad your scuppers awash too often, 'ave yer, chum?"

Taking it to be a query as to his drinking habits, Lazlo shook his head.

"Well then, you take this old rumpot's word and do like your mate says. Close

19

your eyes and swill 'er straight down. In no time yer'll be 'earing chimes sweeter'n the bow bells."

"Painter sweat first" — Hutch tossed down his whiskey in a gulp — "then your lizard pee. See?" He drank the beer straight off too.

Lazlo thought it might be best not to think about it too long. He laid his rifle on the bar, wiped a shaking hand over his mouth, and picked up the shotglass. He nearly gagged on the raw whiskey, but got it down and then took the beer, drinking it down carefully but steadily.

Aussie folded his thin arms and leaned them on the bar, grinning a little. "You done up the town for fair last night, you two."

Hutch poured himself another slug of whiskey. "Yeah, I 'member some of it. Shot up a few things, didn't we?"

"Right you are, guv'nor. This chum of yours is some 'andsome marksman. 'E ought to enter the competition."

"He can handle a long gun mighty peart," Hutch agreed, pouring a third whiskey. "What competition's that?"

"Take it you chaps 'aven't 'eard. There's a show come to town that set up business yesterday, over on 'Umbug Flat. Colonel

Laban Ruddy's Medicine Circus, it calls itself."

"What the hell is a medicine circus?"

"As it 'appens, yours truly took in yesterday's performance. What it amounts to is a patent-medicine spiel with a few sideshows to it. Today, among other things, there's to be a wrestling match and a rifle shoot."

"Hey, you hear that, little pard?" Hutch delivered a mighty slap to Lazlo's back. "Shooting and wrassling! Don't it sound to you like them's right up our alleys?"

This time Lazlo didn't stagger, even though the slap had more force than its predecessor. He stood straight at the bar and turned another look at Hutch.

The "Shawn O'Farrell" had gone down as smooth as honey, and a small miracle had taken place. Lazlo felt like his usual self again. Which was to say, stern and straight-headed and not about to take an ounce of guff off anyone. In fact, his ordinary sobriety ended just short of surliness. He was known by the few who knew him at all as a gruff and short-spoken man.

His legs were braced solidly apart; his stocky and muscular body barely stirred to Hutch's thick-handed blow. His stare held a black warning light that made Hutch drop his hand.

21

"Well say," Hutch said with a kind of lame grin, "you're looking a heap better already, Laz."

Lazlo nodded, holding his stance and stare. "That is what you call the dog's hair, eh?"

"Yeah, well, hair o' the dog, really. Sets a body's humors right up, don't it?"

Lazlo nodded once more, gravely. He lifted his rifle off the bar. "Now I will go home to my claim."

"Hold on there, little pard —" Hutch swung his massive front away from the bar, facing Lazlo. "Let's chaw this business over a mite . . ."

"Breakfast?" Lazlo flicked the faintest of smiles. "I don't need any. You go have yours. All thanks to you for the dog's hair . . . and the other."

"No, damnit! I mean them shooting and wrassling matches Aussie heard tell about. Why shoot, boy, them could be tailor-made for you 'n' me! I'll do the fighting and you do the firing. We will lay bets on ourselves with the crowd and . . . hell, man, we can really clean up!"

Lazlo shrugged. "What is the need?"

Hutch's eyes narrowed; he gave a hitch to his paunch-sagged trousers. "You told me last night you was so busted you didn't know if you could last out in these parts for 'nother month. Said you hadn't sluiced up hardly no color a-tall of late. Told me so five, six times as I recall. You telling me now that you ain't in need?"

So that is what I told him! Lazlo thought with a flood of relief. *But maybe I went too far with it . . .*

Maybe. Just maybe he had. A man's suspicions could be touched as readily by a vehement denial as by an outright assertion. Lazlo wondered if he had done as much with Hutch Prouter.

Damn his own whiskey-loosened tongue! He was relieved that Hutch was ignorant of the reality, but now he must be careful about what he said.

"You are very sure you and me can win."

"Betcher ass I am!" Hutch raised a hand to clap it down on Lazlo's shoulder, but then thought better of it and dropped the hand. "Why hell, betwixt us we can whup the socks offen any sucker in this damn camp! I seen how you can shoot, and by grab I know what I can do in a wrassling fall. Now then — whaddaye think?"

"I think I will have another whiskey."

Grinning, Aussie poured him another drink.

Lazlo fingered the shotglass, turning it

gently in his work-toughened hand. He studied his own reflection in the stained mirror above Aussie's shoulder. Hutch beside him made Lazlo look like a midget, but he wasn't really all that undersize.

Lazlo was a little under average height, square-faced, and wide in the chest and shoulders. His hair was dark brown and curly, clipped close to his head, and his short beard followed the contour of a determined jaw. His swarthy skin was weathered to the darkness of mahogany. His nose was stubby from being twice broken in brawls that had been forced on him because he carried himself too taut and straight to suit the tastes of some belligerent types he'd run into. His eyebrows almost met above his nose, forming a thick straight bar.

His clothes were those of any working miner: a gray flannel shirt, heavy pants tucked into sturdy boots, a battered hat that was weathered to an indeterminate color. If his worn garments differed in any way from those of most of his fellow prospectors, it was that his own were fairly clean, also neatly patched and mended — by Lazlo's own hand.

"One thing you did not think of," he said quietly.

"What's 'at?"

"Money. We cannot get up enough between us to make any bets we place worth the while."

"No need to, guy," said Aussie, still grinning as he glanced from one of them to the other. "I got a good feeling about you two gents . . . and old Aussie 'as never been one as flinches from a strong 'unch. Think I'll ride this 'ere one out. You chaps do the honors in the ring . . . and I'll circulate through the crowd and lay bets for all of us. We'll split the winnings three ways. What say?"

"I say you could stand to lose your shirt," Lazlo said dryly.

"Naw he don't!" roared Hutch. "Come on, Laz. *You* don't stand to lose a damn thing, leastways. And you sure's hell could use the money. What about it?"

Lazlo gazed impassively into his glass. He had no wish to engage in a spate of foolish theatrics for the little extra money it might bring him. He was impatient to get back to his gold claim . . . and something else that was a whole lot bigger.

But again, suppose his refusal were to kindle Hutch's suspicions? It stood to reason that a man who needed money as badly as he did — or as he'd told Hutch he did — couldn't afford to turn down an

25

opportunity as certain as this one. Not when he could handle a rifle as well as Lazlo Kusik could.

Unable to think of any likely excuse, he shrugged and took his second whiskey in a swallow. Then he said curtly, "Yes. Done."

CHAPTER 2

Yesterday Lazlo had come to Bozetown to buy what he needed to implement his plan. This included a wagon and team, some sawed lumber, carpentry tools, and more grub supplies. Yet he'd been sidetracked all too soon.

Ordinarily Lazlo wasn't much of a drinker. But the weeks of work and worry had taken their toll of him. With his tense nerves, he could use a slug of whiskey. Quite a few, in fact: he was in a mood to pull out all stops. So the rest of the day, and most of the night as well, had been lost in a swirl of liquor fumes and drunken doings. He had bought a lot of drinks for saloon hangers-on at every whiskey dive in Bozetown.

Somewhere along the way he had picked up Hutch Prouter. It couldn't have seemed too ominous a development at the time, for Hutch was a carousing companion second to none. He'd known how to turn a modestly good time into a tremendous time; he had suggested all kinds of crazy things that he and Lazlo could do to hooraw the camp.

All Lazlo could do now was to damn his own stupidity for tying one on last night . . .

The humpy stretch of Humbug Flat, just east of town, hardly deserved the name of a flat. But it was the nearest patch of land around Bozetown that resembled one. Quite a lot of the camp people and a number of miners were gathered there by the time Lazlo, Hutch, and Aussie arrived on the scene.

"Blinkin' show didn't pull all this much of a crowd yesterday," Aussie told his companions. "Word 'as got around by now. The colonel's a good 'un, all right. Wait'll yer see 'im in action. Show ought to be starting about now."

The crowd was fairly large, quite boisterous, and all male. A lot of the boys were fortifying themselves from jugs and bottles which they passed around freely and openly. They were out for a good time and were likely to get fractious if the day's offerings failed to provide one.

The traveling show's facilities of shelter and transportation consisted of three large wagons, walled and roofed and painted a bright red. On their sides the legend

"Colonel Ruddy's Medicine Circus" was painted in garish yellow curlicues.

"What the hell does that say?" asked Hutch.

He was surprised when Lazlo easily read the words aloud for him.

A self-taught reader himself, Lazlo had found lots of time since his illiterate boyhood to school himself in printed English. What else did a man do with his days during the long months of being holed up in lonely winter quarters of one kind or another? It was either spend your time reading or else go crazy.

The three wagons were pulled up in a line facing the open stretch of ground where the crowd was milling. The tall back of one wagon was hinged at the bottom; disengaged at the top, it had been swung down to a horizontal position and propped up with blocks to form a little stage platform. Behind the platform, thick curtains of shabby purple velour hid the wagon's interior.

Now the curtains parted. A man stepped out, raising his arms for silence.

When he got a partial compliance, he boomed out: "Welcome, gentlemen! Welcome to our medicine circus. I am Colonel Laban Ruddy."

The colonel was short and paunchy; his gestures were as florid as his face, which was networked with the conspicuous veins of a heavy drinker. All the same, when done up in the latest spit and style of flamboyant fashion, with his fine coat of blue broadcloth opened to a flowered waistcoat, he had a certain dignity of mien. He wore his white hair longish under a pearl-gray Stetson. His white goatee chopped up and down to the sonorous roll of his words.

With many dramatic gestures, Colonel Ruddy told of how a few years ago he had come into possession of the closely guarded secrets of the Medewiwin, the medicine society of the great Ojibway nation of the north. These had been revealed to him by a famous shaman of the tribe, "O-jik-wa-ko-bis," as a token of gratitude after Colonel Ruddy had saved the revered medicine man's life.

". . . and the therapeutic virtues of those secrets can be yours as well, my friends! From 'O-jik-wa-ko-bis' himself I learned the intricate processes of wedding rare herbs of the northern tundras into a potion of miraculous properties. Administered in regular doses, it is a decoction guaranteed to alleviate every malaise to which the flesh of humanity is heir. Momentarily" — the colonel swept up one hand in a histrionic flourish — "you shall witness with your own eyes the dramatic truth of that statement . . ."

"Hey, where's the princess?" someone yelled.

Cheers and whistles from the crowd.

Colonel Ruddy paused, smiling, his hand still upraised. "You anticipate me, sir. But first — I was about to say — I present for your entertainment and delectation a most remarkable demonstration of the terpsichorean art, brought from the mysterious reaches of the Circassian East — land of the savage and the sensuous! From the wild steppes of the Russian Caucasus, I give you the exotic charms of . . . the Princess Shahazar!"

The curtain behind him parted. The colonel bowed and stepped aside as a girl came out on the platform.

She was an eyeful, all right. She had corn-yellow hair piled high on her small head, and her eyes were bright blue above a wisp of veil designed to titillate rather than to conceal. The "Circassian" reference must have been thrown in to explain her light eyes and hair and — so Lazlo guessed — circumvent any erudite nitpicker in the audience who might have the temerity to doubt her Eastern origin.

Not that anyone in this crowd was likely to be interested in questioning a damn thing.

The girl began to do a slow, swaying, sinuous dance that lived up pretty well to the colonel's introductory spiel. Well enough, that is, in a mechanical sort of way. She wore a deep scoop-necked bodice that left her midriff bare and a pair of thin baggy trousers made of some shiny stuff that left her lower legs and feet bare. Metal bangles on her wrists and ankles tinkled to her light, graceful movements.

Undeniably the Princess Shahazar was a very pretty girl, and very well built for being so slim. Rather too slim, Lazlo thought: "thin" might be a better word. He did not think she looked altogether healthy. The fall afternoon had warmed up some by now, yet the princess's pale skin was goosefleshed with cold. A couple of times she tried to stifle coughs and didn't quite succeed. After her first voluptuous impact wore off, she seemed to be just a waif of a girl — and she couldn't be over sixteen.

If any other onlooker shared his thoughts, Lazlo saw no sign of it. The crowd stood gaping and avid. When the princess had finished her dance, the storm of applause brought her back for a couple of lengthy encores before they'd permit her to retire.

Now in a good humor, the audience warmed up to Colonel Ruddy's medicine spiel. He repeated with a few elaborations more or less what he'd said before. This time he capped his introductory remarks with the dramatic announcement that the shaman "O-jik-wa-ko-bis," as a favor to his white friend and blood brother, had sent with him on this medicine tour no other than his own son, "Wa-nit-ka-we-bo," to uphold Colonel Ruddy's true words.

At this, an Indian youth clad in white buckskins stepped from behind the curtains and stood gravely by, arms folded. The sight of him sent a ripple of chuckles through the crowd.

"Wa-nit-ka-we-bo" was about the oddest-looking specimen of the Indian race that Lazlo had ever seen. He had a big head with a flat, broad moon face that was set on top of a wiry, spindly body. Yet when he opened his mouth and spoke, he was almost magically transformed. Suddenly he was a Presence, eloquent and commanding. Gravely, in a deeply modulated voice and in flawless English, he declared

33

that the words of the friend of his father were true words.

And so on.

Lazlo couldn't fault the Indian's performance, but one or two things about him didn't ring quite true. He was too young to show the signs of heavy drinking as much as Ruddy did, but there they were all the same: a hint of bloat in the broad features, a touch of rheuminess in the eye. And what about the way he talked? Lazlo had to cudgel his memory to recall where in the devil he'd come across the likes of it before. Suddenly he knew. Yes. "Wa-nit-ka-we-bo's" style of speech was straight out of James Fenimore Cooper's *Leatherstocking Tales.*

It didn't matter to the crowd. Maybe half of them were taken in, while the other half was having a hell of a good time and wasn't about to spoil the fun.

Colonel Ruddy took center stage once more, this time with a harder-line spiel for his "Celebrated Ojibway Elixir and Vermifuge," at a good gold-camp price: four dollars a bottle. A wizened gaffer of a prospector named Briggs, who'd often complained of his pestiferous gout, bought the first bottle. He took a big swig of it and let a wondering look creep across his seamed face.

"Why, I believe that plaguey pain in my foot is done faded right away," he declared in awed tones. "I'm cured! Praise be to God! Hallelujah!"

Maybe Briggs laid it on a little thick, but the crowd responded with more than good-humored hooting and badinage. They also bought numerous bottles of Colonel Ruddy's wares, pretty well depleting his stock.

Aussie gave sly nudges to the ribs of Lazlo and Hutch, who stood on either side of him. "Ain't 'e the silver-tongued old snake-oil artist, though! I'll lay yer any odds that medicine of his is 'arf straight alcohol. But it'll get a chap feeling 'is oats for a spell, and no mistake."

"You reckon that's what it done for old Briggs?" Hutch asked.

" 'Ell no, guy. Briggsy is just a shill. Like enough the colonel slipped 'im a few bob in advance. More like yet, 'e slipped 'im a bottle full of just 'is basic ingredient. Briggsy was wobbling a bit on 'is pins before 'e took the blinkin' elixir, I noticed."

"I think so," said Lazlo. "Maybe then, this Colonel Ruddy also has some tricks up his sleeve for the wrestling and shooting contests . . . eh?"

Aussie laughed quietly. "You can bet

your bonnet on it, chum. You got to 'and it to 'im. He's a rum customer, 'e is! All the same, gents, I'm of the opinion we can 'oist the old poop from 'is own blinkin' petard. Think I got 'is game sized up proper. Just you wait."

The wrestling competition was held on a scuffed level of ground, with the colonel officiating. But he gave the business a semblance of fairness by letting the crowd nominate the referee, an elderly miner that everyone trusted. Then he introduced, with many verbal flourishes, the two strong men of his show who would take on all comers.

A pair of young men came bounding out of a wagon, and they were something to see. They were clad alike in jaguar-hide breechclouts and nothing else. Their thews swelled and rippled to their exaggerated swaggers as they advanced to the center of the ring. Colonel Ruddy had announced them as "those famous Italian wrestlers, the marvels of two continents — the Altrocchi twins, Roberto and Raphael!"

But while their similarly swarthy looks might pass for Italian, they obviously weren't twins. Brothers no doubt, thought Lazlo, but not twins. Roberto was bigger

36

and more massively muscled than Raphael.

Roberto, living up to the colonel's promise of "a remarkable display of sheer might," raised on high an iron bar he was carrying. With a seemingly contemptuous ease, he bent the bar to a right angle and tossed it aside.

That was impressive. So was Colonel Ruddy's offer to ten-to-one odds on either "twin." He would pay a dollar to every dime if any man in the crowd could defeat either of his strong men.

Roberto would be the first to stand forth against all comers. He strutted up and down, flexing his great thews.

"Hell, I'll take them odds!" yelled a big young miner. "By grab, I'll dump that dago on his dumb ass or my name ain't Brawlin' Billy Griswold!"

A burst of cheers from the crowd.

Brawlin' Billy stood a full head taller than Roberto Altrocchi and was a sight heftier. All the same, the betting ran heavy against Billy. The crowd wasn't about to take even highly tempting odds against any man who could bend an iron bar so readily.

Griswold peeled off his jacket and shirt, his shoes and socks, to even things up somewhat against his breechclouted, barefoot opponent. Brawlin' Billy was a formidable hulk of a man, all right. But his musculature didn't have the swelling, iron-hard look of Roberto's.

Nevertheless Brawlin' Billy won the match handily. He pinned his opponent in two out of three grunting, straining falls. The crowd groaned and cheered, and paid or collected their money. As many had laid bets among themselves as had taken up Colonel Ruddy's offer.

Grinning gleefully, Aussie beckoned his two companions to one side.

"Well, chums, it went like I told yer it would. That dago chap threw the match for certain."

Hutch scratched his curly head, scowling. "You reckon that's so?"

"Can it be?" Lazlo said doubtfully. "I think this has cost the colonel a pretty penny."

" 'E 'ad 'is man throw it, you can place bottom bob on it," insisted Aussie. "That's the 'ole game, don't yer see? 'Ere, take a look at this. I sneaked it off the ground when nobody was looking . . ."

He slipped an object from beneath his coat, holding it closely between Lazlo and Hutch for their examination. It was the bent iron bar that Roberto had cast aside.

"See them marks where it's been worked on with a file . . . 'ere and 'ere? And the cuts 'idden with wax and boot blacking. Took a strong man to bend 'er, all right. But not near as strong as that guinea was letting on."

Hutch shook his head, mystified. "I don't savvy this here a-tall. If that Roberto was in a way to lose, how come the colonel offered odds like he give on him?"

"Why guv, 'e knew there wasn't many 'ud take 'im up on that bet. 'E was casting bread unto the waters, in a manner of speaking. 'E means to get it back manyfold, if yer follow me. I'll tell yer 'ow, chums. 'Ark to me close, now . . ."

Aussie's explanation was hasty but thorough.

The three of them pushed their way to the front of the throng. Colonel Ruddy was offering to cover all bets on his second wrestler, whom he would put against any comer.

Hutch bellied forward, grinning. "Looks like easy money," he declared loudly. "I'll take it. I'll take that Eye-talian to a fare-thee-well too."

Colonel Ruddy took in Hutch's considerable bulk with narrowed eyes. Then he laughed, smoothing his goatee with a finger. His big teeth gleamed above it. "You're on, my friend. Wagers, anyone? Same odds as before."

This time around, the colonel had a mob of takers.

Hutch and Raphael squared off on the circle of packed ground, Hutch barefoot and stripped to the waist. There was plenty of solid muscle under Hutch's blubber, and it was pretty hard-looking blubber at that. He moved with an easy-footed, un-expected grace.

Meantime Aussie was circulating busily through the crowd, laying bets with every-one he could corner, including the colonel. Now he slipped back to Lazlo's side.

"I got every cent riding on our friend," he reported. "We're going to make a killing, chum."

"You think," said Lazlo.

"I been telling yer, I feel it in my bones. There they go, now."

The two brawny antagonists began to circle one another. Both were panther-quick, and Hutch's great size seemed to offset the cable-muscled trimness of his opponent.

The way Aussie had explained it, Brawlin' Billy's defeat of the bigger Altrocchi brother had been a setup to lure the suckers in. The crowd would now be certain to bet heavily against the smaller brother, confident that one of their own could take him even more easily. But Raphael, thought Aussie, was no doubt the really accomplished wrestler of the two. No doubt too that he intended to fetch the crowd a surprise by pinning their man with comparative ease.

Only it wasn't going to be easy. Hutch's mighty heft, taken by itself, would ensure that. Moreover he'd wrestled in a number of camptown dogfalls. Several times, he had put down Brawlin' Billy Griswold himself. Aussie was gambling that Hutch could do the same to Raphael.

He did too.

It was exactly as the previous match had gone, except that it went on a lot longer. Both men were pouring sweat before Hutch won the first fall. They went back at it with an even more ferocious, jaw-locked energy, and this time Raphael won the fall. The third round must have dragged on for nearly a half-hour before Hutch slammed his adversary's shoulders to the ground.

The crowd went wild. Bets were collected — and paid.

Colonel Ruddy effected to pay off cheerfully. But there was a hard burn of blood in

41

his cheeks, and his smile was teeth-clenched. He was a man who noticed things. More than once his gaze sought out Hutch and Aussie with a cold knowledge.

"We dropped some sand in 'is nibs's gear box for certain," Aussie said with a wolfish pleasure. "Let's toss in a little more, gents, what d'ye say?"

CHAPTER 3

The colonel introduced his next attraction as "Sureshot Stell," a lady whom he insisted could shoot rings around even that paragon of riflewomen, Mrs. Annie Oakley Butler.

The crowd hooted a little at this. But they quieted down a bit when the lady in question made her appearance from one of the wagons.

Sureshot Stell looked keen-eyed and competent. After the fashion of Calamity Jane and other celebrated women of the camps, she wore men's clothing, complete with cowboy boots and a horsethief hat. She might have been in her midtwenties. She was on the tall and wiry side but sturdy too, and her dark hair was cut mannishly short. For all that, oddly enough, she wasn't unfeminine.

Most important, Lazlo observed, she carried a rifle as if she'd been born with one in her hand.

"Watch 'er now, chum," Aussie murmured. "Let 'er use 'erself up on a few of these yokels as fancy 'emselves marksmen. Then, you trots out your stuff. But watch 'er close the while."

Lazlo nodded. He was feeling a little dizzy and sickish once more. The pick-me-ups he'd taken had worn off. The sun was quite hot now, baking through his wreck of a hat into his throbbing head.

Sureshot Stell appeared very confident as she sauntered out to the bare stretch of ground, but it didn't really make any difference. A whole lot of men tended to be unshakably vain about their shooting ability, even when they didn't possess any. Most of them believed they could shade any woman who ever lived at any damned pastime under the sun that was a traditionally masculine one.

That, ran Lazlo's shrewd guess, would be part of Sureshot Stell's advantage. Betting went heavily against her as her first opponent, an excessively cocky miner, strutted out to take his place beside her.

The rules, as the colonel loudly declaimed them, were simple. Shooters could use either a rifle or a pistol. Glass balls would be tossed up to serve as targets, and the sharpshooters would try to shatter them before they hit the ground. Each person was allowed only one shot per ball before it landed. After twenty throws (provided that both contestants "made the mark"), "time" would be called for five minutes in order to let the contestants rest and give their weapons a little while to cool off. Then another round would commence. Glass balls, the colonel added, were used as targets because the referee could always tell at a glance if one had been hit. Even "chipping" one with a bullet would count as a hit. The first contestant to miss a shot completely would lose the match. Raphael Altrocchi would pitch up the glass orbs for Stell; the opponent could pick his own ball tosser. Ruddy urged the crowd to give the adversaries plenty of room.

The young miner stayed up with Stell for a toss of six balls. Then he missed. A groan ran through the crowd.

She was good, Lazlo thought. Sureshot Stell was very good.

She was a machine of a woman, calmly and smoothly levering fresh loads into the breech of her Henry .44 rifle, ejecting the spent rimfire shells in a litter around her booted feet. Lazlo watched her with a concentration that made him momentarily forget his growing sickness. He had more than a sneaking conviction that this lady could keep up her performance for a long time yet and never miss a shot.

Her next opponent, using a Colt .45 revolver, knocked out eight balls before dropping one. The third man missed his target on the third throw.

The crowd was starting to grumble. An impression that they had been "had" was starting to percolate into their collective consciousness. But then, as they further commenced to assume, it was likely that Sureshot Stell's eye or arm would begin to tire before too long. After all, she was only a woman.

Now the insistent ache in Lazlo's head was spreading behind his eyeballs. Nervous sweat broke on his temples; he rubbed them with his fingertips. He looked at one of his hands; it was shaking. God, how was he going to manage in this condition?

Even if he weren't on the bad end of a monumental hangover, he wondered how he would fare against this woman. True, he had won a few shooting competitions in the camp, including some like this one — firing at inanimate objects that someone threw into the air.

Lazlo had never begun to burn powder with any idea of gaining an inordinate skill. He had acquired his Winchester repeating rifle several years ago when he'd started to follow the lonely trails in search of gold. It had seemed a common-sense provision — that was all — for his own protection and for securing meat.

But he'd discovered an unexpected affinity for the weapon. He would practice with it on all kinds of targets: bottles, tin cans, twigs, pine cones, wood chips, pebbles. It was fun to do and gave him a release from work and tension. So he had become proficient.

Lazlo knew he was good. But just how good? Even at his best, what sort of show would he stand against a sharpshooter of Stell's caliber?

Aussie was eyeing him with a touch of concern. "Bit under the weather, eh, sport?"

"Yes. I am afraid so."

Aussie dipped into his pocket and produced a flask. "To go up against this lady, you'll need a steady 'and. Take a swig. This 'ere is none of your camptown swill. Cognac, it is, and nothing but the best."

Lazlo uncapped the flask and took a pull. The liquor had a smooth dark glow that warmed him evenly from tongue to belly.

"Take another," said Aussie and grinned.

"I kind of thought yer'd be needing it. That's enough now. Trot yourself out there and throw down your gauge. 'Utch, 'ow about you toss up the balls for 'im?"

Hutch eyed the flask as Lazlo passed it back. He swiped the back of a hairy fist across his mouth. "Sure thing. Reckon my hand could use a mite of steadying too . . ."

"All right, but not too bleedin' much," Aussie cautioned as he handed over the flask. "Our chum 'ere'll be needing a bit more later on, or I miss my guess."

A ripple of excitement went through the crowd as Lazlo Kusik stepped out to offer his challenge to Sureshot Stell.

The camp knew him as a loner who rarely sought the company of his fellow miners. But on the convivial occasions he'd attended, when any test of prowess with a rifle was offered, he'd shot rings around all his opponents. This had occurred only three times since Lazlo's arrival in Bozetown, yet in a small, gossipy camp it had been enough to cinch his reputation as a marksman.

At just this moment, Lazlo was feeling far from sure of himself.

The cognac had steadied his nerves and hands, but it had also left him in a slight, pleasant alcoholic haze that he feared might prove fatal to his eye and aim. Just a hair's breadth of timing could make all the difference when you were firing at a thrown object.

Also he had never shot at glass balls. These appeared to be about two inches in diameter; he'd knocked down much smaller objects, such as two-bit pieces. But he'd noted the harsh glint of sun on the flung balls, which might trick even an experienced eye. A gust of wind might affect a ball's natural arc. He wondered if these factors hadn't disconcerted the previous shooters.

Except for Sureshot Stell. She would know exactly how to allow for such vagaries.

She gave him a brief, speculative glance of her ice-gray eyes as he stepped out to the trampled stretch of ground and took his place about ten feet to her left. Her cool inspection of him showed only a bored interest, but she hadn't missed the crowd's stir of reaction.

This close to her, Lazlo could take a better look at her rifle. He was sure it was a specially crafted piece, probably hand-worked. Lightweight, no doubt, and of a hairline accuracy. The ordinary Henry .44 repeating rifle was a heavy weapon and was likely to tire the arms of even a strong man after a period of rapidly lifting and firing it.

Sureshot Stell was a real professional. She had every reason to be confident.

I think she has got all her bases covered, Lazlo thought with bleak humor. He liked that phrase derived from the ingenious game of baseball to which, at one convivial gathering, some miners had introduced him.

Now his senses felt honed to an edge; all details seemed crisp and sharp in his vision. That was the alcohol working, and he did not trust it, but he trusted the wily saloonkeeper. Aussie, who was again busily circulating and laying bets among the crowd, would gauge things like that to a fine degree.

Hutch swaggered out to the bucketful of glass balls that one of the Altrocchis had set in place for Lazlo. He picked one up and examined it, then gave Lazlo a broad wink.

"Go to 'er, little pard," he said loudly. "We're counting on you to whup the pants off her!"

His own remark struck Hutch — and some of the onlookers — as exceedingly hilarious. He gave a whoop and whipped his hat off, slapping it against his thigh.

Sureshot Stell turned a cool look on him. She said calmly, "I reckon you didn't mean nothing special by that, now did you, Slim?"

Hutch eyed the rifle she held so competently and let his vast grin relax to a polite smirk. "Not a thing under the sun, ma'am, and that's God's truth."

As he had before, the old miner who'd been nominated referee checked out the buckets of glass balls that were allotted to each contestant. He did this by spilling them all on the ground, examining each ball in turn and returning it to its bucket. There were twenty-five balls to a bucket, more than enough for a full round of firing.

At a word — "Throw!" — from the referee, the ball tossers sent a pair of glass spheres winging against the sky.

Lazlo's Winchester swung smoothly to match the climb of the ball. When it hung poised at the peak of its arc, he fired. Although he blinked against an unexpected flash of sunlight on the orb, it dissolved in a shower of kaleidoscopic shards.

A perfect hit. The crowd gave him a mild hand of applause.

Sureshot Stell had made her score too. But something had struck Lazlo as being a bit off-center.

Glancing at Stell now, he said politely, "I would like to call time if it is all right."

"You can't do that, young fellow," Colonel Ruddy said sternly. "No time will be called till this round is over."

"But you would not want your shooter to have an unfair advantage?"

"*What's* unfair?" Stell demanded with a touch of heat. "You better make that clear, Jack."

"There is no offense meant."

Lazlo walked over to her and stood in back of her, sighting over her shoulder. "The sun hits on my targets as it cannot on yours, I think. Where you are standing, that big tree over yonder cuts off the sunlight."

Stell turned enough to let her eyes lock his in a chill meeting. She was as tall as he and they were, eye to eye.

Then she shrugged. "All right, Jack. You can stand any place you damn well fancy. Now. Are you happy?"

"Thank you."

A glint of amusement touched her stare. She was not a pretty woman; "pretty" was too soft a term to apply to Sureshot Stell. But she was a damned handsome woman. And of course she'd been well aware of the advantage she had taken.

Lazlo moved to a fresh position where the same tree shadow would cover his throws. He motioned Hutch to readjust his own position; then he and Stell took their stances again.

Once more two balls were thrown up; both were shattered to pieces.

Lazlo's doubts began to ease. This was not so bad after all, he thought as he levered his Winchester for the third throw. All you had to do was to keep topmost in your mind that you were not shooting to beat anyone, you were shooting only to hit a glass ball. Only that.

It was not nearly so simple, but if you made yourself think that it was, you would be all right. That way you could shut out all thought of personalities, and a glass ball was only a glass ball.

He did not look directly at Stell again. He fixed all his thoughts on the rhythm of his shooting. Lever. Lift. Aim. Fire. Tinkle and splatter of glass. Deafening gun roar that slammed against his ears over and over.

Lazlo felt sweat crawl down his ribs. His shoulder was a little numb from absorbing the recoil of his weapon so many times in quick succession. He did not pause except to reload his magazine. His concentration was so intense that the repetition of his own effort was becoming a kind of punishing deadly ritual.

One that, it seemed, might go on forever.

When time was called, he blinked and lowered his rifle, hardly aware of the noisy applause that swept through the crowd. His eyes met Stell's again. Her face showed nothing, but a sheen of sweat dampened her upper lip.

Lazlo walked to where Aussie was waiting at the edge of the throng.

"You're doing wondrous fine, chum!" the little saloon man greeted him. "I got all the wagers laid. If yer can outlast that blinkin' wench, the three of us'll divide a smart piece of money among us."

Hutch joined them, grinning hugely. "By grab, I think we got that pants-proud filly on the run! What d'you think, little pard?"

"I don't know. I was not watching so close," Lazlo set his hands to his ears. "The noise of the guns . . . I think it is starting to rattle my brain."

"Christ!" Aussie was instantly contrite. "I must of left *my* bloomin' brains in storage today. Should of 'ad yer plug yer ears against the concussion. It gets to affecting a body something fierce after a good spell of steady shooting . . ."

As he spoke, Aussie took a tattered bandanna out of his pocket. He tore off a couple of its ragged edges and balled each one into small wads between his fingers. "There y'are, chum . . . a pair of earplugs that will serve to a fare-thee-well. 'Ow're yer feeling otherwise?"

"I think all right."

"Good. 'Ere now." Aussie got out the cognac flask, took a swallow from it, and shoved it at Lazlo. "Just a little 'un, mind you. Won't 'urt yer none, and I've a 'unch it'll 'it the old spot just right."

It hit the spot exactly right.

Lazlo took his drink and handed the flask to Hutch. His gaze sought Sureshot Stell, who was conferring with Colonel Ruddy a little distance away. The colonel didn't look at all happy. He stood with fists braced on his hips; he was tight-lipped when his bearded jaw wasn't chopping out a rush of hard-clipped words.

Lazlo wondered if Ruddy's irritation stemmed from Stell's having given in so easily to Lazlo's objection. Stell appeared to be dryly amused, not at all disconcerted by whatever the colonel was saying.

Ruddy pulled out his watch and gazed at it. The last seconds ticked off, and the five-minute break was up. The contestants took their places again.

Again the *crack-crack* of the rifles. Bits of disintegrating glass catching twinkles of light as they fell to the ground. The devouring rhythm that numbed a man's mind against everything else.

At first, with his hearing somewhat muffled, Lazlo had an easier time of it. But he could feel a tender ache creeping more quickly now through his arms and shoulders. A lighter gun might have stood him in good stead, for he sensed — without taking a direct look at Sureshot Stell — that she was feeling the strain too. She had the advantage of experience, but quite probably she hadn't often had to face an opponent who could hold out against her so long.

Forget her. Fix on those flying balls of glass — nothing else. Lever. Lift. Aim. Fire . . .

The steady ache spread into the upper muscles of Lazlo's trunk. His arms began to feel heavy, the Winchester even heavier. A red throbbing touched the edges of his vision. He was literally pouring sweat. Fearing it might run into his eyes, he kept swiping a sleeve across his brow. Above all, he must keep his eyes clear.

Lever. Lift. Aim. Fire!

On the fourteenth throw, the crowd let out an involuntary groan.

That riffle of reaction gave Lazlo a start. Till now, during this round, the audience had been silent and intent, transfixed by the duel.

Lazlo had exploded his glass ball.

Glancing toward Sureshot Stell now, he saw the truth in her face even before his glance shuttled to the last sphere that Raphael had thrown. It lay untouched on the scuffed turf less than ten yards away.

Sureshot Stell had missed her shot.

Then Aussie was pounding him on the back, shouting triumphantly, "Yer done it, chum! Yer done it! We've made a bleedin' score, we 'ave!" At the same time, Hutch's massive fist was enclosing his hand in a crushing grip.

Lazlo said, "Just a minute, is that all right with you?" and pulled away from both of them.

He went over to Sureshot Stell, who was calmly inspecting the mechanism of her rifle. Now her face showed only a stony indifference, but she was pale around the lips.

"Ain't nobody ever outshot me in three years of this," she said quietly. "You are some shuckins with that piece, mister."

Lazlo hesitated. He did not know what he wanted to say. Finally he said simply, "I am sorry."

"Not half as sorry as I be," Sureshot Stell said curtly. She brushed past him, heading for one of the wagons.

Looking past her, Lazlo's glance crossed Colonel Laban Ruddy's. The colonel was gazing straight at him, and in his look there was something that went beyond mere irritation. Something like a flicker of venomous fury . . .

CHAPTER 4

Laban Ruddy's hand shook as he laid out a game of solitaire on the small deal table. A lamp with a low-burning flame and a half-empty bottle of whiskey also occupied the table's scarred top. Reaching unsteadily for the glass at his elbow, Laban knocked it over and flooded his cards with whiskey.

"Shit!" Laban exploded. He spat out the shred of cheroot clamped between his jaws, and then sent the glass and the soaked cards flying with a furious sweep of his arm.

"Them's my sentiments exactly," said Sureshot Stell.

Laban swung his head toward the open door of his wagon, glaring at her. Stell was standing just outside, thumbs hooked in the belt loops of her pants, grinning a little.

"What the hell, Pa. You can't expect to rake in the pot every deal. So we took it in the neck once."

Laban felt his usual nudge of distaste at

Stell's crude speech, but it was only a weary drunken flicker. He'd been listening to it for too many years to be much affected anymore. Besides he knew she swore and otherwise acted like a man largely to irritate him.

"'Got it in the neck,'" he echoed bitterly. "What we are, is cleaned out, girl. Those men pulled a setup, and we have gotten taken proper."

"Well, that's fair enough, ain't it?" Stell said promptly. "We done our share of taking, God knows. Look, Pa, that foreign man beat me fair and square. And the big fellow took Bije the same way."

"Haven't you a shred of pride?" Laban asked coldly. "I'd think you'd be up in arms. Whipped on your own grounds by a lowdown hunky miner!"

Stell lifted one shoulder in a philosophical shrug. "I felt a mite peeved at first. But hell, he shaded me by a little, that's all. Today he did. 'Nother day, I might of won. That's how it is with 'most any good shootist. Forget it, Pa. There's other camps. We'll make up our losses next place we come to."

Laban said grimly, "That's a lot of money to drop at one shot." Absently he bent over and picked up a few of the wet

60

cards, then flung them down with an angry oath.

"Such a way to talk," Stell said innocently.

Making a thin effort to conceal his irritation, he said, "How is your sister doing?"

"Myra Mae is taking a nap in our wagon." She shook her head. "Pa, you hadn't ought to take her on the road anymore. She ain't well."

"Hogwash," the colonel said shortly. "Myra Mae is only sixteen and healthy as a horse. Basically she is, I mean. Wager it's just a case of feminine 'blues.' This has been a long stint for all of us, but we'll be packing off to winter quarters soon . . ."

"When?"

Laban frowned at the brusqueness of her query. "When I say so. Go on, now. Go shoot up something with that damned rifle of yours, why don't you? Apparently you could use a little practice."

Stell gave a good-natured hoot of derision.

She said, "Yeah, more than you need with that damned bottle," then turned and sauntered away.

Laban Ruddy dug out a fresh cheroot, bit off the end, and savagely spat it out. Then he sat staring at the tabletop, the cheroot cold between his fingers.

Damn that Australian Duck! He was a sharper for certain — the colonel always knew another of the breed at a glance — and he must have cleaned up on today's heavy betting, collecting from Laban himself and from a number of affluent betters in the crowd. And of course he'd have split his winnings with the other two. Laban hadn't missed how chummy Aussie had been with both the hunky sharpshooter and the big wrestler.

Won fair and square, had they? Well, maybe they had. Even so, Laban had a bitter conviction that he'd been taken. He felt outraged by the mere thought that the Duck had somehow outsmarted him.

Nobody, goddammit, did that to Laban Ruddy!

For a full hour, Laban had been brooding on the matter over a bottle. For several years, during the warmer seasons, he and the remaining members of his family — two daughters and two nephews — had made a comfortable living without too much effort, traveling from one frontier camp to the next and putting on their show. It worked out pretty well, with Myra Mae's youthful concupiscence providing the come-on, followed by his own slick medicine spiel, his nephews' wrestling act, and Stell's sharpshooting. Usually they'd clear enough to live high off the hog at their leisure, for the five or six months of each year when they'd "winter" anywhere from New Orleans to San Francisco.

It was a pleasant way of life, one made to order for an ex-circus barker who'd found he could do better with an itinerant medicine show (with side attractions) than he ever had shouting himself hoarse in Barnum and Bailey's sawdust ring. And he was his own boss. Colonel Laban Ruddy had fallen into a pleasurable rut from which — after a few contented seasons of it — he had no intention of being dislocated.

But today had thrust a shocking reversal on all his expectations. He and the kids had made a real killing this season. They would have gone into "winter quarters" with so much loot that he could have afforded to bank quite a piece of it away . . . against his declining years.

Today Laban Ruddy had recklessly bet nearly every cent he'd made this season on the usual course of yokel-rooking which he followed. And he'd lost damned near all of it on a couple of unexpected upsets: two defeats of his performers within the space of a couple hours.

That damned Australian was to blame. And he had all those winnings, he and his two cohorts. While Laban and his family would face a long, dismal winter of scrabbling and minching just to make it through . . . till they could get on the road again next spring.

Laban retrieved his unbroken glass from the floor, filled it to the brim with whiskey, and gulped it down.

Make up their losses at the next camp? Not a chance! It would take another whole season, and a damned lucky one at that, to approach what they had earned this year. With the high-country winter closing down, soon to shut off the mountain trails, he hadn't planned on extending the present circuit to more than another camp or two.

Laban Ruddy's fist clenched around the empty glass. *Well, by God, we'll see.* His decision was made. He swayed to his feet and moved unsteadily to the door, peering rheumily out.

The setting sun laid a pearly glow over the autumn-brown drabness of Humbug Flat. The three wagons were drawn up to form the partial sides of a triangle with its corners open. One wagon was Laban's own; another housed his daughters. His nephews and Robert Topbear — who was no Ojibway or a chief's son, only a Creek-Cherokee outcast — occupied the third. A supper fire had been started in the center of the triangle.

The dark, stocky pair of brothers known to patrons of the medicine circus as "Roberto and Raphael Altrocchi" were squatting on their haunches over a checkerboard laid out on a flat rock. Both were staring at the board, scowling, arms folded on their knees.

"Pretty intellectual game for you boys, isn't it?" Laban said with a drunken, sardonic leer. "Get in here, both of you. I want to talk to you."

Obediently, Abraham and Abijah Willet got to their feet and tramped over to the wagon. Laban stepped aside to let them climb inside, then closed the door behind them. The girls were in their wagon and "Wa-nit-ka-we-bo" would be sleeping off a head of booze in his. Laban just wanted to be sure that neither of the girls overheard this conversation.

Laban slumped back into the only chair and poured himself a drink. Ab and Bije squatted down facing him, glancing incuriously around their uncle's cramped and sparsely furnished quarters, its walls papered with faded posters from Laban's circus days. Their muscles bulged thickly against the rough shirts and trousers they now wore.

Studying their dull faces through his alcoholic blur, Laban thought: *God, if these two could scrape up even half a brain between them, they'd have about a quarter of what I have dead sober.*

Laban sometimes wondered why that was. The boys' mother, his own departed sister, had been a bright girl of some accomplishments, and Jim Willet, the glib traveling man she'd wed, had been no slouch in the mental department either. But this pair . . . ! If there weren't old Uncle Laban to watch out for them, God knew what would become of 'em.

Important thing was, Ab and Bije were proficient at just about anything that required physical action. They took orders well, and once you dunned into their heads what was expected of them, you could depend on them to do a proper job of it.

Laban leaned back in his chair, crossing his legs. "Boys," he said mildly, "it will be necessary to resuscitate our resources before proceeding on our way."

They gazed at him unblinkingly for some moments. Then Bije, slightly smaller than his brother, younger by a year, and brighter by a hair's breadth, knitted his brows. "What's that there resusci-mabobble mean, Uncle Labe?"

"It means," Laban said in a kindly way, "that we have been done out of a peck of money today, and I have a notion how we can get back quite a lot of it. Now, you two flaming wits pay attention to what I tell you. I don't want to have to repeat it more than four or five times."

After a delighted Aussie divided his winnings among Lazlo, Hutch, and himself, the three of them separated. Aussie returned to his saloon, Hutch set out to "make the rounds" of every drinking dive in Bozetown, and Lazlo headed for the local livery barn to see what kind of a deal he could wangle for a wagon. He also bought a trustworthy mule named Matilda to hitch in tandem with his mule Prunes.

The wagon he chose was a sturdy-looking Studebaker that had seen some use, having served the U.S. Cavalry for several years as a supply vehicle. Lazlo considered it all the better for that, since now the wagon would be nicely "seasoned"; any defects would have shown up before now. Old Gaffer, the livery owner who told him its brief history, had a reputation for fair dealing. And a good solid wagon was a key factor in Lazlo's plan.

From there he went to the local sawmill, where he purchased a dozen fresh-cut pine planks, each about ten feet long and an inch thick, along with several stout two-by-fours. Loading these in the wagon, he made a final stop at the mercantile store. Here he bought a gallon of paint, a paint-brush, a saw and hammer, and a sack of nails.

With some food supplies added to the load, he was starting out of town when Hutch Prouter came lurching out of a saloon. Spotting Lazlo, he bawled, "Hey, little pard! You wasn't fixing to depart 'thout hoisting a victory glass 'ith ole Hutch, now was you?"

Feeling he couldn't flatly refuse without giving a nudge to any suspicions Hutch might harbor, Lazlo joined him for a couple of drinks. Afterward he was adamant about not repeating last night's drunken tear but gave in to Hutch's insistence that they have supper together at the China Café.

"Yessir, little pard . . ." Hutch rambled along between mouthfuls as he tore apart and devoured a roast canvasback duck.

"Ain't but one thing to do with money when a man has it. That's spend it."

Lazlo said easily, "Maybe you are right," as he methodically cut and chewed and swallowed mouthfuls of a thick steak. It wasn't a bad cut of meat for gold-camp fare . . . even at gold-camp prices.

Hutch mopped up the last gravy on his plate with a wad of bread and wolfed it down. He gave a mighty belch of satisfaction, wiping his greasy paws on his pants. "Betcher ass. Well . . . looks like you will be pulling out o' here with a mite o' change in your pockets after all, hey?"

Lazlo nodded. "It was a good day. Even divided between us three, it comes to a good piece of money for each."

"Yeah, middlin'." Hutch patted his paunch and glanced over his shoulder toward the waitress. "Hey, sister! More coffee over here." His veiled glance grazed over Lazlo's face. "But they's plenty loot bigger'n that waiting in them hills . . . if a man could strike it."

Lazlo smiled faintly. "That is the little problem, eh? *If*."

"Well, a fella most always can't tell. Maybe if you was to hang on for another year . . ."

"I do not think so. Soon the snow and

cold will close up the mountains. Now will be a good time to pull out. One can do better with a long winter than stick it out in this place."

"Could be," Hutch said agreeably. " 'Pends what kind o' prospects a man has got. Where you be heading to, Laz?"

"Saba City. I have a little color in my poke. Not much, but I can get cash for it at the assay office here. With what I have won today, I will have enough to get by for a little time. I have not thought what I will do next. But there is always something."

"Sure is, if a man has got wits in his head and guts in his belly. Always something . . . yes sirree." Hutch picked his teeth with a splinter of duck bone. His eyes, now focused on a point above Lazlo's head, held a musing and faraway look. "Y' know, though, be a dandy thing if a fella could pack out o' these digs with more'n a passel of busted hopes in his possible sack. That Saba City'd be some place to start a-spending it, I tell you."

His gaze drifted idly back to Lazlo.

"Sure." Lazlo reached for his refilled mug of coffee. "It would be a fine thing."

He wasn't deceived by Hutch's casual probing. Somehow in an unrecalled slip of the tongue, he must have given away at

70

least a triumphant hint of his discovery during last night's long libations. Enough to put an edge on Hutch's watchful cupidity.

And now Hutch was slyly digging, skirting around the central question but always circling back to it and going out of his way to look sleepily unconcerned about it. His approach, however, was too slyly circumspect to convince anyone. If a man weren't expecting anything of the sort, he might easily be taken in by Hutch's guileless manner. But Lazlo, riding a fine blade of wariness these many weeks, was too jumpy and nerve-knotted to be caught off guard. Right now, if one of the Lord's angels were to confront Lazlo Kusik in all its glory, it would be met by a stony suspicion. He did his best to be casual and pleasant with Hutch and to show nothing else at all.

They left the café. By now the swift mountain twilight had flushed out of the sky; it was pitch-dark. Hutch belched and rubbed his vast belly. "Sure you don't want to take on another bumper o' tanglefoot?"

"I had enough last night. I would think you had too."

Hutch laughed, clapping a hand on Lazlo's shoulder. "Warn't it the truth! But I ain't taken on near enough today, heh-

71

heh. When you figure on pulling out for Saba City?"

"I don't know. Maybe the day after to-morrow."

"Well, I will drop by your digs afore then. Pleasant dreams, little pard."

Hutch lumbered off toward the nearest saloon.

Lazlo's new wagon stood at the tie rail, his team of mules hitched to the tailgate so they could forage on some hay stowed in the wagon bed. He watered them at a nearby trough and hitched them up. Then he headed south out of town.

The muddy mire of a wagon road that bisected the camp petered out in a twisting lane below the town. It followed the west bank of the Mad Mule River, an old game and Indian trail now used solely by the few prospectors who had staked claim along the lower reaches of the river. A quarter moon relieved some of the darkness; a cool wind brushed off the western peaks. Lazlo shivered, wishing that he had his Mackinaw coat along.

After a while, the trail swung away from the river, dipping past the mouth of Trevo Pass. This broad and brush-clogged cleft in the western ramparts of the Elk Mountains was sometimes used by men on foot as a shortcut across the mountains. Lazlo had been over it quite a few times himself. But no wagon had ever tried to negotiate that same rough and rambling trail. A little distance east of the pass lay Hutch Prouter's riverside camp and claim, hidden from the road by trees.

The wagon careened and jolted over the pitted trail. Now it was narrowing to a slender trace that ran between the riverbank on one side and a steep, pine-mantled ridge on the other. The trail was barely wide enough to accommodate the wagon, and Lazlo slowed and guided the mules across it with care. A thin glare of moonlight sent a rippling sheen across the river, but the high pitch of slope and the looming pines made deep pools of shadow that obscured most details of what was around him.

Lazlo had been over this trail often enough to have a pretty accurate idea of the worst bumps and turnings. Even so, at one point he halted the wagon in order to give a little thought to what lay just ahead of him.

Pulling up the team caused the rattle of hooves and harness to ebb suddenly into silence. In that moment Lazlo heard something else: a sound that pulled him alert right away, that didn't belong to the hushed current of river on his left or to the sough of wind through the pines on his right.

It was a light thud of running feet on the trail behind him. And it ceased just moments after he reined in the mules.

Someone . . . following close on his back and catching up fast. No, more than one. At least two of them for sure. He was being stalked in the darkness . . .

Lazlo's rifle was out of easy reach, wedged among the supplies in the wagon bed. Easily, making no sudden moves, he loosened the Bowie knife in its sheath at his hip. He did not look around. The stalkers were close to the ground; he was skylined on the seat. Any obvious move on his part would be spotted. If he glanced backward, he was sure he would see only impenetrable shadow.

He clucked to the team and gave the reins a shake, and the mules slogged forward. But now Lazlo kept his head tipped a little to his left . . . enough to let the tail of his eye register any hint of movement it picked up toward his back.

The creak of wagon and harness, the slow clop of hooves covered any other sound. But the edge of his vision picked up

74

a quick change in the flow of shadows to his left.

The running figure was almost alongside him, a clublike object raised in its fist. In the same instant, Lazlo yanked his Bowie knife from its leather sheath and rolled sideways off the seat, away from the club wielder. He hit the ground catlike on his feet and then wheeled around at once, confronting exactly what he'd expected: the shadowy hulk of the second assailant.

This one, too, carried a truncheon of some kind. He swung it savagely at Lazlo's head. Lazlo ducked and felt his hat carried away by the aborted blow, and then he wove under the man's guard and whipped up his Bowie in a quick vicious thrust at the indistinct form.

The knife went between the body and arm of his adversary but didn't entirely miss. Lazlo heard a startled grunt of pain as the blade ripped through cloth and then flesh.

Briefly the other attacker was cut off by the wagon. Already, though, he had leaped to the seat and was scrambling across it. Crouching just above Lazlo, he swung at the latter's head. Lazlo gave a sidelong twist that saved his skull, but the club slammed his shoulder with an impact that numbed his whole right arm.

Lazlo melted to the ground, switching the Bowie to his left hand as he flung himself under the wagon to escape a second swiping blow by the man he'd cut. The one on the seat leaped down in the same instant that Lazlo squirmed around on his belly, lightning-fast. Lazlo took a sweeping awkward slash at the fellow's leg.

This time his blade struck through boot leather and into the flesh and bone of an ankle. The man screamed and stumbled away, then fell to his hands and knees. Lazlo rolled over twice, away from both assailants, and came out on the other side of the wagon.

Both men were cursing furiously as Lazlo swung to his feet and threw an arm across the wagon's sideboard. At once, by instinct, his hand closed on the stock of his Winchester. He dragged it free of the load and levered it once sharply.

The curses broke off. Both assailants took to their heels, plunging away down the trail — one of them supporting his limping companion. Lazlo had a couple of fleeting glimpses of the men before the shadows swallowed them. He fired a little over their heads, then levered his rifle and fired again.

The running sounds died away, fading off among the shot echoes.

Lazlo stood for a long moment, listening, the wind cool on his sweating face. The hurt of his right shoulder became less intolerable as he gently massaged it. The thumping of his heart slowed. He retrieved his hat and swung back up to the wagon's high seat, gathering up the reins. Both mules had come to a stop and had stood placidly through the brief fracas.

He gave them each a word or two of commendation, knowing it would make no difference. An earnest cussing out was all that Prunes and Matilda would really understand.

As he pushed on along the trail, Lazlo carefully cast back over the brief impressions he'd gotten of his assailants. Nothing in their voices or the dim glimpses he'd caught of them had given him any clue as to their identities. And their heads had been muffled in hoods of some dark material.

Their purpose must have been to rob, which suggested that they knew of his good fortune in the shooting match. If they'd meant to kill, they wouldn't have troubled to mask themselves; they would have used guns or knives rather than clubs. For that reason — even in the violence of the moment — Lazlo had fired after them to scare, not hit, them.

Maybe, he thought grimly, he should have shot with a more lethal intent. He had a lot more at stake than just the winnings of a rifle match.

CHAPTER 5

There were quite a few different ways to hunt for gold. In his lust for riches, Lazlo Kusik had tried all of them. That is, all except the dowsing rod, which some seasoned prospectors swore by — although Lazlo could never understand why. He'd known men who'd spent whole lifetimes tramping the West with dowsing wands fashioned of mistletoe or willow or alder (their preference depending on whatever wood was most available), declaring that "the yellow stuff singing in the earth" would respond to the electricity pouring out of their bodies.

Lazlo's practical mind had scorned that kind of superstitious idiocy out of hand. He'd gone about his own gold-divining with pick and pan and sluice box, and a solid lode of what he liked to think of as good horse sense.

Lazlo had been among the first gold seekers to flock into the Mad Mule River country after word of a gold strike had leaked out and Bozetown, named for the old prospector who had unearthed the first rich pocket of ore, had sprung to slapdash life. Lazlo had staked his own claim at a place far below the camp, where the Mad Mule boiled through a tall arm of rocky hills. Just below that rapids-riddled stretch of river, he had set up his sluice box.

The work had been slow and tedious; it required infinite patience. He had shoveled sandy muck into the long box, opened a floodgate to direct the swift current through the trough, and then scooped out the heaviest gravel by hand so the mud would wash away. He "sluffed" the re-maining sand across the backward-pointing wood-baffle fingers and inspected the corrugated metal bottom to ascertain if he'd trapped any gleaming yellow flakes.

Days had dragged into weeks, long and lonely and backbreaking. And above all frus-trating. He had endured all kinds of weather and the stinging attacks of insects . . . and the monotonous squeak of the sluice box. Whole weeks had gone by when he hardly turned up a trace of "color." The weeks had slid away into months, and still he had clung to his dogged and driven labors.

Lazlo knew that other placer miners, higher up on the Mad Mule, had found rich scatters of free gold. But the upper river was studded with claims, and his loner instincts had pointed him toward the lower stretches which all reports had declared were far less promising.

Maybe they were. But free gold must move downward, not upward. Lazlo had made his sober gamble, and he was too stubborn to give it up. Maybe it was just a blind hunch. He didn't know.

He had labored all day, every day, under broiling sun or cold rains, running tons of tailings through his sluice box. At day's end he would carefully clean off its baffles and then, stumbling with weariness, would make his way up a hillside to the old deserted trapper's cabin he'd found conveniently close to his claim. He would take the time to prepare a hot and hearty supper, knowing that he must eat well to keep up his strength. Then he would spread his blankets on a heap of fir boughs and collapse into a heavy, dreamless sleep.

It became a sodden and lackluster routine that was tolerable only because Lazlo was too exhausted most of the time to become prey to the boredom and loneliness of it. Once or twice a month, he would take Prunes to Bozetown and load her up with enough grub to last him a few weeks. What little "color" he turned up was spent to supply him with nourishing meals. Boomtown prices being what they were, he just managed to eke out an existence. At that he was often forced to take time out to extend his "boughten" supplies with fresh meat or fish.

Lazlo's ready skill with a rifle ensured that he spent little time on chancy, time-consuming methods of angling for fish which he didn't much care for anyway. Game abounded along the lower river; the thickets near his cabin were full of rabbit runways. But experience had taught him that rabbit flesh had no real nourishment, nothing to give strength to a working man's thews. So he'd range far afield in a search for elk or mule deer. If Lazlo were lucky, he would make a quick kill and have his fill of fresh venison and a good supply for sun-jerking. The rest of the animal he'd sell to the China Café in Bozetown, and he needed every cent he could get to supplement his meager gold-pickings.

By the time a spring and a summer and most of a fall had gone by, a leaden discouragement had set in.

Wouldn't it be better just to give up the game and pull out for other parts? He could always revert to the life of his recent past — drifting from one job to the next, never working himself too hard, although he was a willing worker — and he could still manage to save up a little money between gold-hunting stints.

But that would take time. To Lazlo Kusik, time was the implacable enemy. At thirty-three, he could feel it snapping at his heels. No, he would not spend twenty more years in the slow accretion of the wealth he wanted so badly. His goal was the big, sudden, lavish strike. At least a few men he knew had "made their score" — why couldn't he? Surely if he persevered, his time would come. He *knew* it in his bones.

And so it had come. But not by the direct and patient method that Lazlo had imposed on himself. When he did locate his strike, it had been by pure chance. At least at the outset . . .

Lazlo's nerves were pretty keyed-up after the attack as he was returning from Bozetown to his claim. He sat up most of that night with a rifle across his knees, keeping out of sight and trying to stay awake. Yet he dozed off more than once. Then he would jerk fitfully awake, staring wildly around him . . .

The gray light of predawn was cold and

clear. Lazlo was shivering when, long before sunup, he threw off his blankets and broke the ice scum on his water bucket. The ice was a half-inch thick this morning. When he dug a heel at the dirt floor of his shanty, he found it was frozen ironhard. By noon or so, it would thaw out . . . but that was the strongest sign yet of weather that was rapidly chilling toward winter.

Soon the first snow would come. It might be a light fall; it might as easily be a roaring norther that would close the high passes. Once that happened, Bozetown would be shut off from the outside world — except to those few hardy trekkers who might brave the heights by snowshoe — till late spring. Transporting heavy cargo of any kind across them would be out of the question.

Lazlo wasted no time. After a hasty breakfast, he set to work with rope measure and saw, cutting the oak planks he'd purchased into uniform lengths that would span the bed of his wagon. He sawed the pine two-by-fours into shorter lengths to contrive a system of braces that would support the planks once they were nailed into place.

Before noon, the work was finished. He had outfitted the spring wagon with a false bottom that left a good four inches of space between it and the true bottom. The only exposed side of the shallow compartment was at the back, and that would be concealed once the tailgate was dropped into place. The existence of the compartment would not be revealed by any casual inspection. A slight difference in depth between the outside and inside of the wagon bed was unlikely to be spotted by anyone unless he knew what he was looking for.

Lazlo gathered up the wood trimmings and dropped them in a fire he'd built up. Then he buried every trace of sawdust and stowed his tools out of sight. As he prepared a scanty noon meal over the fire, he considered his next moves. First a coat of paint for the whole wagon, to cover any discrepancy between the seasoned wood and the newly installed planks. Already he had picked over the ore in his hidden cache, separating the pure dust and nuggets from the gold-embedded chunks of dross.

Just the pure stuff added up to a small fortune . . . and the rest could wait in its hiding place till he returned next year. Then, with a crew of helpers he could trust, he would transfer the balance to Saba City. With the considerable amount he could smuggle across the Elks right now, he'd have till spring to implement all his plans and make all the necessary arrangements.

Yes. At last he could really dare to believe he was going to "make it safe to home base." Still the spur of urgency, the sense of time running out, drove Lazlo on. He wanted to finish his preparations in a hurry and be ready to roll out by tomorrow.

In the meantime he didn't relax his vigilance.

Hutch Prouter's sly digging had left a deep residue of caution in him. Lazlo had rushed his carpentry work on the wagon against the possibility that Hutch might pay an unexpected call at almost any time. However, it hadn't seemed likely he'd make an appearance before noon. His nightly load of libations usually kept him dead to the world until noon or later.

A little after midday, Hutch did show up.

By then Lazlo was halfway through his painting of the wagon; the fresh planks of the false bottom were covered over. Originally the wagon box had been painted a lead-blue on the outside, a Venetian red inside, showing that it had been a U.S. Army vehicle. The new coat, applied by Lazlo inside and out, was a dull gray.

Hutch didn't seem very interested in Lazlo's activity. He came tramping heavily into sight along a trail in the bend of the river. He walked over to Lazlo's fire where, uninvited, he poured himself a cup of coffee and gulped it down before saying a word. There was a single grunted word of greeting. Lazlo left off painting one of the Studebaker's sideboards and gave Hutch a curious glance. Hutch looked in sorrier condition than could be attributed to a night's carousing. His thick features had a pasty, sickish cast.

Lazlo put on a look of polite solicitude. "You are feeling a little off your feed, maybe?" he asked gravely.

"Kind of, yeah." Morosely and without much interest, Butch blinked at the half-painted wagon. "What you doing that for?"

"Well, the thing was pretty weathered. I think a new coat of paint will help to preserve the wood some."

"Uhh." Hutch poured another cup of scalding black brew and swilled it down. "Jesus, Laz. It is a mighty sorry thing. Almighty sorry."

"What is?"

"About Aussie. I come to tell you he's been murdered."

Carefully Lazlo laid down his paintbrush

87

and then straightened up, twitching a crick out of his back. "What is this? What do you mean? Are you joking with me, Hutch?"

"God, I wish I was. Aussie is stone-dead, little pard, and that's God's truth. He was murdered for sure."

Hutch sat down cross-legged on the ground, running a hand through his matted thatch of hair as he talked. "It happened sometime last night," he said.

This morning Marshal Abe Friendly had noted that Aussie had failed to open his saloon at the usual early hour. That break in routine had seemed odd enough for Friendly to look into it. He had found the padlock on the back door of Aussie's establishment broken and, on the floor just inside, Aussie's cold body. He had been killed by a blow on the head, and the place had been ransacked.

Mechanically, Lazlo bent over and picked up a ragged scrap of cloth. Wiping traces of paint from his hands, he tramped slowly over to Hutch. "Why?" he asked quietly. "Who would kill Aussie? Does Friendly have any idea?"

"Nary a one. I ast him. Whoever done it must o' been looking for something. Money, I hazard." Hutch's big hand paused at the back of his head; he winced. "Jee*zus . . . !*"

"Money," Lazlo echoed. He settled down on his hunkers to face Hutch eye to eye. "I was attacked last night when I left Bozetown. Two men with clubs. I fought them off, but it was a close thing . . ."

"You too?" Hutch's jaw dropped; he stared at Lazlo. "Well, god*damn* now! It happened to me too . . . I reckon the same as to you and poor Aussie."

"You?"

"Damn well told," Hutch said vigorously. "I had took on a good big jag o' tanglefoot and was starting on my way out o' town. I was not steady on my pins and had not got far when — *wham!* — some jasper jumped me. Larruped me over the bean and laid me out cold. When I come to, all the winnings in any jeans, what I hadn't spent buying drinks for half the goddamn town, was plumb gone. Sun was way up by then. Went to tell Abe Friendly what happened. That's when I heerd about Aussie." His eyes narrowed down. "You reckon it were the same crew that give all three of us the what-for?"

"It might have been," Lazlo said in a neutral voice. "You did not see who it was that set on you?"

"Didn't see a goddamn thing. I got larruped from behind, all unawares. How about you?"

Lazlo shook his head. "They had hoods that hid their faces, these men."

"Shitmaroo!" Hutch growled, tenderly rubbing his skull. "Well, they cleaned me out and maybe Aussie . . . 'pending if they found his money. Reckon that's what they was after, what the three o' us collected in bets yestiday."

Lazlo nodded soberly. "It would seem so."

"And that could mean 'most any jaspers in camp who seen the matches or heerd talk about 'em later on." Hutch ran a thick paw through his hair in a final swipe of disgust. "Christ almighty!"

"I am sorry about Aussie. And about your money, Hutch."

Hutch grimaced. "Don't never waste salt o' your tears on t'other fella's grief, little pard. A man has always got enough of his own to sorrow on. If he is up today, you can lay odds he will be flat down tomorrow. That is how the world goes."

Maybe it was just a casual fragment of cynicism. Or was there a deeper meaning hidden in Hutch's words? Lazlo didn't know. But though he had speculations of

90

his own about the attacks on Aussie, Hutch, and himself, he had no intention of voicing them.

Lazlo felt sorry about Aussie but couldn't dredge up any real sympathy for Hutch's loss. He saw no point in mentioning that the weight of his own suspicion fell squarely on the strong, active pair of Colonel Ruddy's performers called "the Altrocchi Brothers." Or that their participation in the assaults — at least in the one on him — would be easy to verify by a knife slash in the one's side, on the other's ankle.

No. All Lazlo Kusik wanted was to get clear of Bozetown, and particularly of Hutch Prouter, as soon as possible. If he'd felt that Hutch deserved better at his hands, it might have been different; he might have done what he could to help Hutch recover his money, even if it delayed his own departure.

The trouble was, he had a pretty fair conviction that Hutch would slit his own brother's throat if he could gain by it. The slight possibility that he might be doing Hutch an injustice didn't cut much ice. In the tough places Lazlo had frequented nearly all his life, a man's survival could hinge on judging the caliber of other men quickly and rightly. And he didn't trust Hutch Prouter. That was all there was to it.

Anyway what had happened to Aussie had left Hutch in a state of mind that was glum and bemused. Consequently he didn't attempt, subtly or clumsily, any more probing into Lazlo's affairs. That was a relief. But there was no telling when Hutch's interest might revive.

Lazlo felt even more relieved when, after a few more blind-alley speculations about the events of last night, Hutch decided to take his leave.

"Just when you figure on packing out o' here, little pard?" he asked.

"Early tomorrow, I think. If this job of painting is dry enough."

"Unh." Hutch scratched his jaw. "Well, you will be coming out along the trail hard by my claim. If t'ain't *too* blame early and I am not sleeping off a load o' corn, I will look for you to drop off for a minute or so, and we will tip a goodbye cup. Hey?"

Lazlo said he would.

They shook hands and Hutch lumbered away. Lazlo watched him till he disappeared around the upriver bend.

CHAPTER 6

Alone now, Lazlo lost no time finishing up the paint job on his wagon. Afterward he tramped up the long ridge above his camp, rifle in one hand, a gunnysack in the other. He crossed the height of land, then went up and down another ridge, keeping a wary lookout all the while.

He hoped that Hutch had really gone back to his claim. It would be easy, once he was out of sight, for him to circle back along the ridges and lay up where he could take a long view of Lazlo's preparations to leave. Still . . . these bald hills had little in the way of good cover, and a watchful man should be able to spot any out-of-the-way movement by a spy.

All the same Lazlo felt nervously exposed as he clambered across the stony crests. His flesh crawled with the thought of what a clear target he might be.

Hutch wasn't his sole cause for worry.

Lazlo couldn't pin down a solid reason for his suspicion of Colonel Laban Ruddy and his crew. Maybe it was the controlled fury he'd noted in Colonel Ruddy's expression after Lazlo had taken the shooting match. Maybe something about last night's hooded attackers had put him in mind of the two wrestlers. Or maybe it was just the cold fact that he and Hutch and Aussie had fetched those "medicine circus" people an unaccustomed upset.

No doubt they weren't used to being outslicked. And Lazlo guessed that probably this was what it really boiled down to. Very likely they had felt driven to recoup their fortunes at the expense of the same three men who were responsible for their heavy losses.

If it had been the "Altrocchi Brothers" who had assaulted and murdered Aussie last night, they might not have intended to kill him. But Aussie was just as dead. So they might figure they'd have nothing to lose if they should kill again. (If Colonel Ruddy bossed the outfit, if he gave orders to the rest of them — and if he had no large scruples about committing actual murder — wasn't anything possible?)

Having failed in their attempt to rob Lazlo last night, what was to prevent their trying again? Not a damned thing that Lazlo could see.

Outside of Abe Friendly's unofficial regulation of Bozetown, there was no law, no legal retribution of any kind to worry about in this whole wild and wide-open gold-strike country. Every man was expected to shoot his own dogs. The occasional vigilante action against wrongdoers only applied if the offender were caught — and nobody had caught the "medicine circus" people at anything. At anything that could be proved.

Lazlo himself could only admit to a silent suspicion. He wasn't sure of anything. But he couldn't shake a sense of continuing danger. Maybe he was only spooking himself . . . but didn't he have reason to?

Well, the job had to be done. Get it over with fast — that was the main thing.

Lazlo had discovered the lode by pure accident. Needing meat, he had set out one dawn, working down the river for a half mile in the hope of sighting a deer coming at this hour to drink. He'd found no game but unexpectedly had come on a quantity of shot-size gold nuggets swirling in a rock basin in the river shallows.

Within the hour Lazlo had moved his sluice box there. The place had yielded about an ounce of gold per hour. He noticed something else: The river at this point was half-filled by an alluvial fan of outwash sand and gravel. The hillside above was flanked with rotted, scaling rock from which the debris must have come.

Had the gold also come from up there?

Gripped by a mounting excitement, he had examined the formation with care, noting that the apex of the alluvial fan, largely obscured by brush, began at the mouth of a deep fissure. Lazlo had clawed his way up the steep incline, avalanches of loose rock cascading away from his driving boots. He had beaten his way through the brush that masked the fissure's mouth and had slogged into the gloom between its towering, crooked walls, still climbing.

Enough light had penetrated into the broad crevice for him to make out the wall of solid quartz that ended the fissure. The band of quartz was maybe six feet in width and just as high. Its surface showed streaks and pits that gleamed a rich yellow in the faint light.

His heart pounding, Lazlo had struck into the rotted granite with his Bowie knife. Big chunks had scaled away with each blow of the heavy blade. After only a half-dozen such blows, he had sunk back on his haunches . . . sweat breaking on his skin, muscles quivering, eyes glazing.

For a moment he'd been almost too stunned to believe what he saw. The broad band of quartz was literally webbed with thick veins of the precious stuff.

He had made it. Lazlo had made his strike.

Almost at once his mind had methodically busied itself with how to make the most of his personal bonanza. First he had applied all the tests for the worthless look-alikes of gold, right out of Bernewitz's *Handbook for Prospectors.* If the stuff couldn't be scratched with a knife, it wasn't pyrite; if it crumbled to powder under the knife, it wasn't pyrrhotite; if it could be beaten into malleable contortions without breaking, it wasn't chalcopyrite. His ore had stood up splendidly to every test.

Grimly, Lazlo had set about keeping his find a total secret. First he'd moved the sluice box back to his claim site and erased the signs of his brief digging in the stream bed below the gold fissure. Then he had continued the daily work on his claim in a lackadaisical way, putting in enough time at it to throw off any casual visitor. One might drop by now and then — Hutch Prouter, who worked a claim a ways upriver, or a few other prospectors. To all of them, Lazlo would complain about his sorry pickings and stress the probability that he'd abandon his claim and clear out of the country before snowfly.

Each evening after it was full dark, Lazlo would quietly repair a half-mile downriver and spend the night hours in the gold fissure, hewing with his pick and shovel at the band of gold-studded quartz. A big open-sided lantern gave him a strong if shadow-marred light to work by, and its glow was entirely pocketed by the steep walls.

While darkness still held, he would sack up as much of his pickings as he could carry at a time and convey them to a hiding place some distance away. This was a deep rock crevice into which Lazlo would dump the ore and then sift a little sand over the top to conceal it. When dawn's first gray tinged the sky, he would quit work and return to his shack to catch a few hours' sleep before breakfast and another day of idle sluicing.

In spite of his precautions, worry hedged all his waking hours. He'd become as tense as a cat, jumping at every sound, gnawed by a fear that somehow, someone would find him out.

Maybe it was just the suspicious old-country peasant strain in his nature. His Hungarian mother had possessed that quality in full, even though she'd always claimed descent from nobility. His father, a Polish political expatriate, had died shortly after their arrival in America. Lazlo had practically no memory of him.

Just maybe, in any case, he was starting to conjure up threats that didn't exist. Yet he knew that the potential for danger was very real. Ungarnished greed was rampant in any gold camp. The setting attracted that kind of person — and Lazlo recognized himself as one — in swarms. Mix the greed with the lack of ethics in most of the prospectors, add a dash of ruthlessness, season with almost no lawful restraint, and you have constant menace on all sides.

Claim-jumpers were as common as fleas. A man who ran into a good streak of miner's luck might promptly find his claim usurped by another or, as likely as not, by several others. He might be beaten within an inch of his life and thrown off — or even, on occasion, killed on the spot, his body buried in an unmarked grave. The killers would circulate a story that he'd sold out and left the country. Even if anyone could prove otherwise, nobody went to the trouble of collecting the proof. Each prospector had to patrol his own claim, and if he struck anything worth- while, that could be a day-and-night job.

Lazlo had good reason to take every pre- caution.

Before the deep pocket of gold-laden quartz was exhausted, he knew he'd made a strike that far exceeded anything that any other prospector had taken out of this re- gion. And he fully intended to take all of it out. Not all in one journey, but if he were to finance the arrangements to get out what remained, he would have to take out a substantial amount now. Therein lay his big problem.

Gold was immensely heavy. Just a block of it, five by five by six inches, weighed nearly a hundred pounds. Lazlo had turned up several hundred pounds of gold-bearing ore, as well as whole nuggets which had fallen free of the rotted quartz. Now that the best of the lode was played out, or seemingly so, he could apply himself wholly to the problem of secretly trans- porting away as much gold as he would initially require. The assay office in Bozetown itself was equipped to handle far lesser amounts of gold . . . but even if he could have gotten cash for a sizable amount, he was wary about letting anyone in Bozetown, even the camp assayer, know of his find.

Lazlo had toyed with several possibilities, weighing each in turn. Could he transport the gold by stagecoach? Once a week a stage crossed from, and returned to, Saba City on the other side of the Elk Mountains, bringing in or taking out passengers, mail, and cargo of various kinds. That stage run would continue till snow clogged the high passes, and this could happen at any time now. But Lazlo dismissed the notion from his mind anyway. If he loaded even a small part of his fortune on the stage and even a whisper of it leaked out, his treasure would never reach Saba City.

Most likely, neither would he. At least not alive. The stage was a constant target of road agents. Every desperado in the Territory must have held it up at one time or another, in the hope of hitting a good-sized gold shipment.

There was his mule Prunes, but he wouldn't burden her with a load of the size he meant to transport. Lazlo was a man who thought a heap more of animals than he did of most people he'd met, and he was damned if he'd drive a heavy-laden Prunes across the Elks in near-freezing weather. Besides, the danger of being held up and robbed would still be as great.

The answer he had hit on had seemed to him — at the time — a stroke of brilliance. In fact, the idea had excited him so much that he'd decided to act on it at once . . .

In a rock-littered declivity now, Lazlo sought the deep crevice in which he'd concealed the loads of ore he had conveyed to this spot. He knelt and scraped away some of the sand that camouflaged the cache of pure nuggets. He filled the gunnysack with as much as he could carry.

Staggering under his load, Lazlo started back to his camp — the sack of precious metal slung over one shoulder, his rifle looped over the other with a rawhide thong. Back in camp, he hastily unloaded the nuggets, jamming them into the space between the true and false bottoms of his wagon. He made two more trips back to his cache. The purest part of his treasure was now rammed inside the narrow pockets of the hidden compartment. Any more of it, taken with the weight of himself and his gear, would burden the wagon too heavily. Lazlo dropped the tailgate to cover the open slot at the rear and then nailed it securely into place.

That done, he felt a little queasy from the strain of nerves and physical exertion. By now the sun was fading toward the west. Its thin pale rays held little warmth, but Lazlo was drenched with sweat just the same. He wanted to sit down and rest.

But he had a piece of business to finish up while daylight held. He started to tramp up the ridge again and then was struck by a thought that made him turn back. He got a piece of rope and a small canvas sack out of his possibles. Then he hurried on up the ridge.

Back at the crevice, Lazlo dug into a little hoard of gold dust that was set off from the chunkier stuff. He filled the canvas sack a third full of the gleaming particles and secured the mouth of it with a drawstring. He tied the sack under his shirt with the rope, patting it out flat against his side so that it made a barely discernible lump.

A hard smile touched his lips. It would not do for a prospector to leave a hard-worked claim with no stake at all under his belt, would it?

Working swiftly now, Lazlo refilled the exposed part of the crevice with sand, then scattered fragments of shale over the seam so it would blend with the rest of this rubble-covered dip. Afterward he headed back for camp, going slowly so he could scan the ground for any telltale signs he might have left. But he'd stuck carefully to bare rock in his comings and goings to his cache. He didn't think that even an Indian could have followed tracks anywhere in the vicinity of the hidden treasure . . .

Just the same, he continued to keep a sharp eye peeled. It was still short of sunset, and the coming of dark wouldn't relieve his anxiety much. He might have waited till nightfall to move the gold, but it would have taken ten times as long, fumbling his way in the dark. And he needed time — not only to let the paint dry on his wagon, but also to rest up for an early morning start out of here.

Tomorrow he would not rest until he had traveled high into the eastern passes, miles from Bozetown and its horde of greedy hardcases.

Lazlo was drag-footed with exhaustion as he tended the mules, gathered wood for a fire, and cooked up a mess of grub. He actually dozed off twice, squatting on his heels while his supper was cooking. It took a vast effort to pull himself alert each time. He wasn't even very hungry, but his body must be fed to keep up his strength. He wolfed down the beans and bacon and pan bread without taste or pleasure. Then he headed for the shanty and some shut-eye.

A sluggish thought hauled Lazlo up short. Maybe he was just light-headed with suspicion, but the idea of spending his last night on his claim in that cramped shack gave him a cornered feeling. Wouldn't it be damned easy for someone to take him by surprise in there?

He got his bedroll from the bunk in the shanty and carried it upslope a ways. Although the crowns of the ridges were bald, there was plenty of brush along their lower flanks. He spread his ground tarp in a hollow place inside a thicket and stretched out. Bundled in his Mackinaw coat and blankets against the increasing chill, his Winchester cradled in his arms, he went quickly to sleep.

A last cold stain of sunlight faded from the sky, but Lazlo was snoring deeply and dreamlessly before it vanished.

It had been his intention to arise in the first gray light of dawn so he could get as early a start as possible. But Lazlo hadn't reckoned with his own utter weariness.

When he did come awake, suddenly and

with a kind of shock, the sun was high in the sky. Christ . . . he must have slept away a good twelve hours or more.

His muscles were stiff with cold as he shed his blankets and got to his feet. God knows, he'd needed the sleep. Too much strain on a man's body and nerves wore him down to a shoestring. That was where he was now, Lazlo knew.

In a few days, he thought, I will be eating prime steaks at the best hotel in Saba City. And washing them down with champagne. It was a promise he had made himself over and over during the most grueling hours since he'd stumbled on his strike.

It was very close to him now. Just a few hours away.

A residue of tension filled Lazlo's belly as he walked down to his camp, but his step was springy, his spirits brisk and almost optimistic. The hour of departure would be later than he'd wished, but he should be packed up and away from here within an hour. Last night he had cooked up enough grub to last him several days. He would make good time on the trail. A few stops to rest the mules and boil up some coffee, maybe a night or two of sleeping out. Then he would be "safe at home base."

Lazlo built his morning fire, added some water and fresh Triple X to the grounds that filled the bottom of his coffeepot, and set the pot close to the fire. Then he carried his few belongings from the shanty to the wagon. The paint job was still a little sticky, but that was all right. A rich man should not mind a few paint stains on his possibles.

The thought made him laugh aloud, suddenly and exultantly.

He sandwiched his prospector's tools among the other gear. All he would leave behind was his sluice box. Maybe some other prospecting fool would try his luck along this stretch of the Mad Mule. He would have need of the sluice box. Lazlo felt cheerful enough to wish that sort of fool well . . .

By the time he had the wagon loaded, the coffee was boiling furiously. Lazlo tramped over to the fire and reached down with a gloved hand to move the pot away from the flames.

A bullet whanged into the coffeepot and set it bounding away.

As the heels of the gunshot crashed against his ears, Lazlo could only stare with stunned disbelief at the perforated pot on its side, the brown liquid gurgling out on the icy ground.

A second shot exploded shards of frozen dirt inches from his boots. It seemed more of a warning shot than anything else. That thought flashed through Lazlo's mind even as he snapped out of his momentary paralysis, turning his head.

He had left his rifle leaning against a rock about twenty feet away. *God!* He should have kept it next to him. His eye gauged the distance, and a clot of reckless anger rose in his throat.

He would make the try. He had to.

Gathering his bunched leg muscles under him, Lazlo made a wild lunge for the rifle. Trying to duck low in the same movement caused him to lose his footing. He felt his feet skid away from under him, and then he crashed on his face.

The unseen rifleman fired again.

This time the flinty chips of earth burst against Lazlo's face. The man had fired that close to it. And he wasn't alone. In the wake of his shot, overlapping it, two other guns spoke at the same time. Both shots gouged up pellets of frozen soil within inches of Lazlo's prone form.

He was trapped. And helpless.

The Winchester was still a yard beyond the tips of his outflung fingers. Lazlo lay very still, feeling the slow trickle of his sweat, the hard pounding of his heart, on the ground beneath him. Slowly, very slowly now, he turned his face toward a growth of brush from which he figured the shots had come.

The foliage rustled. A man stepped out to view. He was stocky and white-haired, with a snapping vigor in his eyes and not a trace of whiskey glaze on them. The rifle in his hands was as steady as a rock; he held it carelessly trained on Lazlo.

"Good morning, Mr. Kusik!"

Ringing out in the crisp young day, Colonel Laban Ruddy's voice was full of hearty good cheer. "Lord alive, lad, but I'm mighty gratified that you decided to show good sense. Who knows? You may still manage to pull out of this unfortunate contretemps with your hide more or less intact . . . eh?"

CHAPTER 7

Colonel Ruddy sat on a boulder and took a long pull at a silver flask he'd taken from the pocket of his belted traveling jacket. The tip of his nose burned with color; a healthy flush of morning chill deepened in his face.

"Ahhh . . . cognac. Nothing but the best. And nothing like it for chasing the cold." Laban tilted a politely questioning brow at Lazlo. "Care for a draught?"

Lazlo shook his head. "No, thank you."

He glanced at the two brothers standing to either side of him with ready pistols. Some Italians, these were. Ruddy had addressed them as "Ab" and "Bije," and had also called one of them "Nephew." He likes to keep it all in the family, Lazlo thought humorlessly. Bije, he had noticed, walked with a slight limp.

"Very well. To business." Laban Ruddy gestured with his flask at the loaded wagon. "I gather, Mr. Kusik, that you're preparing to take your leave of these parts. I should hate to delay your departure.

And have no reason to do so if you choose to . . . cooperate?"

"How can I do that?"

"Very easily," Laban said gently. "We want the money you won from us. And others."

"Take it," Lazlo said coldly. "Can I get it out of my pocket?"

"Slowly, if you please. Very."

Lazlo eased the bulging wallet out of his Mackinaw pocket and tossed it at the colonel's feet. Laban Ruddy merely glanced at it and did not pick it up. "So far, so good. Now. The rest, please."

"It is all there. To the penny."

"Not the cash, my dear fellow. Your *gold*. I really feel we have a bonus coming for the inconvenience you've given us."

Laban rose to his feet, took another swig from his flask, capped it, and tucked it away. "Doubtless you've a poke of dust and nuggets to show for your labors. Or you've secured payment for it at the local assay office." His eyes pinched to wintry slits. "We want it. One way or the other, we intend to have it. How will *you* have it, sir?"

Lazlo shrugged. "The pickings were bad. I made enough to buy supplies — that was all."

Laban's big teeth showed below his mustache. "Ha-ha. Is that right. Go through his wagon, Robert. Dump everything out."

The moon-faced Indian — now addressed as Robert Topbear and not as "Wa-nit-ka-we-bo" — was squatting on his heels and looking on with a glum indifference. Now he got up, shambled over to the wagon, and began throwing out its contents. Afterward he tore apart the packs, went over each item piece by piece, and then glanced at Ruddy with a shrug of his brows.

"If he has any gold or any more cash, it must be on him."

"There's a thought," Laban murmured. "Follow it up, why don't you, Robert?"

Robert Topbear patted Lazlo's pockets and the sides of his Mackinaw. His hands paused. He opened the Mackinaw and pulled up Lazlo's shirt. In a moment he'd cut the thong that secured the goldsack against Lazlo's ribs.

Laban gave a weary shake of his head. "You gold grubbers do manifest a singular lack of imagination in concealing your grubbings." He accepted the pouch from Robert Topbear, undid the drawstring, and spilled a portion of gold dust into his palm. He clucked his tongue, regretfully. "*This* is all you've realized from your many months on the spot, Mr. Kusik? I've made, you see, a few judicious inquiries about the length of your sojourn here."

"Men have prospected longer still and have found less." Lazlo laid a bitter tinge of anger on his words. "It is little enough to show for all that time. And now this little is yours, eh?"

"An elementary but accurate conclusion, my dear sir." Laban showed his teeth again as he returned the dust to the bag, cinched it up, and pocketed it. "I believe that concludes our business, and you may resume your preparations for departure . . . which I suggest you undertake without delay. To encourage your swift exodus, we shall appropriate both your rifle and knife. Both of which, by the way, I must congratulate you for wielding so handily."

Lazlo didn't have to simulate the rush of wrath that bit into his reply. "It is too bad Aussie couldn't do the same. Damn your souls!"

"The Australian?" Laban's brows puckered. "True . . . the boys took his purse. But they took your friend Mr. Prouter's, too. So you've heard?"

"Do you tell me you have not?"

"Haven't what? Make it plain, my friend."

"Aussie is dead. You have killed him. Hutch Prouter brought me the news yesterday."

"What?" The word left Laban as a shocked whisper. His gaze, swiveling from one of his nephews to the other, held a mounting fury. "My God! You damned fools! You *killed* a man? After I gave you *distinct* orders to avoid . . . ?"

The dull faces of the brothers showed flickers of alarmed bewilderment.

"Jeez, Uncle Labe," Bije got out, "we din't mean to. Christ, we din't even know till now! I hit that funny-talking little jasper, and he folded clean up and we took his money and cleared out. That's all, I vow! We din't know —"

"All right — all right!" Laban cut him off with a chopping motion of one hand. He paced slowly up and down for a moment, staring at the ground, then halted and raised his glare to his nephews. "What's done is done. No way to undo it. But damn your stupid, blundering hides!"

His hard glance cut to Lazlo. "So then. You know. But you can't prove it, can you? Your word against ours. And there're several more of us — to alibi one another. If there were any authorized law to alibi to."

Lazlo said nothing.

"I reiterate, Mr. Kusik: get out. Get clear away from this country. With that word of advice, I bid you good day and wish you well."

"Colonel," Robert Topbear spoke in his flat, dispassionate voice, "I suggest we hold up for just a little while."

"What's that? Why, Robert?"

"This fellow might have a lot more going for him than appearances would indicate." The Indian paused and then nodded at the flint-strewn slope above the camp. "When I was reconnoitering the place a little earlier — before I brought you and the boys word to close in — I came on some diggings way up there. There is a fissure in the cliffs that someone has been digging way back into, I'd say for quite some time. There's a big pile of rubble around the mouth. As though someone" — his black gaze shuttled to Lazlo — "had a good reason for concentrating a great deal of time and effort on the project. And I found this among the rubble."

Robert Topbear produced a rough chunk of rock from his pocket and handed it to Laban. "Those streaks in the rock, Colonel — they might be gold or pyrites. My own guess, it's a piece of gold-bearing ore."

"Really?" Laban squinted at the jagged bit of rock, juggled it in his palm, and looked at Lazlo. "You wouldn't have a plausible explanation for so intriguing a development, would you, Mr. Kusik?"

"I dug up there a long time, sure," Lazlo said stolidly. "That's after I found a little color there. Most of what you got in that sack came out of that same digging."

Laban Ruddy rubbed his goatee thoughtfully. "Mmm. Well . . . the matter bears a bit of study. Robert, I think you might show me the spot. Nephews, just keep your guns on our hunky friend here. See if you can manage not to let him run you both off as you did night before last."

Laban and Robert Topbear went tramping up the slope.

Lazlo sank down on his hunkers by the fire, holding his hands to the glowing coals, aware of the brothers' watchful gazes and their ready pistols that followed all his movements. Stupid or not, they wouldn't be taken unaware.

Lazlo's thoughts ranged narrowly over his situation. Damn the Indian. If he hadn't spotted the scars of heavy digging, Lazlo would be safely rid of this crew now and not much the poorer for it. How much more could they tell from examining the place? He hoped not much. He had pretty well cleaned out the pocket, and the handful of gold-streaked chips he'd left shouldn't invalidate his story.

He swung to his feet and walked over to the punctured coffeepot.

"Don't you move around like that, Mister," the one called Ab warned him.

"I only wondered if there's a little coffee that didn't spill out."

"You sit," Bije declared flatly.

Lazlo dropped to his haunches and met their dull, unblinking stares with no particular expression.

Presently Laban Ruddy and Topbear returned. Laban was wearing a sleepy, blandly smug look that made a sudden tension coil in Lazlo's belly.

Laban halted before him, a hand thrust in his pocket. "You'd never guess what," he murmured. "Look."

He took the hand from his pocket. In his extended palm lay a solid gold nugget close to the size of a hen's egg. "That's something, eh? Found it under a few inches of dirt I kicked into. Hard to believe you could have missed it, Mr. Kusik. Why, it's again a third of the amount in that poke of yours — I mean, that *was* yours."

Lazlo gave a wondering shake of his head, gazing at the nugget. (It was as large as any he'd dug out of the fissure, and how in God's name *had* he missed it?) "It is quite a thing, for sure. But it might be easy to overlook if it got under some dirt." He shrugged. "It was my bad luck. I have had a lot of that lately."

"You may be in for a bit more." Laban's voice was low, measured, and wicked. "Just possibly you're holding out on us, sir. Could it be you hit a pay streak of considerable value, cleaned it out, and conveyed the cream of it elsewhere?"

"You are imagining things," Lazlo said stonily. "If I did, this smart Indian of yours could track it down, couldn't he?"

Laban smiled thinly. "Robert's talents in the arts of his ancestors are, I regret to say, sadly circumscribed. About the only thing he's ever smelled out with any ultimate conviction is a cache of hooch. If you *did* convey gold in any quantity from that digging, I trust you'd take pains to conceal it from even a trained eye."

Laban sat down on his heels a few yards from Lazlo, folding his arms on his knees. "Come now, Mr. Kusik. Let's not bandy idle words. Your excavation *was* quite productive, wasn't it?"

"That is a guess you can afford. But you guess wrong."

"Do I?" Laban chuckled mildly. "My sense of logic says — quite possibly. But a feeling deep in the gut of me contradicts all logic. Come now, man. We'll have the truth from you by one means or another. How will it be?"

"You have the gold I found. You found it on me. How much does it look like?"

"Offhand," Laban said affably, "I'd say it looks like a blind alley. A decoy. Oh, you're shrewd enough, my boy — in a hunky peasant way. But the trade I've followed lifelong has an old aphorism you may have heard: Never try to con a confidence man."

"I think I heard it a little different."

Laban let out a hearty laugh. "Good. Very good! But now, of course, you'll have to pay the price of such useless intransigence. Boys, relieve Mr. Kusik of his coat. Then march him over to that dead tree yonder and tie him fast to it."

Standing at the north end of Lazlo's claim line, the tree was a small oak, barren of bark, its top broken off, and most of its branches gone. Only the silver-gray trunk endured, rooted in the frozen soil. Ab and Bije used the ropes that had secured Lazlo's pack to tie him upright against the tree, and they made a job of it. His hands were lashed behind him around the trunk. Loops of rope that circled his chest and waist and upper legs also fastened him tightly against it.

Damn his own carelessness!

But drugged with weariness, prodded by haste, working in half-darkness much of the time, it had been easy to lose even a good-sized chunk of gold in the loose earth. No . . . damn the luck that had led Laban Ruddy to uncover the nugget.

Laban gave his orders. He and his nephews and Robert Topbear would scour the ground all around and above the claim. They were to search every nook and cranny of the surrounding terrain, keeping their eyes open for the least betraying sign.

That, at least, would not do them much good, Lazlo thought with bleak satisfaction. From the original digging, a broken trail of sorts led from the fissure down to his camp: splintered twigs, scuffed ground, bits of broken shale. His many comings and goings had made it inevitable and, bone-tired and ready to drop in his tracks from his other efforts, he'd made no attempt to conceal those signs. But the place where he'd cached the body of his ore was immaculately hidden.

He had one bad moment when Laban Ruddy, poking around the camp proper, laid his gloved hand on the tailgate of Lazlo's wagon. Then he jerked the hand away with a mild curse. The paint was still a little sticky. Would he suspect . . . ?

Apparently not. Laban was too irked by the indelible stain on his fine kidskin glove to attach any importance to the fresh paint job. As Lazlo had told Hutch, it was just a sensible safeguard against weathering. And the damage to his glove diverted Laban from a closer inspection of the wagon.

Somehow that small fiasco of an incident helped Lazlo steel himself against a growing dread. He resolved that, by God, no matter what these bastards did to him, he would give away nothing. *Nothing!*

After nearly an hour of searching, Laban tramped back to where Lazlo was tied. His eyes were red-edged with the heat of impatience and the effects of several more pulls at his flask.

"Here," he said, "is how I have the matter sized. I think you've a considerable cache of gold you've very cleverly hidden somewhere around here. It would be too difficult, for a variety of reasons, to transport it out of the country by yourself just now. But you decided it could afford to wait till a more propitious time. Am I correct?"

Lazlo said tonelessly, "You are the one saying it."

"So far, Mr. Kusik, I have just been playing pat-a-cake." Laban paused. "Be reasonable now. I'll make you a proposition. Show us where the gold is, and we'll divide it straight down the middle. Half for you, half for us. And we'll save you a deal of trouble by conveying it over to Saba City in our three wagons. I'll even return the cash and gold we've taken from you."

"I see." A corner of Lazlo's mouth lifted. "I can see how *you* can call that a fair exchange."

"My dear fellow, nobody said aught about 'fair.' I may just be discussing the price of your survival. Getting a bit chilled, are you?"

Lazlo was. No sun brightened this cold morning. Coatless and immobile, he could feel the chill deepening in his flesh as the minutes crawled on. It was hard not to let his teeth chatter when he spoke.

"I have been colder."

"No doubt." Laban tipped back his head and gazed at the sky. It was a harsh leaden color and clouds boiled over the peaks. "But you'll be a good deal colder yet in a little while, I'll warrant. That sky, now. It could promise rain or sleet or snow." His gaze returned to Lazlo's face. "Why endure needless misery? In the end you'll have to break . . . or perhaps freeze to death."

"There is nothing to tell. Also I do not think you will let me freeze. The killing of Aussie. You did not like that."

"Not at all," Laban said genially. "But I might, with so much at stake, not cavil at letting you freeze a few fingers and toes that would soon require amputation. Think about it awhile."

He turned on his heel and strode away, calling to his nephews and Robert Topbear. When they joined him by the shanty, Laban said, "Boys, our friend over there hasn't decided he'll cooperate. He will, but he needs a space to make up his mind. While we're waiting, we may as well be comfortable. I noticed a stove in the shack. If you fellows will gather some wood, we'll fire it up and be warm in the interim."

The potbelly stove in the shanty was a rusty old affair that Lazlo had used only once; it overheated so badly he'd feared it might burn down the shack. He watched the three younger men round up the needed deadwood from the ridgeside and carry it into the shack. After they'd laid a fire in the stove and had it drawing nicely, the men closed the door of the shack behind them. Smoke bloomed from the roofpipe.

Alone and unobserved now, Lazlo threw all he had into arching his body away from the dead tree, straining against the ropes. It was useless. All he could manage to do was force the knots tighter.

The slate-bellied clouds in the sky were moving overhead now, and the cold was increasing. A raw wind started up. Before long it was picking up a small freight of sleet. Icy rain and pellets of ice slashed against his face and body. The chill was eating into the marrow of his bones now.

Lazlo threw all his strength into another try at escaping his bonds. He knew even as he made the effort how hopeless it was . . .

A tightening of real panic filled his belly.

He had been afraid before now. No man could live for very long as he had, in the places he had lived, and not know what fear was. But this was fear of a different sort. The kind a man knew when he was strapped from taking action against the threat that faced him. He was trussed up like a beast for the slaughter. And he was slowly freezing to death.

Should he give in? Lazlo wavered for a moment.

It would save him from worse. What of Laban Ruddy's promise to share the gold? Half of it would still leave him a rich man. But could he depend on Laban to keep his word? Once he had what he wanted, Laban might even decide to leave Lazlo staked where he was to let the elements finish what Laban had begun.

By now, after all, Laban might have guessed what Lazlo himself damned well knew: that to avenge a steal of this magnitude, he would follow Colonel Laban Ruddy to the ends of hell.

Beyond that was the iron knowledge that he would not knuckle under. Not to any threat under the sun, by God. Part of it was rooted in Lazlo's own stark pride. But weighed into the equation, too, were the endless hours of back-breaking work and nerve-strung worry that had gone into assembling his trove.

It was his. He had earned every grain of it. And he would keep it all, or he would die.

The door of the shack opened. Robert Topbear came out, stumbling a little, toting a wooden bucket that Lazlo had left in the shack. He carried it down to the stream bank and filled it with water. Unsteadily he crossed the open space to Lazlo, the full bucket sloshing at his side.

Laban Ruddy had been watching from the open door of the shack. Now he let out a loud, immoderate laugh and went back in, closing the door.

Robert Topbear halted and gave Lazlo a lopsided leer. "Paleface decide talk now? Uh? Tellum red brother where yellow wampum hid? Uh?"

"All the moonshine is not in your head." Lazlo's lips were stiff, his teeth chattering fiercely now. "There is no gold. Go back, damn you, and tell your master that."

Robert Topbear seemed to take no offense. Still grinning, he glanced down at the bucket he held. "The colonel thought you might still feel just so. That's why he sent me to fetch a pail of water to throw on you. Get a little colder than you are, you might make up your mind faster."

"Go ahead then. Don't keep your master waiting."

For answer, Robert Topbear tilted the bucket in his hands and poured all the water out on the ground. Even in his frozen, half-torpid misery, Lazlo felt a feeble dart of surprise.

"Why?" he murmured.

Robert Topbear's grin faded. "Maybe because liquor never makes a dirty job taste any better."

"This bothers you? You're the one told him maybe I had more gold hid somewhere."

Topbear grimaced. "I didn't think about what it might lead to. The colonel —" He paused and rubbed a hand over his face, as if scraping away the effects of drink he'd consumed. "The colonel wasn't always like this. Always a con man, sure, and a sharper. But he's never been an out-and-out thief before. Nor a man who'd do to another what he's doing to you. Christ, I don't know. Maybe all the booze he takes has eaten into his brain."

Lazlo set his jaws to keep his teeth from rattling together. He spoke through his nearly clenched teeth. "It's good it has not eaten into yours."

"Oh, I don't know." Robert Topbear gave a wry, bitter shrug of one shoulder, as though the irony were lost on him. "I have no morality, you know. Not the integrity of my own people anymore. Not even the morality of you whites, which amounts to damned little. Had a good moral sense once, years ago before I was packed off to the White Father's Indian School at Carlisle, Pennsylvania."

"Is that where you got to reading Cooper?"

Robert Topbear's grin flashed and vanished. "Spotted that, did you — in my spiel? You're sort of a surprising fellow on your own account. Yes, Cooper. And a lot of other things. Learned a hell of a lot about the white man's vastly superior culture. Enough to graduate at the head of my class at Carlisle. Then went back to my reservation in the Nations. But I no longer fitted into the tribal life. Had learned too much, you see. And soon found I did not fit into the white man's society any better. You paragons of the master race don't much fancy uppity Injuns. Especially eddicated-up-to-their-ears ones."

Topbear smiled crookedly; he made an aimless gesture with the empty bucket. "Ah well. Mine's no special case. Happens to a lot of us. When the booze gets working, I talk too damned much. My apologies."

"That's why you got drinking?"

Lazlo said the words with no censure and no real interest. He was too miserable to give a damn. Hurtful needles of cold were tingling into his fingers and toes, driving with a quiet agony into the ends of all his nerves.

"That's why. And why, I guess to my good fortune, I fell in with Colonel Ruddy. He's been more than my employer. He has been" — Topbear hesitated — "my good friend."

"What does he pay you in? Booze?"

A gleam of anger surfaced in the Indian's black eyes. Then he relaxed; his crooked smile flickered again. "What else? But he's been kindly to me. He has kept me with him when, at times, he might have found it convenient to abandon me. Worth a drop of loyalty — don't you think?"

"What I think," Lazlo said coldly, "is that the brains of you both, you and Ruddy, are rotted with whiskey. I would not think that two of you could get so much out of one flask."

Robert Topbear chuckled. "You underestimate the resources of a dedicated boozer, friend. Both the colonel and I have — or had — a few other flasks secreted about our persons."

"I am not surprised. Does the shootist drink too?"

"The what?"

"The lady with the special Henry rifle. She seems to take up with a man's ways pretty good."

"Oh, Stella. She's the colonel's daughter. Older one, I mean. The Princess Shahazar is the other one. Her real name is Myra Mae. 'Member the princess?" Robert Topbear made a few roguish gyrating motions with one hand. "Nope, Stell is a real decent woman."

"It seems so. Otherwise why would she help you sharp the suckers?"

Robert Topbear's glint of humor switched off.

"Watch what you say about her," he said flatly. "Stella Ruddy is a good woman. Sure she talks rough and dresses like a man, mostly to spite her pa. But she has no part of his con act — or mine." Topbear's speech was starting to slur as the full intake of the liquor he'd consumed hit his brain; he blinked rapidly as if to focus his eyes. "Fact is, what the colonel tol' the girls this morning was that he and I and the two boys were going to town for an all-day whoop-up. Meaning, natch'ly, we meant to get falling-down drunk."

"They would have no trouble believing that."

"Natch'ly not."

"In a minute," Lazlo gibed, "I think you will fall on your face anyway. And how will you tell your master why you did not wet me down? I think that will make him mad."

Robert Topbear gave a loud, hiccoughing laugh. "Who'n hell gotta wet you down, f' krissake? You're damn near soaked through already, paleface. Give you another fifteen minutes out here, you be too damn stiff to sing out, even if you decide to talk. Huh?"

Lazlo didn't reply.

Robert Topbear swayed on his braced legs, laughed again, and then turned and lurched back to the shack.

Icy shudders wracked Lazlo's body. He was wet to the skin, all right, and he could feel the last tinglings of sensation ebbing out of his extremities. They were going totally numb.

Maybe you should give in, he thought. What good is gold to a dead man? Maybe they will take it all, but a dead man could not even care.

Panic was edging out resolution now, and he fought the temptation with all his will. Once more he heaved savagely against the pinioning ropes. They held tight.

But he felt a faint grating at the base of

the tree. What was that? Wasn't it set as solidly in the frozen earth as it appeared to be?

Again Lazlo threw his weight forward and then back, rocking against the trunk. There was a sharp crack. From the main root of the dead tree? He kept on steadily and fiercely rocking, a burst of hope feeding fire into his sluggish blood.

Suddenly the tree was grinding loosely in its moorings. Then the last of its network of dead roots gave way and pulled free.

Tipping suddenly forward, Lazlo fought for balance and barely gained it before he fell on his face. God, that must not happen.

For a moment he stood half-bent under the tree's dead weight, mustering the dregs of his energy. His feet, now that he could move again, felt like frozen blocks. He must be very careful. Now he could move a little, even walk a little, but he must go very slow and careful. If he fell down, trussed up as he was, he would never be able to get back on his feet.

At any moment one of the men in the shack might come out again. So he had to get away from here. That came first. Then he must find help.

Hutch. Hutch Prouter's claim was the nearest place. A little distance up the Mad Mule on this side of it. If he could get to it before his half-escape was discovered . . .

Reeling awkwardly toward the north edge of his claim, Lazlo set a painfully turtlelike pace, taking every step as gingerly as a girl with her legs encased in a hobbling skirt. Some of the freezing sleet had crusted on his clothing; it sloughed away in crackling scales as he inched along. He had to keep bent way over just to keep the lower part of the tree trunk on his back from hitting his heels. He staggered and stumbled. He took each step a few inches at a time and with infinite care.

He couldn't even feel his feet any longer. Their clumsy wooden strides at the ends of his stiffened legs, the numbing cold working steadily upward, made him wonder if the rest of him would also give out before he got much farther.

At the same time he felt a driving and dogged urge not to waste a precious second. Now he was away from the open bank on the upriver trail, deep in the trees and out of sight of the shack. Raging against his own near helplessness, he pushed himself too hard. His boot skidded in a puddle of icy slush.

Lazlo twisted as he fell, but all he saved himself from was landing on his face. He landed on his side instead, and he was just as helpless.

He made one mighty effort to tuck his feet under him, to maneuver himself upright, and knew even as he made the try how hopeless it was. He sank back. A groan of despair burned in his chest; the sweat of his rage and his futile efforts began to ice on his face.

He heard a clump of booted steps on the frozen trail. They were coming after him — *damn them to hell!*

The boots came into the tail of his vision. They stopped less than a yard from his head. With his residue of failing strength, Lazlo craned his head enough to let his gaze travel up along the muffled, burly form of the man who stood above him.

"Howdy there, little pard," said Hutch Prouter. "You been caught in a mite of a jackpot, now ain't you?"

CHAPTER 8

Hutch cut him free and dragged him deeper into the trees. Then Hutch shucked off the heavy buffalo-hide coat he was wearing and wrapped it around Lazlo. Even in this weather it had a thick, musky, unpleasant smell, but Lazlo couldn't remember a more welcome warmth. He crouched on the ground with his back to a tree, huddling inside the coat as Hutch briefly told him how he'd come to be here.

Earlier, from his own tree-hidden camp by the river, he had seen Colonel Laban Ruddy and his companions coming along the trail, headed downstream. What were they doing way out here, and where were they going? The question had piqued Hutch enough for him to follow them, keeping out of sight.

Watching from the edge of timber, he'd seen all that had occurred between Lazlo and the colonel. But he couldn't overhear their words and wasn't quite sure what to make of the situation. Being unarmed, he'd decided that if he were to be of any help to his "little pard," he'd better go back to camp and fetch his guns. Having done so, he returned to the spot just as Lazlo had taken his helpless spill.

Hutch was eyeing him closely, brows raised as he talked.

Lazlo answered the unspoken question. "They came to rob me like they did you and Aussie. Yes, it was them did that. Then . . . they thought I had more gold than I do. So they made me freeze awhile so I would talk."

"And you wasn't about to, huh?"

"There was nothing to tell."

Hutch nodded and scratched his beard. "Unh. Well, you are out of one jackpot of trouble, little pard. What now?"

Lazlo's teeth were chattering with cold, but some feeling had flooded back into his chilled body. He could move his arms and legs without much trouble. Sensation was trickling back into his fingers and toes. He flexed them to help the feeling along, ignoring the prickles of pain.

"You went and got your guns," he murmured. "Good. That is how things stand now."

Hutch hefted his old Hawken rifle in one fist. His Walker Colt was rammed into the

136

waistband of his leather pants. "Surest thing you know. You want to roust them gents around some, I take it."

"Yes," Lazlo said gently. "Some."

A silent chuckle shook Hutch's vast bulk. "I got a score to settle with 'em too, Laz. You just say on. I reckon we can light a hotter fire under their britches than they got going in yonder shack."

There were two ways they could come at the shack's occupants: by the door or by a small window over on the south wall. Lazlo figured that he and Hutch could catch the four men between them, and by complete surprise, if they worked in unison.

Hutch nodded. "You want to hang up their hides for good? The Lord hisself couldn't blame you none."

"No. Take them alive if we can." But Lazlo's jaw had an iron set. "Only shoot if we need to."

On stiff legs he moved back to the edge of timber and paused, sweeping a glance over the cabin and the clearing. Ruddy or one of the others might come out at any moment to check on him. But that wasn't what claimed Lazlo's immediate attention. His rifle was still leaning against the same rock. Once they'd had Lazlo in hand, Ruddy and his men had carelessly left it there.

He wanted his own rifle, the good familiar feel of it in his hands. Let Hutch keep both his antique weapons.

Hulking beside him, Hutch said impatiently, "All right now, Laz. We going ahead or not?"

Lazlo said, "Yes," and added a few terse details as to what he had in mind. Then they broke apart, Hutch lumbering toward the door like a great stalking bear, while Lazlo cut across to the rock. His circulation was coming back; his movements were smooth and quick as he picked up his rifle and checked the action.

Another short run and he was over by the south window.

Glass windows weren't a feature of any building in or around Bozetown. Glass was an expensive indulgence to have freighted in, and it broke too easily. What you did, if you furnished your shelter with any sort of window, was to outfit it with a scraped deerhide that was translucent enough to let in light. Or else you covered the aperture with a pegged-together square of puncheon boards that swung inward on rawhide hinges fastened to a side of the frame.

The window of Lazlo's shack was covered with a puncheon-board square. Weathering and warping had strained the puncheons apart, leaving broad cracks through which a man could scan the whole interior.

Three of them — Colonel Ruddy, Robert Topbear, and Bije — were sitting on their heels in a circle, intent on what appeared to be a game of poker, casting the greasy, well-thumbed cards down on the packed-clay floor. Both Topbear and the colonel looked as if they might slide over on their faces at any moment. Gaps in the old stove sent out a fitful orange glare over the scene. The one called Ab was crouched by the stove, not too steady himself as he fed a few lengths of stovewood into the fire.

Carefully, rifle balanced in his left hand, Lazlo planted his right hand against the puncheon square. Suddenly he swung it in, slapping his right hand to the barrel of the rifle and thrusting his arms and head and shoulders through.

He fired into the ceiling.

The shot was thunderous in the shack. It was the signal to Hutch, who gave the door a mighty kick that burst it open. He came barreling into the room. His face wore a huge grin; his Walker Colt was leveled.

The three men on the floor froze in place. Ab came wheeling about wildly, dropping the stove pieces. Then he clawed at the pistol thrust in his belt.

"Don't!" Lazlo yelled, bringing the rifle to bear.

He was pumping its lever on-cock even as Ab yanked his gun free. And Lazlo fired.

The slug's force flung Ab against the wall with an impact that shook the building. He slid down to a sitting position, his eyes already glazing. They turned a last puzzled, unfocused look on his uncle; his mouth opened and worked, as if laboring for speech.

No words came. His head tipped over on his shoulder. The sudden pungence of his released sphincter filled the hot closeness of the room.

A fan of cards in Colonel Ruddy's upraised hand dribbled to the floor. "Ab, boy?" he whispered. "Ab, boy?"

He scrambled on his hands and knees to his nephew's side. His hand searched for a heartbeat. When he pulled the hand back, his palm was a slick wet red and he stared at it, unbelieving.

"On your feet," Lazlo ordered. "Up. Up, damn you! Hutch — their guns, their knives —"

Robert Topbear obeyed, looking sober and careful. Ruddy stayed as he was. So did Bije, his swarthy face shocked and almost uncomprehending. Hutch moved among them, collecting pistols and knives. These he tossed into a corner alongside the rifles leaning there.

"That does it, Laz."

"Keep a watch on them."

Lazlo withdrew from the window and tramped around to the door. He ordered the men outside. Robert Topbear didn't have to be told twice. But Lazlo had to repeat the order three times to get the grief-stunned Bije and the colonel in motion.

They stood in the cutting, sleet-freighted wind that couldn't quench the burn of hatred in the faces of Ab's kinsmen. Both of them still managed to stare straight at Lazlo, grief already submerging itself in a wish to do hot-blooded murder.

Tears iced on Bije's cheeks. "Mister," he said in a quivering voice, "you gonna kill us too, you better do it quick and do it now. I swear, you hold off and I will kill you." His powerful hands flexed and unflexed. "I will do it with no weapons a-tall."

"I was you, Laz," Hutch said mildly, "I would take this boy at his word."

"Shut up, Hutch." A hard pulse pounded in Lazlo's head. "I did not ask you."

"You hear me all the same. Now this

141

sharper and his crew, by God, they killed Aussie and robbed me and set you out to freeze. If that ain't cause enough to put 'em under, they will hang your hide up for sure any chance they get. Look at that old sharper, now. Look at his face."

The colonel's skin had a yellowish pallor and hugged the lines of his skull as if he'd aged many years in a few moments. "Your friend has the right of it, Mr. Kusik," he said. "Perhaps you should heed his word."

"But it will work two ways," Lazlo said quietly. "You will kill me on sight if you can. But I will do the same . . . next time. That is a fair warning. I am very good with a rifle — this you know. So maybe you better see there is not a next time."

"Ah, but there will be." Rimmed by a drip of frosty whiteness that tugged down its ends, the colonel's mustache made his meaningless grin even more grotesque. "And you will not seek us out, I think. But *we'll* be looking for you, sir. Enjoy any speculations you may have on exactly who will have the advantage . . ."

While Hutch held a gun on them, Lazlo thoroughly searched the three prisoners. He recovered his own gold pouch and money from Laban Ruddy and turned up a bulging money belt cinched around

Laban's waist. It contained a good deal of both coin and paper money. In the pockets of Robert Topbear and Bije Willet and the dead Ab, he found only a few loose bills and coins. Altogether, it came to somewhat more than what he and Hutch and Aussie had divvied up between them.

Hutch vigorously declared that they'd be justified in appropriating all of it. But Lazlo scrupulously counted out to the cent what Laban's nephews had taken from them. He didn't know how Laban and his cohorts had come by the rest of it and did not care. He stuffed the remaining money in the money belt and handed it back to Laban.

"And now," Laban said with a wintry smile, "you think that evens our score, hunky? Not by my lights it doesn't."

"I did not think it would." Wearily Lazlo motioned at the upstream trail. "All of you clear out. Do not bother coming back for your guns. They will be at the bottom of the river."

He and Hutch watched them tramp away into the woods, Bije bearing his brother's dead weight across his shoulder. Hutch shook his head, grumbling, "Boy, you're making one pluperfect awful mistake. Couple of 'em, I'd say."

"I am not a killer. And a man does not stay honest by robbing even a thief. So far, Hutch, I have stayed honest."

"But Jesus — !"

"Why don't you chuck their guns and frogstickers in the river? Then we'll cook up something to eat, eh?"

To that, anyway, Hutch had no objection. While he disposed of the weapons, Lazlo went into the shack and stripped down and toweled himself dry in the stove's heat; then he put on dry clothes. Afterward he tended his mules and whipped up a sizable batch of beans and bacon and sourdough biscuits, of which he and Hutch hungrily wolfed down about a third. The rest of it Lazlo packed up for the journey ahead. Once on the trail, he intended to make as few halts as possible; he would eat while on the move.

It was too late, now, to cover much distance in what remained of this day, and Lazlo was dog-tired from his latest ordeal. It would be best if he caught at least a few hours' sleep before starting out.

Hutch, slumped at ease in a rawhide-rigged chair — the cabin's only piece of furniture besides a pole bunk built into one wall — belched and picked his teeth reflectively. "Y' know, Laz," he said idly, "I been thinking. Maybe what I ought to do . . . I ought to ride out o' these mountains with you. Give you an escort, sort of. That ole medicine drummer and his boys will be looking to deadfall you som'eres up ahead. I lay you any odds on it."

Lazlo was sitting on his haunches by the stove. For answer, he reached in his coat pocket and scooped out the money he'd recovered, spilling it out on the clay floor. He divided it into two separate and equal piles and pointed at one. "That is yours, Hutch. To the penny. In it is half of Aussie's share. I think this squares us, and now we go our ways, eh?"

Hutch looked injured. "Why, little pard, I allowed you would be grateful for the offer."

"I am. But I do not like to owe a man, and already I owe you too much. Also, if there are dogs to be shot, I will shoot my own. That is how I do things. Thank you."

Hutch grumbled, but he'd learned to know the steely undercore that sometimes touched Lazlo's voice and what it meant. No argument.

Once more Lazlo wondered silently if he'd possibly misjudged Hutch. And still concluded he hadn't. Hutch's appearance just when he'd needed help had been almost too timely. Mightn't Hutch have been prowling around the camp on his own, looking to spy on Lazlo's activities, just before Laban and his people had shown up?

Well, Hutch declared in a morosely aggrieved voice, if that's how his little pard wanted it, he'd say no more. But he still hoped Laz would drop by his camp for a cup of coffee right after he pulled out.

Lazlo politely said he would. And Hutch took his departure.

Edged by his suspicions, Lazlo curled up in the brush near the shack, bundled in blankets and with rifle at hand. The fall of sleet was letting up, and its few light cold pings on his face couldn't prevent him from dropping into a sound sleep . . .

CHAPTER 9

When he awoke, the last traces of daylight were washing out of the sky. Soon it would be fully dark. Feeling sharply refreshed, he made his final preparations to leave and hitched Prunes and Matilda to the wagon.

At the same time his mind ranged bleakly over what might be ahead of him. Three men would be "laying for" him, and the advantage would rest with them. They might get hold of more guns and try sneaking up on his camp again. But more likely they would bide their time. Lazlo would be burdened with a slow-moving wagon and the need for keeping his full attention on the rough crossing of the Elks. At least twice on the way he'd be compelled to slack his guard in order to catch a little sleep. Once they had him spotted, Ruddy and company could either overtake him or ambush him . . . quickly and by surprise.

Then Lazlo paused on a thought: *But they will look for me on the road to Saba City.*

There is another way . . . and being so new here, they will not know of it.

Another way, yes. But it was across a brutally rugged stretch he'd never think of tackling otherwise. Trevo Pass, cutting through the first western ramparts of the Elks, led to a maze of trails that could be crossed on foot by a man who knew them. Lazlo had done it himself twice. But could a heavily loaded wagon get across?

Head bowed, his hands resting on the harness, Lazlo weighed the idea with care. Carson's Crossing lay on the far side of that mountain arm, and it had an assay office. But it was even farther away than Saba City. What if his wagon broke down on a remote trail? Against those natural perils, however, he balanced the dangers posed by Ruddy and company, as well as by assorted road agents, along the well-graded way to Saba City.

Do you really mind a good gamble so much, my practical fellow? Then maybe you are in the wrong business.

With the wry flicker of a grin, Lazlo swung to the wagon seat and took up the reins, hoorawing the mules into motion. For a moment they strained against the wagon's weight. Then the vehicle stirred and rolled forward, and he knew it would be all right. At least on the early part of the trail . . .

A light sleet continued to prickle his face as he pushed through the gathering dark. Ahead was Hutch's camp, and he'd already made up his mind not to stop if he saw no fire. Hutch *did* know this country, and if he got an inkling of what Lazlo was up to, it would be dangerous knowledge.

Slowly, almost noiselessly, Lazlo eased his team along the road where it curved past the dark grove that hid Hutch's camp. Any glimmers of firelight would show among the trees. But he saw nothing. Hutch had to be asleep, and his fire, if he'd laid one, had died to ashes. Yet Lazlo winced every time his wheels banged against bumps in the frozen trail.

Trevo Pass was very close now, and there was enough light to show where it breached the looming bluffs. He swung slowly into it and gave the mules their head along a narrow trail that ran through rank brush on the canyon floor. The wheels jolted across the rocky roughness, and the wagon sent out a few creaks of complaint but not many. He drove steadily and carefully along the bottom of the pass for about an hour. The sharp thrust of bluffs that marked the first rise of mountains to the west dwindled into a long wedge of flatlands. The trail took a winding course across these flats, beyond which the tough part of his journey would begin.

Then the snow began to fall.

It came down lightly at first, a swirling handful of flakes that mingled with the pelting sleet. Quite suddenly the rattle of sleet on the wagon box ceased, and there was only the spatter of wet snow, thickening fast.

Lazlo hadn't counted on anything like this. He damned his luck with a heartfelt anger. There was always a possibility of early snow in the high country this late in the year, but it had seemed a minimal risk. There'd seemed little danger that in the few days it would take to cross the peaks, the fates would conspire to dump a fall of snow on his trail. Now it was happening.

Lazlo pulled up the team, considering. He could turn back. And what then? Be stalled in the Bozetown diggings for a winter? With Ruddy and his comrades maybe hanging about too, waiting their chance? And what of Hutch Prouter?

His anger prodded up stubbornness. He would go ahead. The risk of getting bogged down in mountain snows seemed less chancy than what lay behind. These early-season snows were only harbingers; almost always they melted off in a day or so.

He urged the team into the whirling whiteness, unable to make out anything beyond a few yards away, not even the mules' heads.

Then, out of the white-black silence, Lazlo heard a muffled tramp of feet. Someone was coming along the trail behind him. He hauled up the team and picked up his Winchester, now kept always ready to hand. He strained his eyes against the pale-shot darkness.

Gradually a man's form came hulking into sight. By his size, Lazlo knew at once who it was. But the knowledge only sharpened his wariness.

"Hutch?"

"Surest thing you know, little pard," came the cheery reply. "Yes sirree . . ."

Hutch halted by the wagon, a bulging warbag slung across one shoulder, and rested a great paw on the sideboard as he squinted up at Lazlo. "Didn't see no sense to hanging on at Bozetown this winter. Have had mighty poor diggings in them parts. That being so, I figured I would pack up and 'winter-warm' over in Saba City or Carson's Crossing, either one."

"I see." Lazlo managed to keep his voice even. "So then, can I ask what makes you decide to do so right now?"

"Oh, I got thinking on't a goodly spell back," Hutch said amiably. "But I didn't really get to considering it till I knowed you was fixing to pull out. I taken a powerful shine to you, little pard. I figured if you did not mind, it'd suit me to share your fortunes for a time."

"Is that right."

"Surest thing, you know. I mean, hell, what you objected to afore is me siding with you in any more rows with that colonel and his crowd. Shit, Laz, I understand how that be. Man is got his pride. But ain't no reason I couldn't give you a mite o' company so far as Carson's Crossing, was there now?"

"That is something else." Lazlo peered through the beating snow at the outline of Hutch's shaggy head. "How did you know I went this way?"

"Didn't take no broad-gauge guessing, boy. I was rolled up for the night when I heard your wagon go by my camp. I'm a light sleeper and got ears like razors; they are that sharp. Then I heard your wagon turn into Trevo Pass. Sound carries from atwixt them stone walls to beat all hell. So

I thought, shit, that makes sense. It come to ole Laz it is the safest way he can clear out. Me, I was fixing to pack out anyway (would of told you as much if you'd dropped by), and so might's well side you out right away. War'n't no great doing. Cached what good-sized odds 'n' ends I own, tools 'n' such, out o' sight for when I return, come spring. Chucked them few light possibles I possess in my warbag, and I was all geared up. Then took me a little deal o' walking to catch up — that's all."

"Convenient," Lazlo murmured. "Very. But it is a tough trip over these peaks."

"Well, that's another thing. Figured you would be pleased to have an assist along the way. Laz, there is places ahead that you will be obliged to practic'ly lift them goddamn mules and wagon acrost. You be glad of an exter pair of strong arms 'bout then. 'Sides, I know the trails 'long this way good as you do. Anything at all should happen to you — an accident like — be me to pull you through. Sort of life insurance, huh?"

Lazlo couldn't make out but could easily picture the broadly cheerful grin that must be shaping Hutch's lips. Yet what he'd said was true. For the moment Lazlo could think of no ready argument to counter the glib offer. Still, whether Hutch was sure of anything or not, he must be downwind of the truth.

Damn him! But what do I do? If I refuse now, he will be sure. But what is to prevent him from following me and waiting . . . till I am dead for sleep? Wouldn't it be better to keep Hutch squarely under his eye? The frying pan could not be any hotter than the fire.

"Done, Hutch!" Lazlo reached down and gave the bigger man a friendly slap on the shoulder. "You will be a welcome companion. You surprised me is all, coming upon me so sudden."

"Yeah." Hutch might have been a little disconcerted. If so, he covered it by adding, " 'Course I was a mite peeved, you not stopping by my outfit like you promised."

"Your fire was out," Lazlo said with a forced joviality. "When Hutch Prouter is full of booze, he is dead to the world as a man can be, eh? I would not disturb your sleep."

"Oh, yeah. Well, I didn't drink nothing stronger'n river water last night."

"Why, now I see it is so." Lazlo shifted sideways on the seat. "Come up beside me and ride. Throw your pack in the wagon."

Hutch laid his warbag in the wagon bed with lighthanded care, explained by a distinct clink of bottles. *Maybe,* Lazlo thought grimly, *he looks to booze to give him belly for a nasty piece of work . . . but how can I be sure?*

He couldn't be. Otherwise he'd do what he must to protect his gold and his life. But Lazlo's conscience chained him to certainties where right and wrong were concerned. He *had* to be sure. So he would have to wait. And stay alert. Somehow he must manage to do both, during this long crossing of the mountains. Even if it lasted only a few days, it would still be the longest trip of his life.

And maybe the last.

Soon the falling snow slacked off to a few drifting flakes. At least the way ahead would not be blocked by deep snow. Unless another storm came along soon, and that wasn't likely.

Hours passed. The double strain of guiding the team along a mushy nightbound trail and worrying about the man beside him told badly on Lazlo's nerves. Before long he would need rest and sleep. How could he get them?

The wagon creaked more than ever as it

jolted along the rough road; Hutch's vast weight caused the whole vehicle to lean increasingly askew on that side. Lazlo was about to say so when Hutch himself spoke up affably: "Seems I am adding a passel exter to the load. Mought be best I light down and mosey 'long on foot."

Lazlo stopped long enough for Hutch to clamber down and then shook the mules into motion again. By now his visibility was better. He could make out details of the wide flats they were crossing: trees, boulders, even the black humps of distant bluffs against a lesser darkness of sky. The only sound was a crunch of hoofs and wheels on crisp new snow.

Hutch's heavy tread should also have been loud in the snow, but Lazlo suddenly noticed that it wasn't. A quick glance showed him that Hutch was no longer tramping beside the wagon. He'd fallen back behind it, striding along with head bent, as though scanning the ground.

Lazlo no longer needed to guess. He knew.

A moment later Hutch was back trudging alongside the wagon. What he'd been studying, of course, were the deep-sunk ruts of the wagon's wheels in fresh snow. The wagon was a light one; if it were heavily weighted in any way, the wheelprints would show as much. Not that a cursory examination of the ruts would leave Hutch really sure of anything. What mattered was that he'd given himself away. Lazlo could be sure now that Hutch posed a certain and murderous danger to him.

Soon he must somehow make a move before Hutch made one. But God — what move? Would he be forced to kill the man in cold blood?

Maybe not. Lazlo felt a sudden leap of hope.

Staring ahead of the team into a slowly lightening darkness as false dawn drew on, he saw the faint prints of wagon wheels in the snow. Another party had put a wagon, in fact several wagons, into the westward pass ahead of him. They'd come this way just hours before, the night's snowfall having only partly obliterated their wheeltracks at this point. They weren't very far ahead.

Hutch also saw the ruts and dourly commented on them, grumbling, "Blamed funny thing, any folks choosing a way acrost these peaks this time o' year."

"Yes," Lazlo agreed soberly. "It is strange, all right."

Pretty soon the tracks were more clearly

defined, showing how far the wagons had gotten when the snow had ceased falling. He would, Lazlo knew exultantly, overtake them before long.

Meantime he kept a close watch on Hutch.

CHAPTER 10

Within another hour, as the dawn light grew, the white landscape ahead was broken by a motte of pines. The trail led into it. Through the trunks now, Lazlo made out ruddy gleams of firelight. The sound of childish voices and laughter drifted toward him.

So many kids, he thought, must mean a large party. But he was baffled. What kind of people (discounting his own case) would be fool enough to try crossing the high passes at this time of year — with wagons and children?

Before Lazlo and Hutch reached the camp, a young man came tramping out of the woods to their right. He was bearing an armload of dead branches.

"Hello," he said pleasantly.

Lazlo pulled to a full stop, gave him a civil nod, and then glanced at the young girl, who was also carrying a load of branches, and had now moved up beside the man. She was small and dark, quite pretty, and he guessed not over fourteen.

She had a fresh, scrubbed look that was nice to see, and her shy, quiet manner did it justice.

"I'm Mark Bly, and this is Cissie O'Halloran," said the young man. "We were out gathering wood when we heard your wagon coming."

"That is your camp ahead?"

"It is. If you gentlemen would care to breakfast with us, you'd be welcome."

Mark was tall and gangling, probably not much past twenty. He had a courteous and well-spoken way about him. His thatch of crisp carroty hair topped an open, trusting face that Lazlo immediately liked.

Glancing at Hutch, Lazlo said, "That sounds fine, eh?"

But Hutch paid no attention. He was gazing at Cissie O'Halloran with a kind of lewd, slack-jawed grin. The girl saw it too. She moved a little closer to Mark and lowered her eyes. Lazlo had never seen this side of Hutch, and it wasn't reassuring to note.

Lazlo felt a mounting curiosity as he put the wagon into the grove, following Mark and Cissie into a wide natural clearing. Three covered wagons were drawn up in the trampled snow to one side; their team mules were hobbled nearby. There were kids all over the place, chattering and yelling and clowning around . . . both boys and girls. But no sign of adults that he could see. *What sort of outfit is this?* he thought in bewilderment.

The kids were working mostly in twos, coming out of the trees with armloads of brush and branches and dumping them by several fires in the center of the clearing. Others were heading back into the woods to scour up more firewood. All of them halted and stared, their voices dying away, as Lazlo checked his team and swung to the ground. They seemed to range in age roughly from four or five to their midteens; there must have been twenty or more of them.

Mark and Cissie were moving over to one of the fires where, Lazlo now perceived, there was another grown-up besides Mark. She was sitting on her heels, cradling a small girl on her lap, spooning gruel into the child's mouth as she made little clucking sounds of encouragement.

Mark added his armload of wood to a pile and turned to Lazlo and Hutch. "My sister, gentlemen, Miss Aretha Bly."

Although she had doubtless noted their arrival, the woman only now looked directly at them. She set the little girl on her feet gently and stood up.

She was a small, trim-bodied woman whose hair flamed red where it puffed from under her gray bonnet and, like many redheads, she was pale-skinned and freckled. Her face was plain and snub-nosed; her mouth was compressed but not severe. She looked almost frail in a flowing gray dress and a man's heavy Mackinaw coat. Although she hardly came to her brother's shoulder, she must be a dozen years his elder, and plainly she was in command here.

Lazlo pulled off his hat. "My name is Lazlo Kusik, ma'am. This is my friend, Hutch Prouter. We are crossing the mountains and came on your tracks a ways back. Mr. Bly thinks maybe we can get breakfast here."

"Indeed you may, sir. You're welcome to share what we have, although I'm afraid it's little enough."

She gave him a quick, strong handshake but didn't offer to do the same with Hutch, who hadn't bothered to remove his battered horsethief hat. Lazlo, who'd met all kinds in his roamings, placed her accent right away: like Mark's, it was that of a cultivated New Englander. Next to the forceful thrust of Aretha Bly's personality, her brother seemed gentle, almost anonymous. Her eyes were a calm bright blue like his, but hers held a kind of solemn rectitude that was almost pushy.

She handed the bowl of gruel to Cissie O'Halloran. "Cissie, take Abigail to the wagon and bundle her up warmly. Then try to coax her into eating a bit more."

"Yes'm, Miss Aretha." Cissie took the little girl by the hand and led her off.

Lazlo didn't think the small one looked well. Her face was pinched and pale, and she had a weak, unsteady walk, although she was well past babyhood. In addition, most of these children were poorly clad. Their clothing was threadbare, inadequate for the season, and much of it looked like oversize castoffs.

Charity kids, he thought abruptly. *That is it.*

"Please help yourselves, gentlemen. All of us have eaten." Miss Aretha motioned to the pots simmering by the fire, then turned to the watching children and clapped her hands together sharply. "Come now! You all have duties to perform. You know what they are."

As the kids dispersed, Lazlo and Hutch hunkered down, accepted the plates, tin cups, and forks handed to them by Mark, and served themselves gruel, sidemeat, and coffee from the pots. Hutch loaded his plate, but Lazlo, not wanting to impose on such a charity outfit as this obviously was, skimped on his helpings.

The two Blys crouched down on the other side of the fire, courteously saying nothing as their guests took the first edges off their appetites. Then Miss Aretha said, "I take it you gentlemen are making for Carson's Crossing?"

Hutch, wolfing down his food, didn't look at her or reply. Apparently he'd taken as instant a dislike to Miss Aretha as she obviously had to him. It was to Lazlo that she spoke.

"We are, ma'am. And you too?"

"Yes. Are you familiar with that place, Mr. Kusik?"

"Yes."

"A good place to live, would you say?"

Miss Aretha's face wore a peculiar look. Somehow it made Lazlo uneasy. "I would say that," he answered warily. "Do you mean to settle there?"

Carson's Crossing, where he had been more than once, lay in a fertile river valley to the west. It was in the center of a prosperous stock-raising region, and there was some mining and lumbering activity too. Not a bad place to be, if you could get across to it all right.

"In a manner of speaking." Miss Aretha spoke very crisply; her gaze was almost fierce. "I wonder, sir, if you have ever heard of the Children's Aid Society?"

"Uh, no, I have not."

"Well, it was founded some years ago by a Connecticut minister, the Reverend Charles Loring Brace. I suppose that you are not familiar either with the condition of homeless and abandoned children in the city of New York . . ."

Lazlo nodded a little wearily. "Yes'm, I know it very well."

"Oh?"

"I grew up there. At the Five Points on the Lower East Side."

"Ah! Then I hardly need tell you of the horrible circumstances in which these waifs exist. There are nearly ten thousand of them in the city of New York, Mr. Kusik. *Ten thousand!* Children living in squalor, filth, disease, misery . . . when they are permitted to live at all."

The light of a true zealot blazed in Miss Aretha's eyes now. Lazlo cleared his throat awkwardly. "Uh, yes. I believe —"

"That is not the worst. Unwanted babies by the hundreds are abandoned every year. Sometimes on the doorsteps of the well-to-do . . . but more often their pathetic little forms will be found dead and stiff in ashcans and back alleys — or floating in the East River. Many more — the *fortunate* homeless who survive — will eke out an existence in the alleys, eating bits of garbage from the streets, clothing their nakedness with rags . . . and of course filching and stealing!"

Miss Aretha's small fists clenched in her lap. "Boys, Mr. Kusik, become hardened criminals by the age of twelve or thirteen. Girls become women of — of the . . . female vagrants." She flushed, lowering her eyes. "I crave your pardon. I fear I am always carried away by the subject. It is all-absorbing to me. But you will be aware of the conditions I describe."

"I can say that I am —"

"Well, sir! — when the Reverend Brace founded the Children's Aid Society, it was with the intention of placing the orphaned and abandoned children of the slums with good families throughout New York and New England. Of course orphan asylums have been common in our eastern states since the 1830s, but the institutionalized care and raising of a child — Mr. Brace was certain — could never substitute for the virtues of a family upbringing. Genuine love and affection, along with the particular care and sound education that only a real home could provide, would not only alleviate a host of social problems, but it would also produce useful citizens.

"Indeed, his plan succeeded beyond all expectation! Not only has a sizable portion of the city's destitute youth been uplifted, their lives redeemed for gainful employment in farm and manufactory, but many have gone on to responsible positions in law, business, the professions. From potential menaces have been wrested worthwhile assets to society. Agents of our society are constantly in the field to call on applicants for foster parenthood and to verify their worth. They also follow closely the careers of those children whom their efforts have placed in foster homes. The evidence they have gathered to confirm the value of the society and its work is irrefutable!

"Well . . . after the initial success of his undertaking, Reverend Brace found that the demand for foster children was so widespread and the number of homeless children in the city of New York so great that he deemed it advisable to extend the society's activities westward — first, to such states of the Middle West as Michigan and Indiana. Again results were so encouraging that orphan trains were soon rolling toward Nebraska and other western states!"

Lazlo gave a polite, wary nod.

The woman's fervor was so genuine and passionate that he felt more than a little embarrassed. Also, sincere or not, all that she'd said sounded pretty much like a set speech. Not too surprising, at that. A lot of suffragettes, militant feminists, and the like were marching along the lecture circuit these days, even in remote parts of the West.

"My brother and I," Miss Aretha went on, "are in charge of this party of twenty orphans, under the auspices of the Children's Aid Society. Unfortunately our departure from New York was plagued by one delay after another. We were due in Carson's Crossing a full month ago. All was arranged many weeks in advance, you see. Every child in our party has the prospect of a good home, in town or on a ranch or farm."

Mark Bly cleared his throat — as if he too were a bit embarrassed by his sister's intensity. "We've come a long way, Mr. Kusik. By steamer on the Great Lakes and from Chicago by train. At Saba City, where rail connections terminate, we purchased several wagons and teams of mules, and from there came across the mountains as far as Bozetown."

Hutch gave a sardonic grunt. "You picked y'self a prime time for crossing these peaks." He picked up the scalding-hot coffeepot in a callused hand that was impervious to heat and freshened his cup again. "Ain't no daisies growing up here this time o' year, son. What you ought'a done, you ought'a took the stage route to the south and west, around the mountains. It is a farther piece to go, but a heap safer. Ain't that right, Laz?"

Lazlo said, "Mmm," sort of noncommittally. His mind was ranging ahead, ferreting out what this situation might hold for him.

Miss Aretha looked directly at Hutch for the first time.

"We deemed it urgent," she said in a chilly voice, "due to unavoidable delays and the lateness of the season, to reach Carson's Crossing as soon as possible. We were told in Bozetown that in this mountain country winters are early arriving and that severe weather may be expected any day now."

"Yes'm." Hutch's mock-politeness was so elaborate that it bordered on insult.

"That is more or less my point, ma'am. Ain't exactly the season for kiting across this here country, if you fetch my meaning, ma'am."

Miss Aretha clasped her finely shaped hands together in her lap, turning her gaze down at them, perhaps to offset modestly the tempered-steel flash of her eyes. "Mr. Kusik, perhaps *you* might give us credit for being greenhorns only up to a point. With winter coming on, naturally our first thought was to get our charges to their destination as quickly as possible. With that in mind, and in my admitted ignorance of the country, we chose the most direct route from Saba City to Carson's Crossing. None offered advice to the contrary . . . until we sought the advice of the officer of Bozetown camp, Mr. Friendly. By then, however, we had come that far. In any case, as I understand it, the southern route also holds its dangers. There has been Indian trouble along that way, and the stages are sometimes menaced by desperadoes. Also, may not winter conditions sometimes shut off those roads as well?"

Lazlo frowned at his empty plate. Unsure just what advice he wanted to give, he felt decidedly uncomfortable. "Well, once in a while. But mostly the stages get through all right. Maybe, with these wagons of yours, you can go on west through Trevo Pass. But when that ends, the trails over the Elks are very bad. They were made by animals and Indians. It will not be easy to get a wagon over them."

Too late, even as he spoke, Lazlo realized he'd erred.

Miss Aretha pounced on the point at once: "If the western way across the peaks is so inadvisable, sir, why are you traversing it *with* a wagon?"

"I have my reasons," he said stiffly. "In any case, it does not matter much for me. If my wagon cannot get across, I will leave it and go on foot. I am in no danger of my life."

"Nor, in that event, are we. At least a half-dozen of our youngsters are older boys — large and husky enough to wrestle a wagon over the rough places on those terrible trails of yours. Should we be forced to abandon them, however, we would simply complete our journey on foot . . . although it would work a hardship on the younger children."

Her words tripped a trigger in Lazlo's mind.

His own heavy wagon might need just that kind of assistance. Those husky boys could be useful to him. Above all, in the company of the Blys and their wards, he would have around-the-clock protection against anything Hutch might be minded to try.

Then his conscience balked, sharp as a blade. It would be wrong to use these people that way. He shook his head almost angrily. "These mountains are nothing to take a bunch of kids across this time of year. You are crazy to try it. You'd do best to turn back to Saba City."

"Mr. Kusik! —"

"Sis," Mark interposed gently, "they can't know how serious our straits really are. Our funds have just about run out, Mr. Kusik. We can't afford to retrace our steps and then make a long and circuitous detour to reach Carson's Crossing. Our provisions are nearly gone —"

"And," Miss Aretha cut in crisply, "it will take only a few days — four at the most, Mr. Friendly estimated — to get across the peaks to the west, even allowing for ordinary difficulties. But to return to Saba City and then make a wide swing along the southern route would take the Lord knows how many days! Surely the gamble is worth it. We have enough provisions for several days — and the sooner we get to Carson's Crossing, obviously the less danger we face of being caught in an early blizzard."

"But some snow has fallen already. Why not turn back and lay over in Bozetown till spring?"

"We can't!" she said vehemently. "How would we feed and shelter twenty youngsters through a long winter? How could we risk holding the young lives entrusted to our care in that wild and lawless place all those months? Their souls already have been bruised by low passions to which I will not permit their being subjected any further. No, sir! We shall push on, and without delay!"

Lazlo gave a short, grim nod. She was determined to be insensible to any risk. These damned zealots usually were. But if she were bound to be a fool, why should he scruple at turning her stupidity to his advantage?

"Well," he began sourly, "since you're set on —"

He jerked and swore.

Something had stung him in the back of the neck, a smart pelletlike blow. He swung his head, rubbing his neck. A small boy in a man's ragged cutdown ulster stood a few yards away. He was bright-eyed and towheaded and held a peashooter in his grubby fist. He grinned impudently at Lazlo's glare.

"Cyrus —" Miss Aretha was sharply reproving. "You've been warned time and again! Mark, take that thing away from him."

The boy fled across the camp and into the trees. He trailed a taunting laugh. Mark loped after him.

"I'm sorry, Mr. Kusik. You were saying — ?"

"Since you will go on no matter what," Lazlo said doggedly, "it would be good for us to throw in together. You could easily go astray on a wrong trail. Game trails and Indian trails — they twist all over and cross each other in the high passes. I know the best and shortest way . . ."

"Me too," chimed in Hutch. "Reckon you could use both our services, Miss Bly, ma'am."

Hutch's manner had changed abruptly. He was grinning almost handsomely as he waggled his shaggy head up and down.

Miss Aretha's manner softened perceptibly. She looked from one to the other. "That is a generous offer. I am grateful to both of you . . ."

CHAPTER 11

The wagons moved out within the hour. By now a weak diffusion of daylight filled the broad stretch of the pass, although the sun never showed on the slate-banded horizon. But the sheen of new snow picked up what light there was and clearly etched the whole landscape.

Lazlo took the lead, breaking track for the Blys' three wagons.

The land ahead of them still rolled flat and even, so that in places the snow had drifted enough to obscure the faint trail. Hutch tramped beside or behind Lazlo's wagon, sometimes well behind it. Lazlo knew he was inspecting the wheel tracks again, comparing them to those of the other wagons.

I will still have to keep an eye on him. But now it will be easier.

After a while, wanting to stretch his legs, Lazlo asked Hutch to take over the driving chore. Dropping back a little along the line of wagons, he grimly noted that the Blys' larger and, on the face of it, more heavily loaded wagons left far lighter wheel indentations than his own.

If Hutch hadn't been reasonably sure before, he was now.

The kids, anyway, were having a great time with the moist, crunchy snow. A few of the youngest, and a couple of really sickly ones, rode in the wagons, but most of the boys and girls were cavorting around the slow-moving vehicles, packing and flinging snowballs, their childish cries ringing in the frosty stillness. Miss Aretha made a half-hearted effort to shush them, but presently, smiling and shaking her head, she gave it up. Who could suppress a bunch of kids full of coltish energies and still wearing an early-morning edge?

Miss Aretha was handling the team behind Lazlo's with a brisk, no-nonsense competence; Mark was on the driver's seat of the next in line; a husky fifteen-year-old named Tim brought up the rear.

Lazlo was tramping alongside Mark's wagon, idly chatting with him, when a snowball whizzed past his head, missing it by a couple of inches. He turned in time to catch a glimpse of Cyrus disappearing around the tailgate with a thumb-to-nose *"Nyaaah!"*

Grinning, Mark said, "He likes you. I can tell. Better be on your guard. I didn't get that peashooter away from him. Couldn't catch him."

"That does not surprise me," Lazlo said dourly.

"I imagine not. I've a feeling, Mr. Kusik, that you have no great opinion of us — or our mission. We must impress you as a pair of errant and hare-brained do-gooders. And all-around incompetents — eh?"

"I would not say that."

Lazlo was merely being polite.

In fact, probing back into his memory, he realized that he *had* heard of the Children's Aid Society before. It had already been operating on New York's Lower East Side when he was a kid. But although he and his mother had known the worst kind of poverty, she had lived till he was in his late teens. By then a brawny youth well able to take care of himself, he'd had no use for social services. That was when he'd departed for the Middle West, to spend the years of his young manhood following the harvest crews. He knew as well as anyone how the poor of New York festered out their lives in the dreary stews of their ghettoes. But he'd paid his own debts all his life, never asking any assistance outside of his own resources.

Maybe he wasn't being fair. But experience hadn't equipped him to think in any other terms. Possibly the kids *would* be better off out here in God's clean country . . . but life in the West was rough and raw, any way you tried to live it. And people were disappointingly the same any place you found them. That was the cynic's definition, Lazlo supposed, but to him it seemed right on the head. It would be a waste of time telling young Mark that, though. Or that rock-ribbed sister of his.

He expressed his thoughts aloud more obliquely: "What I wonder is why a pair like you got into this kind of work. You are gently bred, you and your sister."

"You might say that," Mark said affably. " 'Retha and I were born into fairly comfortable circumstances, as children of a Boston mercantile merchant. But our mother died bearing me, and our father followed her when I was five and 'Retha was seventeen. We were farmed out to relatives much less well off, and on 'Retha fell much of the burden of seeing to my upbringing and education. It marked both of us, I suppose. Too, we're Quakers. It seemed natural for us to take up charitable work, at first for the Society of Friends, later for Reverend Brace's Society."

"She is a strong-willed woman, your sister."

"Mmm. Well, *I* tried to talk her out of this mountain crossing, Mr. Kusik. But she was adamant."

"You would be in a pretty pickle if I had not come along," Lazlo said bluntly. "Didn't your sister think of hiring a guide?"

"Oh, certainly. In fact we approached — with Marshal Friendly's guidance — a number of men in Bozetown. All thought we were crazy. None would consent to undertake the job for as little as we could afford to offer — except for a couple of men 'Retha didn't like the look of."

Lazlo's grunt held a tinge of contempt. "So. And if you didn't get caught in a blizzard, still you might get good and lost and then starve or freeze up there. Did anyone think of that?"

Mark flushed a little. "Well, we have a good compass. 'Retha thought that with its aid we couldn't go far astray. After all, Carson's Crossing is almost exactly due west . . . isn't it?"

Sweet God Almighty, Lazlo groaned inwardly.

He inspected the sky above the saw-toothed range ahead with grim care. Any

179

frail sign of how the weather might turn over the next few days would be a help. So far he could tell nothing. The temperature was crisp but not too cold. If it went way up, fine. If it hung steady, though, more snow might fall.

For a lone husky man making his way across the peaks, it would not matter. But these kids — some of them looked so puny and sickish. Too much snow or too much cold: either could spell disaster. Then . . . another Donner party? A party of *children?* Lazlo shut his mind against the thought. Hell, a man had forebodings all the time. Almost always they came to nothing.

What really bothered him was that he was actually starting to feel concerned about this passel of damn fool innocents.

The wagons rolled steadily west through a long day. By first dark they'd crossed the last of the flatlands and the end of Trevo Pass. Beyond lay the imposing arm of mountains, and in its foothills by a rushing stream they made camp. Tomorrow the real ordeal would begin.

The mules were unhitched, watered, and fed. The children gathered dead brush, and roaring fires were built up. Everyone huddled around them and thawed out while Miss Aretha, bustling about and seeming to be everywhere at once, got preparations for the evening meal underway. Her mouth was set in a tight angry line all the while, and Lazlo knew why.

Hutch Prouter's upswing of mood hadn't lasted long. For most of the day he'd been dipping into his store of gin and whiskey. Now he shifted around the camp like a blubbery baboon, cursing and muttering to himself, openly leering at Cissie and other young girls.

Maybe I will have to put him down after all, Lazlo thought narrowly. *Best, though, to say or do nothing right now; it might only worsen matters.*

Supper was dished up, and everyone was served a portion. Miss Aretha motioned them all to gather around a central fire, and there, in a primitive flicker of light that seemed a kind of brave beacon against the darkness all around, she bowed her head and led a prayer of thanksgiving. The children bowed their heads too, the boys pulling off their ragged caps.

Miss Aretha looked up and shot a meaningful glance at Lazlo. In belated realization, he yanked off his hat and gave Hutch, glaze-eyed and swaying at his side, a hard nudge.

Hutch, however, not only refused to doff his hat, he barely touched his meager serving of supper. It wasn't like him, but Lazlo, thinking that Hutch had drunk too much to be very hungry, gave it only a passing thought. He paid little attention when Hutch wobbled off into the darkness as Miss Aretha led the children in singing "Shall We Gather at the River?" Likely he was going off to be sick, or to relieve himself, or to swill down more booze; whichever, he would doubtless pass out before long.

Then, unbidden, a thought struck Lazlo. He left the group by the fire, swiftly following Hutch toward the south edge of the camp, where his wagon was.

As he'd expected, he found Hutch there. But he was not engaged in digging out another bottle. Instead Hutch was bent down, muttering to himself in a fierce, slurred undertone as he peered at the wagon's tailgate and underside.

So, Lazlo thought coldly, *now he is starting to think. With all the booze in him, he is starting to think.*

"You are all right, Hutch? Eh?"

Hutch straightened up with a jerk. In the dim reach of firelight, his bearded face seemed as malignant as a troll's. He strained out a laugh through his big teeth.

"Oh. Sure, little pard. Fine as frog's hair. Felt a mite sickish back there, was all."

"I thought that might be it," Lazlo said mildly. "I do not think this Aretha Bly takes very kindly to you, Hutch."

"That is God's own truth." Hutch belched, swaying tubbily. "Goddamn high-hat bitch," he rumbled. "Where'n hell does she get off, looking at me like I was a god-damn pig?"

If you look like a pig and act like a pig, you will be taken for one, Lazlo felt like saying but didn't. "Come, Hutch. They are gentlefolk, these Blys, and we are too rough for them. You're tired, eh? Get some sleep, why don't you?"

"Yeah," Hutch said groggily. "Mebbe that is what I need some of. Sleep."

Lazlo got Hutch's blankets out of the wagon and spread them out close by, then supported the big man's sagging weight as he maneuvered him over to the blankets. Hutch toppled into them with a sodden grunt.

"You're a honest-to-Christ nice fella, Laz," he groaned, pulling the blankets around him. "Gonna side with you all the way, li'l pard. You believe it. Yessir. Alla way . . ."

That was Lazlo's biggest worry. But he thrust it and all other worries to the back of his mind. He needed sleep too. He carried his own soogans off a little ways, spread them out, and rolled into them. He'd just composed himself for sleep when a smarting blow on his face brought him half-upright, his heart pounding.

The faint sound of boyish laughter came from the fringe of the forest. Lazlo knew the voice. Fleetingly he saw the small dark form of Cyrus vanish into the woods. He felt something reposing in the front socket of his collarbone. He rolled it between his fingers, knowing sight unseen what it was. A dry, hard, wrinkled pea.

Lazlo swore once and loudly in the badly remembered tongue of his parents. Even as he was running over sadistic possibilities of how he might satisfactorily get back at the little bastard, his thoughts broke apart and threaded away. He slipped into the sleep of complete exhaustion.

It didn't last long — an hour or maybe less.

At first the sounds dripped like slow strands of molasses into the deep well of his slumber. Then they pulled him upward and outward toward a muddy awareness.

Sounds of . . . *breaking glass?*

The giant roar of a man's voice shook him completely awake. Lazlo sat bolt upright in his blankets, blinking his eyes, listening. Then he scrambled to his feet, hand closing over his rifle, and stumbled toward the sounds.

He hadn't far to go. Light from the fire picked out the scene in hard relief. He pulled to a stop, hands tight around his rifle but not bringing it to bear.

Miss Aretha stood by the side of his wagon, clutching a hand ax. At her feet lay a crumpled bundle that he recognized as Hutch's sack of possibles. It glistened with a dark spreading wetness. Mark was beside her, his face pale in the orange glow.

They were confronting Hutch like a pair of bantams. He stood a few yards from them, his mighty shoulders drawn up and his great hands fisting and unfisting at his sides. Lazlo could see his bearded face only in quarter-profile, but in the dancing light it looked mean as hell. He appeared ready to kill.

The children were gathering around too, but at a safe distance. They looked frightened, confused, dismayed. Miss Aretha's small face wore a quiet look of iron. Mark appeared less sure of himself, but just as determined as his sister.

Lazlo stepped into the space between Hutch and the Blys. "What is going on?"

"That tony goddamn bitch!" Hutch bellowed. "Ask her! Ask her what she went and done."

Lazlo glanced at Miss Aretha. She stood very stiff and straight, her chin up. "Mr. Prouter," she said icily, "has given us no opportunity to explain. I fear, even so, that he will not accept the explanation. Our children, Mr. Kusik, have gotten into the liquor your friend so providentially packed along."

Lazlo said tonelessly, "The kids?"

"Exactly. The kids. I noticed, some minutes ago, that several of the boys were behaving strangely. And then I realized why. They were drunk!"

Her eyes blazed with a kind of blue fire. In that moment, just passingly, Lazlo wondered why he'd ever thought of this small woman as plain. She might not even be pretty. But plain? Never.

"And you thought —"

"Not right away. But I wasn't long arriving at the answer. What else could it be? There is no liquor among our supplies, not even for medicinal purposes. We've taken especial pains to ensure as much. So the liquor they found and consumed could only

186

have been among your supplies, sir, or" —
the full venom of her look pounced on
Hutch — *"his."*

"Didn't give her no call to get out that
goddamn hatchet o' hers and bust up my
cache o' redeye," Hutch rumbled. He lifted
his big hands, palms up, fingers curling
into thick hooks. "Now you get clear out o'
the way, little pard. I got me some damage
to do . . ."

"That is enough." Lazlo wanted only to
keep the peace, but he swung up his rifle to
lay emphasis on the order. He looked at
Aretha Bly. "What kind of kids are these,
to go into things belonging to a man? And
then drink themselves drunk on his
booze?"

"*You* ask me that, Mr. Kusik?" Her blue-
fire eyes impaled him. "You who claim you
grew up at the Five Points?"

"Well, I did. But —"

"Then my God, sir! Why question the
fact? Surely you're aware that many of
these slum children, through no fault of
their own, are addicted to monstrous vices.
Not the least of which is *drinking gin!*"

Lazlo dipped his head up and down,
wearily. "Something of the sort was known
to me."

"Well, sir! If you can still fault my reason

for appropriating and smashing this . . . this fellow's supply of it, you're considerably less than the man I'd taken you to be."

Miss Aretha stood with arms folded, her stare fierce and imperious.

What she didn't understand was that Hutch too was an addict and that cutting him off from his beloved hooch, suddenly and cold turkey, had turned him into an ugly and dangerous brute. One who had to be placated — somehow. Or stopped dead in his tracks.

"What is done is done, Hutch," he said mildly. "In three days, maybe, we will be across the peaks. Then I'll buy you out a whole saloon. How is that?"

"Three days . . ." Flamelight raked Hutch's eyes with a red heat. "I could walk back to Bozetown a heap quicker."

"That is up to you. Do what you must."

"I'll tell you what you best do, boy. Move away."

Hutch took a lumbering step forward. Lazlo leveled the rifle on his chest. Hutch came to a stop, but his face was working maniacally.

"You want to stop me, Laz boy, you better use that straightway and make your first shot count. Won't be no time for a second, as before that I will have you busted in two."

"You will make me kill you?"

"Come to that, I will." Hutch's voice was guttural and implacable. "You don't mix in this now. Step off."

Lazlo's gaze swept the ground and lighted on a fallen branch. He walked over to it, still holding his rifle pointed one-handed, and bent to close a hand on it. He set a foot on the branch, broke off the thick butt end, and then, experimentally, swung it back and forth. It would do.

He walked over to Mark Bly and handed him the rifle. "You know how to use this?"

"Yes. But —"

"If I lose, shoot him."

The calm order clearly shocked Mark; even his rock-ribbed sister paled a little. What in hell did they think they'd bought into, breaking up a drunk's liquor cache? A tea party, maybe?

Lazlo did not want to shoot Hutch. He still had the raw taste of one man's recent death at his hands.

With time to take a good aim, he could shoot to cripple, not kill. But it was too easy for a man to die even of a crippling wound, given what medical care he could expect in this country — usually none. Lazlo had seen it happen too often.

Men did not die of beatings so often. If

he could fetch Hutch a sound beating, it might head off worse. He didn't press the thought of how much chance he'd stand against Hutch's bearlike bigness and sheer strength.

Go ahead and do it; that is all. If you can.

Hutch grunted and belched and showed his big teeth. It might have been a grin. He waited, hands loose at his sides now.

Would the liquor he'd taken slow him? Lazlo hoped so. He knew how fast Hutch could move in spite of his sway-bellied bulk. If he ever got those huge hands on a man of ordinary size, God help that man.

Don't give him any time to think about it!

Hutch might be fast on his feet, but how quick of wit was he?

Lazlo rushed in, raising his club two-handed above his head. Hutch's fist pulled back. At the last moment, Lazlo swerved aside, evading the mighty swing Hutch intended for his head. He brought the club down in a crushing blow on Hutch's extended arm.

It had enough force to break bones. Even Hutch's. But the big man's arm was corded with resilient muscle that padded the impact. Even so, the pain made Hutch stagger backward, his eyes glazed with shock.

Lazlo whirled in two quick steps around and slightly behind the big man, pivoting on his heel. Another two-handed swing of his wood billet, this time in a horizontal arc, slammed Hutch across the kidneys.

Hutch howled and dropped to his hands and knees. Lazlo took a sideward step to get Hutch's thick knob of a skull squarely in range and raised the club again. Now he had time for a full overhead swing that would pound Hutch into oblivion. It would be over that swiftly — that easily.

He hadn't reckoned quite enough with Hutch's stamina and cunning. On his hands and knees, wagging his head back and forth as if to clear it, Hutch suddenly shot out a long arm. He grabbed Lazlo by the ankle and yanked. Lazlo's feet shot from under him, dumping him flat on his back.

Hutch kept a bruisingly powerful hold on Lazlo's ankle as he floundered forward to get the final grip he needed. His face was discolored with pain and whiskey and triumph as he got his knees under him, free arm crooked at an angle that would protect his head against another swing of the club.

Lazlo kicked futilely at Hutch with his other leg. His leverage was bad; Hutch easily blocked the awkward kicks. Hutch was raised above him now, teeth bared with a feral and murderous expectancy.

"Go on, little pard," he husked, "try'n hit me —"

Something else hit him.

Lazlo didn't see what, but it caught Hutch in the region of his right ear. He let out a high-pitched yowl and clapped a hand to his temple. In the same moment he swung his head sideways, not yowling now.

He was bellowing. Shouting imprecations at a small boy with a peashooter.

Cyrus, bless him!

It gave Lazlo the momentary opening he needed. Hutch's arm had dropped, leaving his bearded head wide open. For Lazlo, it was a bad position from which to administer a *coup de grace;* flat on his back, Hutch's weight half-pinning him, and damned little room in which to swing a club.

Still he tried. He swung with all his strength.

The billet broke in half on Hutch's thick skull. The blow would have laid out a lesser man for hours. Hutch just swayed above him, glassy-eyed and stunned. Lazlo followed up fast — with a fist still wrapped around the billet stub. The punch had enough power to swivel Hutch's head, forcing an explosive grunt from him.

Slowly then, he toppled sideways.

Lazlo heaved off Hutch's weight and climbed to his feet. He limped over to Mark, took the rifle from him, and went back to Hutch, who was climbing laboriously to his knees.

Lazlo put the rifle muzzle to the back of Hutch's head.

"Now, Hutch," he said between his teeth, "you have got me just about mad enough to blow out your brains. So don't tempt me. Get your stuff and clear out of here. And mind . . . if I find you dogging my trail again, I will not talk anymore." A long pause. "What I will do is, I will shoot you on sight."

Hutch rubbed a hand over his face and looked at it, smeared bright with his blood. Finally he spoke, "You have said it all, little pard," followed by a chest-deep chuckle.

The liquor had washed out of Hutch's voice. It was strained and wicked. He turned his head enough for Lazlo to see the grinning grimace that shaped his fleshy face so that somehow it seemed as gauntly cruel as a skull.

"I will be dogging you right enough.

Only you won't noways see me when I come. Time you do, it will be way too late. That is God's own truth."

CHAPTER 12

Arms folded on the table, Laban Ruddy eyed the man sitting across from him with a frustrated swell of anger that he was careful not to let show. You could smooth-talk a man like Creed Jacks all day and all night, Laban was bitterly convinced, and never dent his dry composure.

Creed Jacks looked like anything but a man whose reputation with a gun had run ahead of him even to this remote corner of the West. He was slight of build, under medium height, with a voice so whisper-soft that you had to cock your head to make out what he said.

Everything about him seemed sort of nondescript and washed-out. The gray that streaked his hair was almost imperceptible against its dead paleness. His eyes were of no particular color. He might have been anywhere from thirty-five to fifty-five. Anyone trying to describe him after once seeing him, Laban thought, would have a hard time remembering how he looked.

A man would remember his clothes, no doubt. Creed Jacks wore fine black broadcloth of a conservative cut, tailored to his slight frame, along with a pearl-gray Stetson and a handsome sheepskin coat. A diamond stickpin glittered in his cravat. Quiet and tasteful and expensive: the costume of a man used to having plenty of money and spending it in a casual but never flashy way. God knew what whim or idle purpose had brought him to this remote gold camp.

One thing was sure: he was a man utterly sure of himself, utterly unconcerned about anything or anyone else, unless they got in his way or could be used to his advantage. When Laban had approached the table where Creed Jacks sat alone and asked if he might join him, Jacks had nodded courteously even while his pallid gaze briefly and impersonally sized up Laban and then dismissed him.

Though irked, Laban had bought Jacks a drink and then laid it all out for him in the plainest terms, underpitching his voice against the raucous, smoky din of Red Mike's saloon.

For two days and nights Laban Ruddy, his remaining nephew, and Robert Topbear had kept a watch on the road to Saba City. They'd taken up positions on the flanks of two high ridges that formed part of the pass through which the road ran, about a half-mile east from Bozetown.

It was a cold, cramped, and tedious vigil. And to Laban's disgust, Lazlo Kusik had failed to show up.

This had puzzled him. All signs had indicated that Kusik intended to pull out soon. If he did, they'd be sure to spot his slow-moving wagon by keeping a watch on the road to Saba City. What had gone wrong? Had the hunky changed his mind? Surely he'd anticipated that Laban and his boys would get hold of more guns and make another try at him. With that thought, Laban had sent Robert Topbear to reconnoiter Lazlo's claim camp. Returning a couple of hours later, Topbear had reported that the camp was deserted. Kusik, his wagon, and all his belongings were gone.

But *where?* Topbear couldn't say. Snow had fallen, but the wind had drifted over any tracks.

The question fed Laban's growing angry bafflement. He'd been told back in Saba City that the only way in or out of the Mad Mule River Valley by wagon was through the deep pass that ran east between folded ridges and flanking mountains all the way to Saba City. What could they do but keep watching it?

Finally, after another fruitless day and night of chilly vigil on a ridgeside, Laban, viciously sober and out of whiskey, had left Bije and Robert Topbear on watch and tramped back to Bozetown where he could pick up more liquor and, just maybe, some trifles of information that would put him on the right scent.

Engaging the bartender at Red Mike's in talk, Laban had asked first about Kusik's ally, Hutch Prouter. He might get a line on Kusik's whereabouts through Prouter. Informed that Prouter's camp lay on the Mad Mule a little way above Kusik's, Laban decided to try his luck there. Maybe —

Then, right out of the blue, the barkeep said idly, "Say, you see that fella over in the corner drinking by hisself? Know who he is?"

Laban gave the man an indifferent glance. "No, I don't."

"Creed Jacks, that is. Used to see him a lot when I was tending bar at the Silver Eagle, way down in Tombstone. He was mixed up with Sheriff Behan and that Clanton crowd against Earp 'n' his brothers —"

Laban cut in, "I've heard of him," and eyed the slight, unimpressive man with a fresh interest.

Creed Jacks. A man deadly with a gun. That, Laban Ruddy was now convinced, was what he needed more than anything. More even than good luck or a sound lead on Kusik and Prouter.

Truth to tell, much as he was set on tracking down Lazlo Kusik, the fellow had Laban Ruddy more than a little spooked. There was an edge of danger in Kusik. You could feel it, by God, under that quiet hunky manner of his. He'd already demonstrated that he was a mean customer to tangle with. That friend of his, Prouter, wasn't to be taken lightly either.

If they tackled Kusik again, it had to be a sure thing.

Laban himself was a stranger to violence and firearms. So were Bije and Robert Topbear. Stella's prowess with a rifle might have been turned to good use, but Stella was less concerned with getting back at the man who'd slain her cousin Ab than with caring for her sister Myra Mae, who'd come down with another of her periodic bouts of severe coughing. So the two girls had remained in the camp on Humbug Flat.

Creed Jacks was a killer. His worn-handled Colt in its worn holster, the skirt of his coat pushed back to keep the butt clear, was the only outward sign of it. Only his reputation was right out front for anyone to see. It preceded him wherever he went.

The problem was that Creed Jacks hadn't bought any of Laban's pitch.

He'd listened to Laban's story patiently and politely, staring with show-nothing eyes at his glass of whiskey on the table between them, twirling it gently between his fingers. When Laban was done, Creed Jacks had said mildly, "Well now, sir, let's look at what we have got here. Way I understand it, you have a mere pittance in your poke. Hardly enough to make it worth my while to waste a twitch of my little finger on your behalf."

"I told you —"

"What you've told me," Creed Jacks went on, "is that you assume, on a basis of far from conclusive evidence, that a certain hunky miner has made himself a quite lucrative strike. In toto, Mr. Ruddy, what you've offered me in support of that contention is considerably less than convincing."

"Mr. Jacks . . ."

Sweat damped Laban's face. He was feeling a need for support that verged on desperation. And he wanted that support from Creed Jacks. "You're a gambler, I have heard. Listen then. Here's a gamble worth the taking. Side with me in this, and I guarantee you'll have your hands on half of whatever Kusik's strike amounts to. Even at a gamble, sir, that should prove to be considerable."

Creed Jacks remained politely smiling and wearily skeptical. "I am a cynical man, Mr. Ruddy. In my time I have heard about every story under the sun. I do not believe in purple cows. Nor pigs in pokes."

That was where the matter rested for the next twenty minutes, during which Laban wracked his brain for all the arguments he could summon from a lifetime of experience at snake-oil persuasion, none of it to any effect.

Creed Jacks nursed along the whiskey Laban had bought him and politely refused to drink up so that Laban could buy him another. He replied to anything Laban said with a murmured word or so, and his gaze was faraway.

Laban was about ready to give up when, casting an idle glance around the room, he saw a big man push his way through the swing doors on the far side of the dim, noisy, log-walled room.

It was Hutch Prouter. The sight of him did nothing to improve Laban's state of mind.

Hutch bellied his way over to the bar and brought a big fist crashing down on it. He roared that he wanted a bottle, *goddammit!* — and his stentorian bellow caused the hubbub in Red Mike's to ebb momentarily into silence. Prouter got his bottle, paid for it, and tipped it to his mouth. His head went back; his Adam's apple bobbed for a quarter-minute. When he lowered the bottle and swiped a hairy hand across his mouth, the bottle was a third empty.

Prouter's gaze moved across the crowd and stopped on Laban Ruddy. Laban felt his innards squeeze up under Hutch's stare. A moment later they crumpled even tighter as Prouter shoved away from the bar and started across the room toward him.

Judas Priest in a jug! Laban thought wildly. He sat in a paralyzed panic that increased with a closer sight of Prouter's face.

Before, the fellow had seemed as jovial as a clown. Hadn't appeared very temper-

tight even when he'd helped Kusik over-
come Laban and the boys. But now his
broad face wore as purely mean and ugly a
look as Laban had ever seen.

My God, what does he mean to do!

All Prouter did was grab the third chair
at the table in a hamlike hand, yank it out,
and slack heavily into it.

"You 'n' me," he growled at Laban, "got
medicine to make. Best hear me out."

Prouter paused for another belt of liquor. He set the bottle gently down, and it
was half-empty now. Laban, himself a
steady but slow drinker, felt a proper awe.
Prodigious feats of "putting it away" were
nothing unusual in a mining camp, but
he'd never seen the like of this.

A half-quart of booze had done nothing
to soften whatever devil was working in
Prouter. His face was craggy with temper,
and now Laban noticed the crusted scab of
blood that had dried on his temple.

"Who's he?" Prouter motioned curtly at
Creed Jacks, who was giving him a bemused, mildly interested stare.

Laban performed the introductions.

"Heerd o' you," Prouter told Jacks and
leaned his massive forearms on the table.
"I got som'at to tell you, Ruddy. 'Bout Laz
Kusik and a mess o' gold." He jerked a

thumb at Creed Jacks. "He 'ith you? Want him to hear this or not?"

Laban hesitated, his brain working with a swift sure instinct. Whatever Prouter was on the peck about, his wrath wasn't directed at Laban Ruddy. "Why not? Say what you want to."

In less than five minutes, even allowing for Laban's own excited interjection of questions as he sought clarification on details of what Hutch told him, the situation was clear.

When Hutch paused at last, taking another hefty pull at his bottle, Laban shuttled his gaze to Creed Jacks. He looked at ease, leaning back in his chair and smiling very faintly. His eyes no longer seemed colorless. They held the cold gray sheen of half-thawed ice.

"What you told me before," he murmured, "commences to interest me, *Colonel* Ruddy."

It ought to. Hutch Prouter had practically handed them on a platter a convincing affirmation of Laban's own argument, along with a plan of operation. Out of what Hutch had said, the few things of importance could quickly be isolated: Prouter had reason to be sure of Kusik's cache of gold and where it was hidden.

The falling-out between Prouter and Kusik had left Hutch in a seething rage — as ready as Laban himself to kill for revenge and money.

Best of all, he could guide them right to where Kusik was. All they'd need to implement the plan was some saddle mounts that could be bought or rented from the livery barn.

Not stirring from his slack position, Jacks reached out and picked up Hutch's bottle, saying genially, "Mr. Prouter, I hope you didn't intend to drink this up all by yourself. After all . . ." He filled his and Laban's glasses from the bottle and handed it back to Hutch. "I think the occasion calls for a toast to what appears a most promising partnership. Gentlemen — here's to ill-gotten gains. And a three-way split on them."

CHAPTER 13

After Hutch's departure, Lazlo got a night's sound sleep, for which he was grateful. Mark and a couple of the older boys took turns on guard duty, just in case. Lazlo had inspected the weapons owned by the party. These consisted of a battered Winchester and a vintage Hawken rifle much like the one of which he'd relieved Hutch, along with Hutch's old Walker Colt.

Weaponless, Hutch wasn't likely to sneak back. Possibly he could rearm himself in Bozetown and then overtake their slow wagons on foot. But one man shouldn't pose much of a danger as long as they stayed on their guard.

Lazlo's biggest worry now was nature's own temper.

Throughout the next day of climbing through the foothills and into the high passes, the weather held steady. They made pretty fair time. Wherever the going was rough for wagons and mules, the combined young muscles of boys and girls alike were enough to wrestle the wagons across.

It was a long and grueling day. Everyone was wrung out, literally exhausted, when the early darkness of late fall forced a halt. They had covered, Lazlo estimated, about half the distance. If he got them on all the right trails, and barring accidents or bad weather or other obstructions, they should be across the worst of it in another two days or less.

Keep your fingers crossed.

By midmorning of the next day, he had the sinking knowledge that it would take a lot more than crossed fingers to bring them safely through. The sky beyond the peaks was a raw gray sludge. Fierce churnings of wind tumbled the clouds ahead of them like masses of dirty fleece. Before long they'd be directly overhead. There would be no nooning today. They must push on quickly, covering as much distance as possible before the storm hit.

The first flakes of snow whirled down as light as dust. The snowfall picked up rapidly in an hour or so, and then what Lazlo had feared was confirmed: This wouldn't be another light snowfall. They were pointed into the teeth of a full-fledged blizzard.

It struck almost abruptly and with a blinding ferocity that cut off the world all around. It didn't merely destroy visibility; it wiped out a person's sense of direction and almost knocked him off his feet.

Lazlo had already prepared the Blys, and they were quick to follow his direction. The wagons were pulled into a square, and everyone huddled in its center, blankets clutched around them, using one another for windbreaks and warmth. There was little talk because you had to yell to be heard. The howling wind snatched ordinary speech away in dim tatters . . .

It was nearly midnight when the storm began to let up.

Lazlo was the first to break out of the shroud of snow that covered him. He shrugged free of his crusted blankets, stood up, and looked around. He couldn't make out much in the darkness and slackening fall of flakes. He tramped around, testing the depth of fallen snow. Not as bad as he'd feared, but deep enough to impede their progress. Up ahead, for all he knew, it might be too heavily drifted for wagons to buck through. Or the maze of trails might be obscured enough to give him the devil's own time trying not to lead them on a wrong turn.

He didn't say his doubts aloud. Not right then.

As the snow and wind continued to die off, Miss Aretha gave the kids orders: Gather wood (not easy to scour up at this height, almost above the timberline), get the fires going and a supper cooking, and tend the needs of the younger or ailing children first. As always, her calm crisp manner and her undiminished store of energy got into everyone else. After the camp was bedded down, the kids nestled in the wagons, Lazlo and Mark and Miss Aretha remained by one of the fires, sitting on their heels and sipping coffee.

"Well, Mr. Kusik," Aretha Bly said with a wry smile, "you said we were crazy to attempt a crossing this time of year. I am bound to confess you were probably right."

Lazlo sipped the dregs of his coffee. "It could be. But we've come this far. We have crossed most of the way. Now we must keep on. It may be bad ahead, but it could be just as bad behind, after this blizzard. We don't know."

"We don't, do we? I believe I told you that even if our wagons were marooned up here, we could continue on foot. We can, of course. But . . . some of the children are not in the best of health. And going through snowdrifts, it will take longer than we'd thought. Can we all make it, even so? What do you think?"

Lazlo felt only a sour trace of satisfaction in having this iron-willed woman defer to his opinion. Just now his thoughts revolved around his private dilemma. If the passes were closed off to wagons, he might lose the biggest gamble of his life. At the least, he'd be forced to abandon his gold till spring opened the high trails once more. That could be six months from now. The idea of waiting that long fretted him.

Worse: Hutch knew he'd come this way. If, later, Hutch followed up the trail and found the abandoned wagon, he would tear it apart to verify what he suspected and then would make his own plans for getting the cargo out. He would have other plans, too — for nailing up Lazlo's hide. Hutch was not stupid. He would lay those plans with care.

I have got to get through now, Lazlo thought doggedly. *There can be no waiting.*

Unwilling to show the Blys these thoughts, he let the cold anger he felt roughen his voice: "I think we better try to get across. We better try like hell . . . *now.*"

Miss Aretha colored. The way her blue

eyes sparked was neither prim nor zealous. Mark Bly cleared his throat and unfolded his lanky frame, getting to his feet. "Um, think I'll turn in now, sis. G'night. Night, Mr. Kusik."

The crunch of his boots died away in the dark. Miss Aretha stared at the fire and said, "I do not require coarse-grained sarcasm in reply to a simple question, Mr. Kusik. I have already confessed my fault. What more would you have me say?"

"I am sorry," he said lamely. "I was thinking . . ."

"Yes?"

"Of something else."

"Oh."

A little enigmatic smile brushed her lips. She rose and walked over to a tall snow-covered rock. Laying a mittened hand on it, she tipped back her head as if listening to the moan of wind from the craggy heights above.

"How much of a fool have I been, Mr. Kusik?"

Lazlo lifted one shoulder in a mild shrug. "It is as you have said. If we're shut off, we can go ahead on foot. But it will take much longer, and some of these kids of yours are not in such good condition. Also, if the trails are drifted, I could lose my way. None of it can be helped. We have come most of the way, and now we must go on. The trails in back of us are blown over too, now. If it's a choice between going on and turning back . . ."

"Of course," she murmured, "we must go on. You're kind not to say I'm a fool woman."

"If you are a fool, I do not think it has to do with being a woman."

Miss Aretha laughed, shortly and sharply. "What an arch flatterer you are, sir!" Her jaw clenched; she looked away from him. "I have taken a number of wrong turns in my life. Perhaps this was just another."

"Wrong turns? I cannot see you taking even one."

"More than a few, I fear. Some years ago I was denounced at a meeting of the Society of Friends . . . for defending the feminist doctrines of Susan B. Anthony and Elizabeth Cady Stanton. That was when I quit their society and took up with the Reverend Brace's. Mark followed my lead, even as he wryly observed that no matter what I do, I'll always need a cause. One cause or another to follow. Oh well . . ." Her laugh was quiet and self-deprecating. "I suppose I just take too much on myself.

For years — being a mere woman — I was relegated to all kinds of minor tasks for the Children's Aid Society. Now, finally, I've been given an assignment of some responsibility. I am the first woman to be put in charge of shepherding a party of orphans to their new homes in the West." She bit her lip and shook her head. "Now . . . oh Lord."

It was, Lazlo realized, a rare moment of weakness in a woman like this. It embarrassed him. He had been a fighter all his life, and he hated to see a feeling of failure in anyone. But it showed in a woman like Aretha Bly, with all her spirit and courage, far more obtusely than in most.

Not knowing quite what to say, he got to his feet and walked over to her. "Listen, how have you done so bad?"

"How have I *not?*" She swiped a mitten across her nose. "I started out so full of self-assurance — with no understanding of what I'd have to face. What a fool I was!"

"No. It is a mood you are in. That passes."

"Sir, I have made *little* mistakes along the way. But pride can suffer those. This one might cost some children their lives. Do you think —"

"What I think," he broke in roughly, "is

that you are one hell of a woman, and you do not seem to know it. Or is that, also, too coarse?"

"I don't think so." She was still-faced, head tipped back a little. Somehow, maybe it was only a trick of the firelight, she looked softer and even vulnerable, in a feminine way. And there was no mistaking a tiny smile that upcurled the corners of her lips. "But I believe you'd best let it go at that . . ."

Not listening now, he reached out, pulled her against him, and kissed her. In the back of his mind, he felt a flicker of surprise at her response. It wasn't overwhelming, but it lasted a few heartbeats before she pushed him firmly away.

"Why did you do that?"

Lazlo felt the hotness in his face. "I thought maybe you needed it. Or you would like it. Maybe I just wanted to. I don't know. Good night."

He turned and tramped away, but her voice brought him to a halt. "Mr. Kusik —"

"Yes."

"I did like it," she said very gently. "But don't do it again. Good night."

The next day's journey was far tougher than any that had gone before.

214

It got worse as the day stretched on and all their early steam ran out of them. Even where the snow hadn't piled too heavily, it was like slogging through a shallow lake of molasses. In places where the snow had drifted deeply, they bucked through by sheer force. The mules strained at their harness while the children hoorawed them.

Tying up with this party had been a wise move of his, Lazlo decided. Alone he never could have gotten past the worst stretches. Time and again he, Mark Bly, and several husky youngsters found their combined strength taxed in lifting the wagons bodily to get them across bad spots and rolling again.

Mark commented on the unusual difficulty of tussling Lazlo's apparently light wagon into line with the others: "Gadfrey, Mr. Kusik, this outfit of yours must weigh a ton! If I didn't know better, I'd swear you were toting all the crown jewels of Europe and their royal wearers too."

The observation didn't worry Lazlo. Mark was too innocent to suspect the real nature of Lazlo's cargo, and he had an inexhaustible good humor that extended to everything except the fact that pretty Cissie O'Halloran seemed constantly to linger in his vicinity. The young girl obviously had a case on Mark Bly, and he just as obviously was flustered and embarrassed by it.

By nightfall the weather was turning stone-cold. That was good in a way. No more snow was likely to fall while it stayed this cold, and the gusting winds finally thinned away and died off completely.

When they made camp in the early dusk, the mountain heights all around were clear, still, and dead-cold. It was a good while before the roaring fires they built up began to thaw the numbness of chill and exhaustion that seemed to penetrate to their bones.

Again, after the tired kids were bedded down, the three grown-ups crouched around a dying fire, drinking coffee and talking.

Earlier in the day, Lazlo and Aretha Bly had been quite constrained with each other. By now they were both so raveled with weariness that neither could dredge up any real feeling about their small interlude last night. All that any of them felt right now was drowsy gratitude at having gotten through a long day and being done with it.

Mark gave voice to the unspoken thought in a wry, oblique way. "Well, we didn't make very good time today, did we?"

"Not very good," said Lazlo. "Still we are a good three fourths of the way across."

Miss Aretha said quietly, "And how will it be up ahead? Better or worse, do you think?"

"It will not be better, that is for sure. But we are this far."

A lame sort of answer. Said not to deceive them, only to soften a harsh fact. The last remaining miles would be across very bad terrain. With drifting snow it would be worse yet but no telling how much worse.

Miss Aretha's glance at him was sober, friendly, and tired. "Oh," she said, that faint upcurling of a smile on her lips, "then things don't look *altogether* badly for us, I take it?"

"I think that is right, yes. If . . ."

Lazlo let his voice trail off into silence. He did not look up or around.

The noise had been soft but distinct in the crisp stillness. A sound of snow crunching under a footstep. Maybe one of the children leaving a wagon to relieve himself or herself in the dark. But he could have sworn the sound had come from beyond the square of drawn-up wagons.

Their camp was in a pocket of looming

boulders on the gradual slope of a mountain base. The tall, snow-capped rocks provided a sort of cozy enclosure for the site but also might lend cover to anyone stealing up on the camp. Lazlo inwardly cursed his own thoughtlessness. Dead tired, he hadn't given thought to posting a shift of guards that night. Any danger Hutch might have posed now seemed far behind them.

But was it? Driven by his rage, Hutch might have followed them even this far, biding his time.

Mark cleared his throat. "You were saying . . . ?"

"Be quiet," Lazlo said mildly. "Maybe we are being watched. Don't look up. Don't say anything. Stay like you are."

Idly he turned his own gaze away from the fire. A man looking at fire was blinded for a few precious seconds if he peered suddenly at darkness. Now he heard it again, sure and unmistakable: the crunch of a heavy boot in fresh snow.

Fool! he thought fiercely. He had left his rifle in his wagon, and it was a good twenty paces away. They were unarmed and in plain sight of whoever . . .

Again the crunching sound, but now from the *other* side of the camp. *More than one?* Lazlo didn't let his thoughts dwell on the fact. He had to make his move now, and he must be easy and casual or he might never finish it.

He got to his feet and stretched, then turned and strolled toward the wagons. The flesh of his back crawled. Sweat stood icy on his face. He had the feeling, bone-deep and sure, that if he'd ever stood in mortal peril, it was here and now.

He came against the sideboard of his wagon and very casually reached under the seat, closing a hand over the stock of his Winchester.

A bullet smashed into the sideboard inches from his elbow. The whipcrack of a gunshot beat down the stillness.

Before the craggy echoes died away, Lazlo had yanked his rifle free and was melting to the ground. Rolling sideways under the wagon and into its deep shadow, he levered the rifle as a second shot chewed up snow and flung it stinging into his face.

CHAPTER 14

Lazlo saw the orange flare of gun flame from the camp's edge and fired at it. There was a bawl of pain or anger: he was on target or close. At the same time Lazlo rolled sideways again, pumping the lever, firing.

A man yelled out there, this time giving a garbled order, and now guns opened up from three sides, all the firing directed at Lazlo's position. He rolled out on the wagon's other side, lunged to his feet and across the squared enclosure, and scrambled out under the opposite wagon. With the square of wagons cutting between him and the firelight, he ran for the rocks, bending low. He dived for the nearest one and saw, too late, someone's dark form crouched behind it.

Lazlo veered at the last moment; he slammed into the man full tilt and bowled him over. He couldn't make out the face and, in the flurry of the moment, didn't try to. He swung his rifle in a tight savage arc that ended against the man's skull and broke off his choked cry. He went limp.

A pistol gleamed in his loose fist; Lazlo kicked it away. He wondered only fleetingly why the fellow hadn't cut him down before he reached the boulder.

Lazlo flattened against the rock, levering his rifle again, just as a running figure crossed the clearing and was briefly limned by the firelight before it reached the square of wagons and was lost in its shadow.

Damn! He could not shoot in hopes of drawing that one's fire. Not with all those kids bedded in the wagons. They were fully awake now, and their shrill lift of voices was querulous and scared.

"You kids stay in the wagons!" Lazlo roared. *"Don't come out! Stay like you are!"*

His yell drew fire from at least two hidden rifles. One bullet spanged off his sheltering boulder. All he could make out were powder flashes off in the rocks. He returned fire at both, but it was blind shooting.

It wasn't pitch-dark. The sky was clear, a dark cobalt blue in color, and the stars were bright. They laid a milky sheen on the snow cover that reflected much of the surrounding scene, now that his eyes were accustomed to the off-shade light. But the shadows deeply swallowed whatever lay within them.

221

Now at least he was on even terms with these people. But who were they? *Christ!* The Blys must still be crouched by the fire, helpless and exposed to gunfire, and so were the children in the wagons.

That, in a way, made Lazlo Kusik just as helpless.

The thought had hardly crossed his mind when a child's shrill cry split the abrupt silence. Then there was a man's calm voice, like silk over steel. It came from the wagon square.

"I advise you to stay as you are, my friend. Don't move. Just listen. I have taken one of these budding blossoms of the slums in hand. I have a pistol set against its head."

The sharp *snap* of a pistol hammer being cocked rose above the children's whimperings. Lazlo strained his eyes against the shadows. He could make out nothing inside the square.

"I will twist the child's arm," the voice went on in the same dead calm way. "Listen."

There was a short childish scream of anguish.

"Do you believe what I say?"

"Yes," Lazlo said hoarsely. "All right."

"What you will do, then, is step out and

come this way with your hands high and no weapons in them. I will give you ten seconds to do so. If I do not detect a sign of compliance after my count of ten, I will pull the trigger."

Lazlo didn't know the voice. But he knew with an icy and absolute certainty that this was no bluff.

"Yes! All right, I am coming."

Maybe to be shot down the moment he showed himself. That tug of alarm gave him a moment's pause, and then he heard the man he'd slugged groan with returning consciousness.

Maybe, he thought, *they would shoot me but not risk shooting him too.* Lazlo laid down his rifle, bent and grabbed the man's wrists, and hauled him upright. The man's head lolled back; starlight fell on his face. Robert Topbear. Lazlo caught the reek of whiskey, and then he knew why Topbear had not shot at him. Topbear had been stone drunk.

Lazlo ducked his shoulders and let Robert Topbear collapse across them. He tramped slowly out from his shelter, around the wagons, and over to the fire, where the Blys still crouched, frozen in place by a violence with which they couldn't cope.

"Show yourselves!" Lazlo yelled in a burst of fury and frustration. "Damn all of you, show your skulking faces!"

"We are about to, Mr. Kusik!"

The orotund and genial voice of Colonel Laban Ruddy rolled out of the dark. "Now, if you will lower Mr. Topbear to the ground. Nobody will open fire on you. Gently, if you please . . . That's it. Hands high above your head now. Splendid."

Laban and his companions came out of their places among the boulders and into the firelight.

They must have surrounded the camp with an ignominious ease. Coming up the trail, they would have spotted the campfire and then, aided by starshine on fresh snow, spread out and eased themselves into various positions among the rocks. All seven of them.

Lazlo felt only a dull surprise at seeing Hutch Prouter among them. How else could they have managed to follow his trail?

Laban Ruddy motioned at the Blys with his rifle. "Up — up. Surely a pair of bluestockings such as I'm told you are know how to receive guests properly. Come, on your feet."

" 'Guests!' " Miss Aretha stood up,

small and very straight, angry color in her face. "You assault our camp like brigands and call yourselves *guests?*"

"A hundred pardons, dear lady." Laban inclined his head. "The expected intransigence of our friend Mr. Kusik made a clandestine approach unavoidable. Search his clothing, Mr. Jacks, will you? Might have a nasty trifle or two concealed on him. Keep those hands well above your head, Mr. Kusik."

The slight, mild-faced man — the only member of the party Lazlo hadn't seen before — came over to Lazlo and began to search him. Moving like a snake, smoothly and lithely, he did it quickly and expertly. He turned up Lazlo's Bowie knife and jackknife and then stepped away.

Robert Topbear raised himself on his hands and vomited. He got unsteadily to his feet, rubbing his head and looking rheumily around him.

"Everything's in hand, Robert," Laban said coldly. "No thanks to you. Go and lie down somewhere. It's what you seem to do best . . . You — the Blys, is it? — get those children out here and over by the fire. And stop their damned caterwauling! Bije, Mr. Prouter, go with them. And search those wagons for any weapons."

Hutch stood hulking in the orange leap of light. His eyes were bleary and bloodshot; a wicked grin split his bearded lips. He was savoring this moment.

Again, silently, Lazlo raged at his own negligence. Something that hadn't crossed his mind was that Hutch might return to Bozetown and make common cause with Ruddy. For all of them to catch up with the Bly party so quickly, even allowing for how long it had taken Hutch to tramp back to Bozetown and make alliance with Laban, they must have come on horseback. Once they had spotted the camp, they would have tethered the horses back on the trail and then stolen in on foot.

Hutch lumbered along behind Miss Aretha and Mark as they headed for the wagons. Bije Willet followed them, taking his eyes off Lazlo for the first time.

Another one who would like to cut out my heart, Lazlo thought almost wearily. Hutch and Ruddy and him. It was just a case of who got his execution in first.

Laban Ruddy smiled his genial smile. "Well, Mr. Kusik, didn't I assure you we would meet again? Beg pardon . . . I've neglected to perform the amenities. Mr. Kusik, may I present Mr. Creed Jacks, who has discovered an interest in common with me. And Mr. Prouter."

Creed Jacks. The name rang a bell at once. Those top guns who frequented the remote camps weren't so many in number that their names didn't often come up wherever men got together to swap trail gossip. Considering his reputation, Jacks looked colorless, almost ineffectual.

But he did things with a terrifying precision. He had been ready to kill a child. God, the man was worse than the others put together!

Lazlo turned his head enough to catch Sureshot Stell in the corner of his eye. She had added a heavy Mackinaw coat to her rough man's costume and beneath her hat wore a thick scarf tied under her chin to protect her ears from frostbite. She held her rifle on him with a negligent ease. The stony set of her face was uncompromising.

She must have gotten a dandy account from her daddy about how her cousin Ab had died at Lazlo's hand. And for damned sure nothing in it would have put Lazlo Kusik in a good light.

Tipping his head the other way, Lazlo studied the colonel's younger daughter, Myra Mae ("The Princess"). She looked as toughly primed as her sister. Now dressed in a man's clothing much like

Stell's, with a droopy slouch hat that partly shadowed her face, Myra Mae held a rifle on him exactly as if she knew how to use it.

The children were rousted out of the wagons and herded into a group by the fire. Most of them were blinking and confused; some looked defiant. The youngest ones were softly whimpering. The oldest boys looked both downcast and sullen, no doubt ashamed of their failure to bring the handful of guns into play at the first hint of danger. But none of them were to blame. The sudden invasion of the camp might have paralyzed any grown man. All that resistance would have gotten them was being shot down.

"Shut those brats up," Laban said impatiently. "We don't intend them any harm. Get that through their heads, will you?"

Miss Aretha's gaze snapped with a blue and bitter fire. "Perhaps I might," she said icily, "if I could only believe it myself."

"Madam, I have no designs on anyone's life. With a single possible exception." Laban's glance shuttled briefly and wickedly to Lazlo. To his nephew: "Bije, fetch our horses in and tend them, will you? Now, Mr. Prouter, why don't you put your theory — and your brawn — to the test?

Go tear the endboards off that wagon of Mr. Kusik's, and we'll see just what —"

Laban was interrupted by a fit of coughing from Myra Mae. She bent over and dropped to her knees, her body wracked by the violence of the attack.

"Myra?"

"It's all right, Pa. I'm all right."

Stella took a step toward her. Myra Mae motioned her sister back with an irritated gesture. Slowly she straightened and dragged herself back to her feet, her jaw set and rifle trained. But she was shuddering all over. Her face was blotchy, and her eyes were glazed from the coughing attack.

Or maybe from worse.

It took Hutch only a few seconds to rip off the nailed-on tailgate of Lazlo's wagon with his bare hands. It took him a couple of minutes — by simply grabbing and raising up the front of the wagon and using his enormous strength — to shake the contents of the false bottom out on the ground.

Lazlo's strike. There was the proof of it, glittering in the snow at their feet, polished to a rich promise by the fire. It occupied the avaricious attention of Laban, Hutch, and Creed Jacks for a brief time. They picked up chunks of ore and turned them in their hands, while Laban's daughters went on holding Lazlo at gunpoint.

Laban tramped back to the fire and halted a few feet from Lazlo. A cold venom etched his warm and plummy tones. "Well, Mr. Kusik, we've gotten a part of what we came after. Can you think of a good reason why we shouldn't have the rest of it?"

"I take that to mean my life."

The lack of concern in Lazlo's reply seemed to touch a raw nerve in the colonel. "That — exactly! A life for a life. Why not?"

"Because then," Lazlo said calmly, "you will not get the rest of the gold."

"The rest . . ." Laban's brow wrinkled; his eyes narrowed. "More gold than this?"

"What you see here is what little I could take out in one load. Yes, there is more. I hid it. And your tame Indian could not find it, so I guess I hid it pretty good, eh?"

"More gold," Laban murmured. "How much more?"

Lazlo shrugged. "Four, five times as much. I cached all of it away to come back for later. Maybe there is a lot more on my claim that I did not turn up. Still, the claim is in my name. This is something to think about, eh?"

Laban stared at him a long moment.

Hutch stood by, scowling, and Creed Jacks's face was expressionless. The short silence was broken only by a crackle of flames.

"I think," Creed Jacks said quietly, dryly, "we might hold our horses a bit. I should like to hear the man's proposition."

Hutch stirred ominously, grunting, "Shitmaroo. This hunky son of a bitch is looking for a way out. I wouldn't trust him no way whatever. Sure, that is what he's doing by God, stalling for time."

"Possibly," said Creed Jacks. "Quite possibly, Mr. Prouter. But as I say . . ."

Laban tugged at his goatee. "We can listen at least. Very well, Kusik. Have your say. What do you want?"

"To stay alive. To keep these people alive also."

Lazlo nodded toward the Blys and the children. Miss Aretha's chill and angry gaze met his. No doubt she was thinking, now that his hidden cargo was revealed, that he'd taken advantage of them to get his gold across the mountains. True enough, but they had benefited too. Let her think of that.

"Reasonable," said Creed Jacks. "But their lives are not at stake. Only yours."

Lazlo shook his head. "The trails up

here twist every which way. Now the snow has blown them over. These people need me to lead them across. They want to go to Carson's Crossing. Why don't we all go there? Now it is a lot closer than Bozetown. And the gold can just as well be sold there."

Creed Jacks showed the wintry wisp of a smile. "True . . . true. But we don't know the trails up ahead, sir. We've trusted Mr. Prouter to guide us this far . . ."

"And I will guide you the rest of the way. I brought everyone this far, eh? I know the trails."

"So do I, you hunky bastard," growled Hutch.

Lazlo looked at him and smiled. "That is right, big pard. If they can keep you sober that far."

Creed Jacks flicked a warning glance at Hutch. "Go on," he murmured.

"I will lead you across all right," said Lazlo. "But there is rough going ahead. We will need all the strong arms we can muster, even those of the kids, to get the load of gold through. If we all go together, we'll be sure of making it, eh? And you will get all you want."

"And what," Creed Jacks said affably, "is 'all'? Clarify your terms, sir."

Somehow Jacks had slipped into complete command. It was as though Laban, Hutch, and the others had been washed into the background. Avoiding Jacks's eyes, Laban got a flask out of his pocket and took a pull at it. Hutch glowered and said nothing. Neither did Bije. Lazlo shared their feeling. Meeting Creed Jacks's opaque stare, he felt sweat dampen his clothing to his skin.

"Well, it is simple," he said. "The gold in my wagon is yours. The gold I left hid on my claim is yours. So is the claim itself. A quitclaim can be made out to sign it over to you . . . to whoever you want. Maybe all of you, eh?"

"Well enough," said Creed Jacks. "Provided you are not bluffing, I should hate to say lying, about that hidden cache of gold."

"Of course I cannot say how much gold I may *not* have found. But that which I found and left — it is there. Waiting."

Creed Jacks grinned. "And it is really 'four or five times' what's contained in your wagon?"

Lazlo forced a grin of his own. "Well, maybe I exaggerated a little. But not much. What's left is a lot more than I could pack out in one trip. And you will not know *where* it is till I show you, eh?"

"And meantime we depend on your word for all this?"

"No more than I depend on yours." Lazlo paused. He tipped his head toward Hutch and Laban and Bije. "These three want to see me dead. I will depend on you to see that they are disappointed."

Creed Jacks's wispy grin turned to a laugh. It was thin, shallow, and not very amused. "Quite agreeable to me. I trust Mr. Ruddy and Mr. Prouter will also find it so."

A long pause, during which Jacks didn't trouble to glance at his partners. Neither of them commented.

"That being the case," Jacks went on, "we'll proceed as you suggest. One thing, however. You are a fighter, Mr. Kusik. It shows in every move you make. In every lineament of your face. It is not in your grain to yield the whole pot — particularly as rich a one as you've tantalized us with — so glibly and easily."

Jacks smiled through an even longer pause. It lasted maybe ten seconds. Lazlo merely stared back at him. There was nothing to say.

"The reason, of course," said Jacks, "is patently obvious. You have now gained yourself a little extra time. You'll wait on happenstance to provide a fillip of diversion that might enable you to turn tables on us. On *me*. When it occurs, you think you will seize your advantage. When you do, Mr. Kusik . . ."

Jacks pushed back the skirt of his sheepskin coat and tapped a forefinger on the butt of his pistol. "When you do, you will be dead. Do you understand me? Instantly dead."

CHAPTER 15

As Creed Jacks had readily guessed, Lazlo had given up so easily because he'd every intention of watching for his chance to catch Jacks and his party off guard. Now he privately, wryly, admitted to himself how slight that chance was. But he'd try if he could. Jacks was right. He was made that way. Even if all odds were against him, he was damned if he'd yield all that he'd slaved and sweated out his guts to realize: the strike of a lifetime.

Not even if resistance cost him his life.

Probably it would. Jacks's party had complete control of the situation. All the weapons were in their possession. They had solidarity — of a sort. Laban and Hutch might resent Jacks's assumption of leadership, but they'd accept it, and whatever Laban accepted, Bije, Robert Topbear, and the daughters would also accept.

Lazlo hadn't the least confidence, anyway, that Jacks would keep him alive a moment longer than necessary to cinch the location of the gold ore back on his claim. *Why should he?* Lazlo thought coldly. *I would not in his place.* Maybe he was not the same kind of man as Jacks, but he understood that kind of man only too well.

The wagons were rolling out as the bleak dawn broke, making their slow way up the tortured windings of old mountain trails overlaid with only a little snow in some places, deeply drifted in others. A cutting wind built up through the long gray day, skirling the snow in biting gusts that slashed at their faces and then settled, only to kick up again.

The higher they advanced into this last treacherous arm of the western Elks, the more difficult the going became. With three quarters of the distance to Carson's Crossing already covered, they were now held to a snail's crawl next to the ground they had covered on previous days.

More and more often the line of wagons was stalled by the necessity to boost them, one by one, over rock- and snow-laden parts of the trail. Hutch and Bije added a lot of welcome muscle to the effort, and every bit of it was needed.

It wasn't a congenial day in any sense. The biting cold and bitterly rough trail would have ensured as much. Meantime, the entire company was divided against it-self. The only goal they held in common was getting across the peaks. And Lazlo had the sure and cruel knowledge that no one person of the party was regarded with more suspicion or downright hatred than he was.

Only Mark Bly didn't seem to share the general animus toward him. For most of the day Lazlo and Mark plodded along side by side, their faces bent against the blizzardy blasts. Sometimes they talked, often raising their voices against the cut-ting swell of wind.

"Sorry everything had to turn out as it did, Mr. Kusik," Mark ventured.

"No sorrier than I am," Lazlo said grimly. "It is the breaks of the game."

"My sister, I'm afraid, hasn't altogether thought through your side of the matter. She appears to feel that, well, you have used us in a way."

"She is right. No blame to her for that."

"But it's not that simple!"

"Nothing ever is."

Mark gave Lazlo a brief and baffled glance. For a half-minute, he bent his head out of the wind and then said hesitantly, "Mr. Kusik . . . is it true what you told these fellows about the gold that is still on your claim?"

"Yes," Lazlo said wearily, "it is true."

"Then it'll be all right with you, won't it? I mean — of course it's outrageous that you should lose all the fruits of your labor. But at least you'll stay alive."

"Yes, that is a very good thing."

The irony was lost on Mark. His thoughts were already veering on another tack. It took him a few more minutes to come out with it, sort of obliquely: "That girl . . . Myra Mae. She's very sick, isn't she?"

"I would say so. When they cough like she does, like they are throwing up their insides, usually they are very bad. We call them 'lungers.' The best thing for them is to winter in a dry place with a good warm climate."

"Yes, so I've heard." Mark was silent for another interval as they tramped along. Then he burst out: "What a damned shame! A lovely girl like that . . . and her life wasting away. Mostly on account of her father's greed!"

Lazlo gave him a brief, mild and wondering look. "Sure. It is too bad, all right . . ."

By early afternoon the wagons crossed the highest point of their journey, a saddle-shaped dip between two peaks, and started

239

down its other side. Ahead, Lazlo was pretty sure, lay the worst part of the whole trip.

So far, they had labored along an upward ascent all the way, and now they were over its hump. But it wouldn't make the going any easier. To the contrary. The steep twisting trails ahead skirted tall cliffs and followed hairpin bends that hung over sheer drop-offs. Lazlo figured that all the trails he'd mentally mapped were wide enough, even at their narrowest, to accommodate the wagons. They might run into tight squeezes here and there, but they could make it through all right.

Trouble was that the shallow fall of snow had added to the problem. In many places the footing was dangerously slick. Where wheels could otherwise take a grip on rough rock, they'd be likely to skid and slide precariously from one side to the other.

Unexpectedly, it was Laban Ruddy who supplied the know-how they needed at this point. Laban had taken the wagons of his medicine circus over all kinds of terrain and through the worst kinds of weather. Cold sober now, he offered crisp pieces of advice that made sense. He stressed the importance of not letting any of the wagons or their teams get out of control. Once they did and were on a runaway course going downslope, nothing could stop them.

What they had to do at the bad places was to evacuate all the youngsters, even the sick ones, from the wagons. They would cut down some of the stunted mountain saplings, trim them to poles of the right length, and lash them between the wheel spokes as rough brakes. Yes, the locked wheels were sure to skid on the slippery places, but if they weren't turning, they could be controlled. There'd have to be someone on the drivers' seats to handle the reins. And a couple of men up ahead to grab the headstalls of the lead mules and steady them. It wouldn't hurt, either, to have another pair of men positioned at the back of a wagon to throw their weight on the rear wheels in case they threatened to slough out of control.

No need to hurry any of it, Laban said. The wagons could be maneuvered across the rough places one at a time. It would take them a day or so longer than expected to complete the whole journey. But they'd be sure of making it.

For the next several hours, they worked at it as Laban had suggested.

An hour or so of guiding a team and bulky wagon along the hairpin turns of trails that often verged on sheer drop-offs was enough to melt the starch out of anyone's nerves and muscles. So each of the men and older boys put in an hour-long shift apiece on a wagon seat. Sureshot Stell served her stint along with them. Lazlo drove his own heavily laden outfit, taking turns with Laban and Robert Topbear, who were the best teamsters. They wanted to take no chances with its cargo.

Robert Topbear was in a black mood all day. When he'd come groggily awake in the morning, he'd found his long braids missing. Someone had sneaked up on him in the night and cut them off. Also, Laban had clamped down on his drinking after giving him hell for being drunk when they'd taken the camp. No more of it, Laban had warned.

As sunset drew on, they were easing down away from the most precipitous stretches, and everyone was starting to relax a little — even Robert Topbear. At a stop, as Lazlo swung off his wagon to be relieved by Topbear, the Indian was almost jaunty.

"Enjoying the trip, paleface? I hope so. It's likely to be your last."

Robert Topbear tilted his head toward Creed Jacks, who was standing a ways off but always keeping a vigil on Lazlo. "Or do you believe that once that fellow has what he wants, he'll let you go free to pose a future threat to him?"

"We will see."

"That we shall!" Robert Topbear said jauntily. He climbed laboriously to the driver's seat and took up the reins, saying across his shoulder, "I'll think of you when I'm sitting in an exotic bistro in N'Awleans, dining on *omelette aux fines herbes* and *fraises de bois,* and washing them down with twenty-dollar-a-bottle champagne — name your preference. I'll even tip a glass to your memory . . ."

Lazlo narrowly wondered if Topbear had been tipping a bottle or flask during the last hour. His spirits had picked up pretty fast. It would do to keep an eye on him.

When they started rolling again, Sureshot Stell had taken over the wagon ahead of Lazlo's while Mark Bly and the husky youth named Tim brought up the last two in line. The men tramped alongside the wagons, ready for any emergency, and Lazlo stayed close to his own . . . and to Robert Topbear.

There was a bad place ahead where the

trail clung to a precarious shelf that was hedged on their right by a vaulting wall of granite and, on their left, shouldered out over a nearly perpendicular drop. The trail slanted downward at a slight pitch but not enough to warrant braking the wheels. All the drivers had to do was hug the granite wall and watch themselves on the turns.

Knowing of a particularly bad one just ahead of them, Lazlo tramped up by the lead wagon and offered Sureshot Stell a word of caution. She only gave him a tight-lipped nod. He could see that she had her team under expert control.

He halted and turned back to pass the word to Robert Topbear. He surprised Topbear in the act of dropping a pint bottle into his pocket. Either he'd taken a pull at it or was about to. Lazlo started angrily toward him, but Topbear gave a defiant shake to his reins, hoorawing his team sharply ahead.

A ripple of panic ran through the mules.

Lazlo yelled, "Don't, you fool!"

Then he leaped aside, flattening himself against the granite wall as the gold wagon jolted ponderously past him.

Just forward of them, Sureshot Stell was carefully reining the mules on the sharp bend. As she began to swing around it, slowing to a crawl, Prunes and Matilda — Lazlo's mules — shied at the prospect of a sudden collision. But the weighted wagon behind them pushed them hard, and the squealing mules smashed at an angle against the rear right side of Stell's wagon.

It skewed wildly around on the slick rock and then tipped slowly outward, hung for a moment on two wheels, and crashed on its side. It didn't go over the brink of the precipice but lay tilted a foot or so from it while the mules thrashed against the tangle of their harness.

The impact brought Prunes and Matilda to a trembling, uncertain stop, with Robert Topbear sawing wildly on the reins and yelling, "Whoa!"

Lazlo was already running toward Stell's overturned wagon. It had stayed on the trail. But where was she? Thrown clear of the seat, she must have gone over the edge . . .

At first, scrambling onto the lip of the ledgerock, Lazlo saw nothing of her. And then, looking downward, he realized that she'd escaped death. But narrowly, and only for the moment.

She had tumbled maybe thirty feet down the slight outslant of the escarpment before she'd been brought up hard by a narrow ledge of rock. It had stopped her fall. But her body was twisted awkwardly across it. Any movement, even a slight one, might roll her off in a nearly straight fall down the remaining hundred or so feet to the base of the cliff.

"Don't move!" Lazlo yelled at her. "Just do not move!"

She managed to turn her face up toward him. It was set and white with pain. "Move . . . hell." She managed a husky whisper that barely reached him. "I think my arm is busted . . . Buster."

That tough streak of her humor . . . showing at a time like this! Lazlo thought, *God what a woman!* And forced a tight grin to his lips.

"Stay still," he told her. "We will get you up."

By now the others were pushing up alongside him.

The flush of cold died in Laban Ruddy's face as he looked down and saw his daughter's predicament. His face became as white as paper. "Oh, sweet Jesus. Stell . . . !"

Lazlo caught hold of his shoulder and gave him a hard shake. "Don't go faint now. Later if you need to. Now we must get her up. Do you have a rope with your stuff?"

Laban rubbed a hand across his temple. "A rope . . . a rope? Yes." He turned on his nephew. "Bije, dammit, get that cowman's rope out of our gear!" He swung back to Lazlo. "But *what?*"

"Her arm is broke, she thinks. So if we let a rope down, she cannot tie it around her. One of us must go down to her and bring her up."

Creed Jacks stood by, his flat gray eyes as bland as slate. "That should be interesting to see," he murmured. "Care to volunteer for the job, hunky?"

"I already have," said Lazlo. "All of you help me set this wagon back on its wheels."

The men pitched in to heave Stell's wagon upright, back off the rim; then they calmed the mules and cajoled them into hauling the wagon forward a few yards. It cleared off the rimrock above where Stell was stranded.

Bije came loping back with a coiled rope. Lazlo took it and shook it out: a cowman's fifty-foot lariat, never before used from the look of it. It would do fine.

Lazlo made an end of the rope fast around his torso under his arms as he gave instructions. Hutch and Bije, the two strongest of them, would hold their weights against the rope at the edge of the drop. The others would lend a pull behind them — as many of them, men and boys, as the rope's length would permit.

Hutch rolled his bloodshot eyes, grinning. "Hey there, little pard. You reckon you can trust me all that far?"

Lazlo smiled. "I think I can."

Glancing at Laban Ruddy, he said, "Colonel, can I trust you to put a bullet through my big pard's head if he lets go the rope?"

"You can," Laban declared flatly. "You can depend on it. Damn it, Kusik, get going now!"

Lazlo let himself down over the rim, gripping the rope in both hands and walking backward, feeling the strain of his weight on the tough hemp. He didn't look downward any more often than he had to. Just a glance at the almost sheer drop was enough to chill a man's guts.

Fleetingly, though, he had to look down now and again so he could maneuver himself close to Stell's side.

"All right!" he yelled at the men above. "Hold steady now!"

There wasn't enough room on the ledge for him to place his feet and settle his own weight. He would have to get Stell off it while he dangled on a rope above a free fall

. . . and trust that the men's braced strength could handle their combined weight.

Sprawled on the rocky projection, Stell turned her pain-glazed eyes just enough to meet his. She whispered, "What now, Buster? Best make it good and fast because this arm is paining me something fierce. I might just go and pass out on you."

"You do," Lazlo said quietly, "and it could get a lot worse. You have one good arm, and I think we will need it to get us both out of this."

"Good. How do we do it?"

It depended on his getting both arms tightly around her waist and, if she could manage it, getting her good arm around his neck at the same time. Then they could be pulled up. All the way they would have to hold to each other as tightly as they could.

"I cannot walk back up like I did coming down," he said. "So it will be very rough."

"It was easy enough coming down for me too, Buster . . ." A grin twitched the corners of her mouth. "It's just that it hurt like hell after I got here. All right. Let's get us on up."

Somehow they managed it.

Lazlo worked himself into a position to

circle her body with his thick arms while she got her sound arm fast around his neck. He had a hard time getting his right arm under her waist where it rested against the rock — and every movement cost Stell excruciating pain. Once he heard (or thought he heard) the sickening grate of bone on bone in her shattered arm. He feared she'd pass out before he could get a secure hold on her.

But she didn't. Awkwardly the two of them worked her weight over to the lip of the ledge till she rolled off it and swung heavily against him, and they clung together over the yawning gulf.

Now, with her good arm crooked as tightly as death around his neck, she managed to whisper, "All right, Buster. Best we lose no time."

"Haul away," Lazlo yelled at the men above. "And do it slow, you hear?"

It was no easy task. She was a good-sized woman, on the thin and wiry side but big-boned, and his arms grew numb as he and Stell bumped slowly upward along the flinty irregular wall. All the way Stell's face was close to his, almost bloodless with pain, her eyes and lips shut tight. But she never relaxed her grip.

Then their bodies were jogging along the

rimrock and hands were dragging them up and over it.

Stell gave way to her pain and passed out almost at once. The attention of Laban, Myra Mae, and Bije was entirely on Stell. They were worried about her arm, but nobody had a clear idea of what to do about it. Then Miss Aretha pushed herself abruptly to Stell's side and knelt by her, eyes snapping.

"Get away, all of you! You'll do her more harm than anything, poking around at her. I have nursed people through sickness, and I know about broken bones . . ."

Nobody seemed to care what shape Lazlo was in, so he lay quietly on his back for a few moments. As he started to get up, Mark Bly came over and extended a hand to him. Robert Topbear, on his other side, did the same.

Lazlo grabbed their hands and they swung him to his feet.

"You're quite a fellow, Mr. Kusik," Mark said fervently. "I swear to you — nothing in God's world could make me try such a thing as you just did!"

"You would try it," Lazlo said quietly, "if it was something had to be done. And someone had to do it. Then you would."

His gaze swiveled to Creed Jacks,

standing a little ways off, his mouth fixed in a small nerveless smile. He shook his head once, as if unable to fathom all this commotion and yet mildly intrigued by it. His glance crossed Lazlo's, and his lips parted in a silent laugh.

You cold-blooded bastard, thought Lazlo. *Anybody could be alive or dead; it's all the same to you if you get what you want.*

He looked at Robert Topbear.

The Indian's brown face seemed grayish in the fading light. He met Lazlo's look stonily. Nobody but him, Lazlo was sure, had noticed Topbear's secret tippling or how it had led to an accident that had nearly cost Stell Ruddy's life.

I will say nothing, Lazlo thought. *Now it is up to him.*

The others were moving away with Stell, carrying her to a nearby wagon where Miss Aretha could properly treat her arm. Robert Topbear remained as he was, standing close to the rimrock like a man frozen in place. Lazlo lingered near him, wondering if Topbear might try something foolish.

Foolish or not, Robert Topbear did it. He fumbled in the pocket of his Mackinaw, pulled out the half-empty bottle and gazed at it a moment. A long shudder ran through him. He pulled his arm back and flung the bottle out over the gulf. It spun end over end, arced inward to meet an angle of black snow-veined rock far below, and shattered to bits.

CHAPTER 16

Aretha Bly set and splinted the broken arm as expertly as any sawbones. (Somehow, Lazlo thought, you'd expect exactly that of her.) She gave Stell a dose of laudanum from her small but well-stocked trunk of medical supplies. Very brusque and businesslike about it all, Miss Aretha then turned her attention to getting supper prepared. When Laban Ruddy tried his best to express his thanks, she all but ignored him. For once Laban's eloquence failed him; he could only stammer. From the outset she'd made no effort to conceal the icy contempt she felt for Laban and his crew, and that was enough to squelch anyone.

Maybe, too, it was why Laban showed not a fleck of gratitude to Lazlo Kusik, who hadn't expected any. Lazlo didn't blame him. Badly shaken by his daughter's brush with death, Laban was also a man sadly confused . . . trying to sort out a scramble of balances in his mind. The man he'd set out to rob and kill had saved his daughter's life.

254

How could he square that with himself?

Laban didn't try. At least not right away. Predictably, he took refuge in his bottle. Robert Topbear, however, held to whatever resolve he'd made for himself there on the canyon rim. Keeping himself busy helped.

When they made camp for the night, in a sheltered swale a half-mile farther on, Topbear took charge of the wood detail, sending the kids out to scare up brush and then showing them how to build their fires Indian-style, small and clean and almost smokeless. He even kept his temper when Cyrus (who else?) came capering up with Topbear's confiscated braids flapping from under the edge of his ragged cap, while he gave out loud war whoops. Some of the other kids followed him in a wild, leaping dance around one of the fires.

Robert Topbear watched them in tight-lipped silence. Finally his moon face broke in a rueful smile. Then a burst of laughter rolled out of him.

Lazlo sat off by himself on his blanket roll, grinning a little at the kids' antics, drumming the fingers of one hand on his knee. But he felt withdrawn from all of them. His own situation hadn't changed by a whit.

Or had it? The odds against him must

have softened a little. Laban and his people, outside of Bije, couldn't help but re-weigh their intentions toward him. That Lazlo had saved Bije's cousin wouldn't balance off his killing of Bije's brother. Probably nothing would. But maybe Laban could keep Bije in check.

Nothing at all would sway Creed Jacks.

No matter what sort of move Lazlo made, Jacks was there, hovering on the edge of his awareness, staying at a distance but always in sight of him.

It would be a lot easier to circumvent Hutch, if a man got the chance. Hutch was now steadily and sullenly drunk nearly all the time. He shambled about the camp muttering incoherently to himself. His face twitched with a bloated and bleary hatred every time he looked at Lazlo. He was, Lazlo decided, a man losing his grip on sanity, making him the one to watch most of all. While Creed Jacks had an impersonal interest in keeping Lazlo alive, Hutch was now consumed solely by a hunger for retribution that fed on itself and grew hourly.

So did his lust for nubile young Cissie O'Halloran. He made it so obvious with his long burning stares at the girl that finally she retreated inside one of the wagons and stayed there.

Hard to do anything about a man just staring, no matter what you were sure was on his mind. Briefly, earlier in the day, Lazlo and Mark Bly had talked it over. They'd agreed to watch out for Cissie, one of them trying to stay in her vicinity all the time. What else could they do?

Myra Mae Ruddy came walking across the camp, straight over to Lazlo. She stopped in front of him, saying in a half-shy, half-embarrassed way, "My sister wants to talk to you."

"Does she. What about?"

"I just know what she said to tell you." A trace of color rose in the girl's wan face. "Mr. Kusik, I . . . well, I just want to say *I* am mighty grateful to you, anyway. For what you did for Stell."

Lazlo rose to his feet, nodding. "So then, I will —"

Myra Mae bent over in a sudden fit of coughing. When it ended and she'd straightened up to meet his gaze with a defiant, bitter stare, he went on mildly, "I will go talk to her. Thank you."

He tramped across the camp to one of the wagons, where Sureshot Stell sat on a ground tarp, wrapped in thick blankets. Her back was propped against a wagon wheel.

Lazlo halted and gazed down at her. "Hello. How are you feeling?"

"Rotten."

"Maybe you should get some sleep now."

"Sleep, hell," she said irritably. "I tried to and couldn't. God, if I could get any sleep, I'd damn well be getting it."

She leaned her head back against the wheel, shutting her eyes. Her face was colorless and drawn and tired. Her broken arm was muffled in a blanket wrapped many times around the splints and bandages. The pain must be considerable, even if dulled by laudanum. Too bad that something more up to date, like morphine, was not available.

Suddenly her eyes opened, darkly snapping at him.

"Will you for God's sake hunker down so's we can converse better? Or do you like to just stand there with your face hanging out?"

Lazlo dropped down on his haunches beside her, saying gravely, "Well, it is good to see you have changed only one way."

"Yeah. That's pretty obvious." Stell grinned very faintly. "The busted arm, huh . . . Buster?"

"No. I mean this is the first time I have not seen you with a gun or reins in your hands."

For a moment she eyed him almost angrily and then let out a soft burst of laughter. "I reckon it is. And I reckon my days as a shootist are done with, too."

"That does not follow. Maybe the arm will heal up good as new."

"Sure. And maybe Arctic owls will winter in N'Awleans some of these times. And maybe, just maybe, I am sick to death of being a trick shot in Pa's little circus." Avoiding the question in his eyes, she tipped her head forward, lowering her gaze. "Anyway . . . reckon I just wanted to say thank you to your face. You got that coming."

Lazlo said dryly, "Thank *you*."

"Don't you sound so damn smart!" Her eyes became hard and bleak. "You killed my cousin Ab. You expect me to just up and forget that?"

"No," he said quietly, "it is not a thing anyone forgets, ever. I never had to kill a man before. You think I will forget? How did your pa tell you it happened?"

Grudgingly, Stell told him what Laban had told her of the incident at Lazlo's claim. Robert Topbear, she added, had corroborated Laban's story.

"Mostly, then, they told you how it happened," Lazlo agreed soberly. "Save for one thing. Your cousin Ab went for his gun. I had no choice but to shoot first. Did they tell you that?"

"Well, no," she said sullenly, not meeting his eyes. "No, but even so —"

"Even so," Lazlo broke in roughly, "even if I had shot him in cold blood, he would have earned what he got. So would your pa and the others. They jumped my claim. They would let me freeze to death to get out of me what they wanted."

"All right," she muttered, "you don't need to spell it out no more."

"You believe me then?"

"Yes, damn it! What more you want?"

"That much." Lazlo rocked his weight back on his heels. "Something else too. If you want to say it. How do you like what he — your pa — and Hutch and this Jacks fellow have set out to do to me?"

Stell shook her head from side to side, slowly and wearily. "Like? What's liking got to do with it? You think I come along on this party to help kill you and take your gold? I come along to . . . oh hell."

"To what?"

"You can believe it or not," she snapped. "I couldn't care less. What I come along for was to see if there was some way I could lend you a hand. I mean, hell, there was no way I could keep all of 'em from going after you, if they was set on it. But maybe, if I come along, I could keep 'em from going too far."

"Such as killing me, eh?"

"Yeah. All of 'em was minded to. And I wasn't about to let Pa and Bije murder a man if I could stop it." Her tone was still half-angry; she turned her gaze down. "I was damn sure there was more to the story than they told. I mean, I just never had you pegged as that sort. An honest-to-God killer."

"I am not." Lazlo picked up a handful of snow and juggled it in his palm, scowling at it. "What do your pa and his friends really mean for me then? Do you know?"

"Nothing for sure. You reckon they confide in me?" She paused, frowning. "I did catch a mite of their talk off and on. What I gathered they agreed on was letting you get this party of orphans through to Carson's Crossing, to suit your wishes. Also they would sell the gold in your wagon for current value on the market, then backtrack with you to Bozetown where you was to sign over your claim to the three of 'em — Pa and Jacks and Prouter. That's about all I got. I was pretty sure, even so, that they would try to do away with you right after that."

Lazlo nodded. Why shouldn't it work out that way? The mountain arm they were crossing formed a divide between two counties. There was a sheriff in Carson's Crossing because it was a county seat. But he wouldn't care less about what happened in a place such as Bozetown, out of his jurisdiction, so isolated it didn't even have a deputy sheriff of its own county to keep order. The county board wouldn't grant funds for such a deputy's salary. Marshal Abe Friendly was paid out of the pockets of Bozetown's own locals. Even if the authorities of either county got word that something crooked was afoot, what would they do about it?

"I reckon the same as you," he said. "Now tell me this, if you can, Stell —"

"My name's Stella. Damn it, call me that if you got to call me som'at!"

"All right. Can I ask how your pa feels about me now, since I helped you out?"

"Lord, I don't know." Stella rolled her head back against the wheel rim, tiredly. "He was so hell-afire to catch up with you. Hired horses for all of us at the Bozetown livery barn and left our wagons sheltered there, which cost a pretty penny Pa couldn't afford to pay. Not since you and Prouter and that Limey fellow won so

262

much at our expense. Prouter and Creed Jacks, they footed our bill to the livery man, which only made Pa the madder. His pride felt stung. Now . . ."

"Now what?"

"Well, I just don't know, Buster. I reckon neither does he. I'd hazard he is more kindly disposed toward you than formerly. But when he ain't sure what he thinks, he crawls back into his bottle. Which he has done, you see."

Lazlo scrubbed a palm across his jaw in a savage wash of irritation. "Yes, I see. That way, anyhow, he is never at a loss. And if he runs low on good booze, there is always his patent medicine."

To his surprise, Stella chuckled in a quiet, friendly, tired way. "Yeah, there sure is. 'Colonel' Ruddy! He's never been a colonel of a damn thing. Ain't even a courtesy colonel like they have in the South. What the hell, though, Buster — he's still my pa. You know what I mean?"

"Yes," Lazlo said gently. "But I wonder what you think of some other things. Those nephews of his, your cousins. They killed Aussie . . . the 'Limey fellow' you mentioned."

"Pa told me. I know."

"What did you feel about that?"

"Purely sick," Stella said very quietly. "So did Myra Mae. And Bob Topbear. But Ab and Bije claimed it was an accident. Don't tell me that don't make what happened to your friend any better. I know it don't. But it's done. So what's the good of raking it up now?"

She was right. In a civilized place, civilized men would pass a civilized judgment on it all. But here?

"No good." Lazlo echoed his own thought. "Still, there is Creed Jacks." He paused, holding her eyes intensely. "He would have killed that child if I had not given up."

Stella looked down, pressing her lips together. "I know it. I had no idea of how far a man like that would go. I am pretty sure Pa didn't either."

"Now Jacks has taken over the whole game."

"Don't reckon any of us looked to that either." Stella moved her blanketed arm in a slight, angry, hopeless gesture. "Now there's not a damn thing we can do about it. I vowed I would keep a sharp eye on Mr. Jacks. But what in blazes can I do with an arm out of commission? Can't even hold a long gun now, much less shoot one."

Lazlo didn't have to look around to be

sure that Creed Jacks was standing not too far off and that his stare was boring into the back of Lazlo's head.

"Can your sister? She holds a gun like she can use one."

"You blamed right she can use it. I learned her myself. And she don't hone for your scalp any more'n I do, but damned if I'd let her go up against that Jacks."

Lazlo nodded soberly. "She is a very sick girl, your sister."

"Yeah. Damn Pa! Myra Mae needs to winter-warm. But we're all of a part, us Ruddys. When Pa had to go kiting after you . . . well, even Myra Mae had to lug along."

Mark Bly had been keeping as close an eye on Myra Mae Ruddy as Creed Jacks was holding on Lazlo Kusik, only more surreptitiously. After she spoke briefly to Kusik and Kusik went over to talk with her sister, Myra stepped off by herself into the pale darkness beyond the fires.

Mark moved in that direction himself, hesitantly. Then, hearing the girl's fitful, wracking bursts of coughing, he quickened his pace. He came on her standing out of the firelight, in the lee of a great boulder, a mittened hand braced against it for support. Gradually the fit subsided and she straightened up, pulling a sleeve across her tear-streaked face. Now she saw Mark standing a few yards away — tall and gauntly awkward and not knowing what to say.

"You looking for som'at?" she said stonily.

"Oh, no." Mark moved his hands aimlessly. "Nothing. It's just . . . well, that terrible cough of yours, I wondered if there was something I — we," he amended hastily, "my sister and I, might do. She knows something of medicine."

"I saw that. She did almighty well by my sister." Tipped up, Myra Mae's pale face seemed sort of ethereal in the dimness. "I meant to thank her for that. But she ain't — isn't too approachable, you know? I allow she don't — doesn't think any too highly of our crew. Not that I blame her."

"Well," he said awkwardly, "she can be quite reserved with strangers. But she could have been an outstanding physician, had she set out to be one."

"A lady doctor?"

"There are a few of them, you know."

Myra Mae opened her mouth to reply, but the words dissolved in another terrible paroxysm of coughing. She swayed forward, and Mark moved swiftly to catch her by the shoulders. She turned her head from him as the fit went on. When it ebbed at last, she did not step away from him.

Clumsily, he took a hand from one of her shoulders, gently, so that she could draw away if she wished. But she didn't. She leaned tiredly, gratefully, against his arm and side. He felt her violent shivering even through their heavy clothing.

"Reckon I am about done up," she said quietly. "Just a question of how long I have got."

Her tone was calm and fatalistic. But under it he sensed a cry of despairing protest against the wasting of a life so brief she'd barely tasted the fruits of living. And felt the protest rise, unbidden, in his own throat and push out in sharp, angry words:

"You'll have time! My God, you must have time. You can't just . . ." He paused, swallowing. "Look, Miss Ruddy. Haven't you — or any of your family — consulted physicians?"

"Oh . . . sure." Her head stirred listlessly, a pale coil of her hair brushing his cheek. "The best that Pa could engage in N'Awleans. That's Dr. Terrebone. All he could give was advice. Good enough advice, I reckon. Mostly it came down to that I should not exert myself any more'n I had to. But our outfit travels a lot, you see, and I was not about to be left behind this season. Thought I could weather it out all right. Maybe . . . maybe I am sicker than I knew."

"I should say so! I'm surprised your father permitted . . ."

"Pa? He wanted me to stay in N'Awleans with a lady cousin of his. So did Stella. I argued something fierce and they gave in. It's just, I don't know, you get used to being with your people all the time, and you don't want to shake loose of 'em, even for a spell."

"I know," Mark said wryly.

"You do?"

"Well, I've followed my sister's lead all my life. Guess I'm of an age where I should 'shake loose,' but . . . it's a hard habit to get out of."

"It sure is," she said wearily. "I reckon that . . ."

Her voice trailed away.

Laban Ruddy had come on the scene, stepping just a little around the rock, halting for a full sight of them. Drink and anger and firelight deepened the florid hue of his face.

"May I ask, sir, what you are about?"

"Nothing at all." Carefully, Mark took

his arm from the girl's shoulders and moved away from her. He felt a heavy warmth beating into his own face. "Miss Ruddy was taken with a violent cough. I hoped I might help her. I meant no harm."

"Pa —" Myra Mae began.

"Be still, girl." Laban stared fixedly at Mark for some moments. At last, slowly, the tension ran out of him.

"I believe you," he said tonelessly. "You are a gentleman, Mr. Bly. And, it's clear, hardly one of the rakish kind. But I'd prefer that you not converse with my daughter, at least in this clandestine manner. Pray don't let it happen again. Back to camp with you, girl."

Quietly and wearily, Myra Mae shook her head. "Pa, it can't matter now, can it? He was just being nice. Why can't a boy talk to me if he wants? Why can't I talk to him? There's not a whole lot else anyone who's in the condition I am can —"

"That's not true!" Laban spoke sharply, angrily, but under his words Mark sensed a chill of fear. "Good God, Myra Mae! You're going to be all right. Do you hear? Shortly we'll be in Carson's Crossing, and we can winter there. We needn't stir from the place till you're fit! I promise — !"

He broke off.

269

The terrible coughing came again. Myra Mae was convulsed by it. She took a single groping step and then, like a puppet with all its strings cut, bowed over and crumpled to the ground.

But it wasn't just another fit. The girl rolled onto her back, hands scrabbling at the snow. Her whole body writhed and twisted. Her eyes were wide and unseeing, the whites of them marbled by starlight. Mark heard awful rasping sounds. Even in this bad light he could see, to his horror, the whiteness of her face darkening, swelling with congestion.

Her hands came up to her throat, fumbling and clutching, as if to tear away other, invisible hands that had already fixed on it.

"Myra!" her father screamed.

Even in that frozen moment, paralyzed by his own helplessness, Mark remembered a long-gone night of his childhood. A New York settlement house to which Aretha had been summoned, he accompanying her, where they had seen an elderly man, stricken by grippe and asthma and consumption, slowly dying before their eyes in this exact way.

Myra Mae Ruddy was strangling to death.

CHAPTER 17

Mark and Laban carried her over by one of the fires. Aretha was already hurrying up, dropping to her knees by the girl as they set her down in the flickering light. The children came running up too, murmurous and wide-eyed.

"Clear away, all of you," Aretha snapped without looking at them. "Fetch more wood here if you want to be useful. Build up this fire!"

All the kids hurried to comply.

Thank God, Mark thought fervently. *Thank God 'Retha is here to take things in hand!*

Maybe it was too late, even so.

Myra Mae's hands had dropped away from her throat. Her convulsions had ebbed to a faint twitching. Her head had turned crookedly to one side, eyelids closed and the lashes veiling her cheeks. Even the congested darkness seemed to fade out of her face except where it pulsed in the veins of her temples. Only her mouth kept working like that of a grounded fish, the guttural sounds rasping out of it with an ominous rhythm that seemed to dwindle off even as he listened.

In a dim corner of his mind, Mark noted that Lazlo Kusik had come up with Stell Ruddy leaning on his arm. The terror that Mark himself felt was mirrored on Stell's face and on Laban's too.

Myra Mae was dying before their eyes. They knew it. And knew there wasn't a thing they could do.

But Aretha was steady as steel of course. She lifted the girl's wrist and took her pulse, her own lips silently counting off the seconds. Then she looked at Laban, saying flatly: "Mr. Ruddy!"

"Yes," Laban said shakily. "My God, Miss, if there is *anything* — !"

"There may be," Aretha said crisply. "Is it remotely possible that your daughter has been attended recently by a physician who had ample opportunity to study her condition?"

"Why . . . yes. Dr. Terrebone —"

"Terrebone of New Orleans?"

"Yes, the same. He is —"

"I know who he is," she said impatiently. "Possibly the nation's leading authority on malaises of the respiratory tract. What did he have to say regarding the health of your daughter?"

Shaking and distraught as he was, Laban got out in a garbled way enough of what Dr. Terrebone had told him to satisfy Aretha. Essentially, Myra Mae's affliction was asthmatic rather than consumptive. Just now, probably, her throat had reached such a crucial stage of getting clogged with matter that it was choking away her life. Aretha didn't bother to say as much. Typically, all her attention was for the dying girl. But Mark knew. Knew from his remembrance of that night when, as a child, he had seen a man strangling the same way. And he also remembered how Aretha had saved the man.

Aretha turned sharply toward him. Before she could speak, he said, "You need a tube, 'Retha. A narrow tube of some kind —"

"Yes! But what is there?" Her brow furrowed. "Nothing in our supplies that will serve —"

"Just a minute."

Mark was hurrying off even as he spoke, and Aretha called after him, "Be quick! She may not have even a minute."

Mark found what he was looking for at the clearing's edge where a clump of winter-killed plants — or weeds — stuck out of the snow. He didn't know what they were and it didn't matter. All that mattered was that the stems were thin and tough and hollow. He knew as much because earlier, out of idle curiosity, he'd broken one off and examined it.

Digging out his pocketknife, he unfolded the small blade and clipped off one of the straight brown stalks. Then he cut off the upper part with its cluster of withered leaves. He peered through the six-inch reed that remained. It was clearly hollow to the end.

Mark returned to the fire and handed the stalk to Aretha. She pointed at the knife in his hand and said, "Give that a turn in the fire, Mark. Quickly!"

Mark turned the small blade several times in the flames and silently handed it to her.

By now Myra Mae was no longer moving. Only a faint noise gurgled from her throat. Aretha had already opened her coat and the collar of her shirt. Now, in a crouching position, she raised Myra Mae's head to her knees and placed the point of the blade to the base of the girl's throat.

"My God, woman!" Laban Ruddy burst out. "What in the devil are you about?"

"About, I hope," Aretha said very quietly, "to save your daughter's life, Mr. Ruddy. You may find it —"

"You'll kill her!"

"I will not kill her. But she will surely die if the substance that has filled her throat is not removed. There is no other way. You may find it harrowing to watch. I suggest you avert your eyes."

Laban's face worked with a kind of wild-eyed frenzy. But he didn't move, nor did he look away, as Aretha made a small deft incision in the girl's throat. Blood streamed down each side of her neck as Aretha sank an end of the slim pipe into the wound and set her lips to the other end.

She sucked audibly. Then turned her head and spat out a mouthful of thick yellow-white fluid stained with blood. The onlookers murmured. Dimly Mark recalled what Aretha had used that other time to save the elderly man: a hollow bamboo pen.

Aretha repeated the procedure, at the same time pressing firmly on the girl's chest with a steady rocking motion, pushing down and then letting up.

She sucked out another mouthful of discolored matter and spat it aside. Then another.

Suddenly Myra Mae's lips parted. Mark heard a deep rushing sigh. God. It was working. Thank God. He felt his own throat fill with a prayer of thanksgiving. Why should the saving of this girl's life be so important to him? He only knew that it was.

Barely pausing, Aretha said crisply, "Cissie!"

"Yes'm?" Cissie O'Halloran said in a hushed voice.

"You know where my sewing basket is, in the wagon. Get it, please."

Aretha did not cease drawing up and spitting out the fluid that had stopped up Myra Mae's throat. And she kept up the steady in-and-out pumping of her hand on the girl's chest. Now the yellowish poison was dwindling to a few saffron streaks in the bright flow of blood.

Aretha pulled the reed out of Myra Mae's throat and then turned her head sideways so the wound would drain freely. Aretha pressed her fingers over the incision to stanch the blood flow. Meantime she continued an even, rhythmic pressure of her other hand to stimulate the girl's respiration.

Cissie came running back with the sewing basket.

"Thread a needle," Aretha told her. "Make haste, girl. I'll want at least a foot of doubled thread on it . . ."

Myra Mae was still only drowsily conscious as Aretha stitched up the muscle and tissue and skin of her throat. She did it as quickly and neatly as another woman might have stitched up squares of fabric over the stretch of a quilting frame.

Everyone, all of the grown-ups and children who were gathered around, looked on with a kind of awed wonderment. All except Mark. He was used to this sort of thing.

Aretha, always reticent on such matters, wouldn't readily reveal how she'd come by the precise, lifesaving skills he'd seen her use with an assurance that would put some certified practitioners of medicine to shame. She'd always been so full of surprising revelations of that sort that over the years Mark had ceased to wonder. Aretha had a total dedication. Maybe a lot of it was just instinct with her. All you could do was accept and not try to understand it.

Aretha said tiredly, "There you are, Mr. Ruddy. Your daughter is saved. For the time being. I would suggest that as soon as we get to Carson's Crossing, you place her in the local hospital — I understand that some Catholic sisters have established a very good one there — and have her remain there until she is quite recovered. I can give you no other advice."

Laban had nothing to say. Neither did anyone else. Maybe some of it would come out later.

Gently Aretha shifted the girl's head from her lap to a folded blanket provided by one of the children. Then she stood up and walked over to the fire that blazed in front of the wagon where she and Mark had their belongings stored. She picked up a canteen of water near the fire, took a swallow of water from it, rinsed her mouth, and spat. She did the same again and then wiped off the mouth of the canteen. She poured the rest of the water into a blackened coffeepot, dumped in some Triple X, and set the pot by the fire's edge.

Mark tramped over and halted beside her. She gave a little start, as if roused from a private revery, and smiled at him.

"Oh . . . Mark. It went quite well, didn't it?"

"I believe it did." His tone was stiff, almost angry. " 'Retha . . . will you for God's sake say out loud what you're thinking?"

"All right." She shook her head once,

gently and tiredly. "You're fond of that girl, aren't you?"

"Yes."

"May I ask why?"

"I don't know," he said woodenly.

Nor did he. Myra Mae Ruddy was very pretty — no, she was a truly lovely girl — and her being ill and despairing had made him feel protective toward her. Otherwise she didn't seem exceptional in any way. A very ordinary girl and practically a stranger to him. Also, to judge from appearances, she didn't come from anything like worthwhile blood.

No need to say any of this to Aretha. She'd know. What he did say, quietly and stubbornly, was: "None of it makes any difference, 'Retha. I can't say why. That's how it is."

"Very well, Mark." She brushed a hand across the soaked skirt of her dress. "Goodness, all this blood! I guess I had better go and change —"

" 'Retha!"

Mark said it so sharply that she turned her head and looked straight at him. He went on doggedly, " 'Retha, I think Miss Ruddy is a pure girl. Notwithstanding her . . . relatives, I believe she is."

"Oh Mark . . ." Aretha bent her head,

again gently shaking it. Suddenly he realized she was quietly laughing. "Do you know something? It's only to the impure that all things are impure."

Mark stared at her in a baffled and slightly outraged way. "What do you mean?"

"Mark, dear, listen. Through all your growing up, you accompanied me I don't know how many times on my calls to settlement houses and the like. Don't you think I've seen it all? The whole range of the human condition? And haven't *you*?"

"Well . . ."

"As to the kind of thing a man and woman can find between them, I believe I understand it well enough. I can even feel it in a way. But" — her hands made a small graceful movement of negation — "it is just not in my stars. Do you understand? I can't go that way. If you can, all blessings to you!"

Mark swallowed. " 'Retha . . . what are you saying, exactly?"

"That it's about time you cut free of my apron strings. It's just that up till now, you've never given me a hint that you cared to. If you can now, Mark, do it!"

"Even if I . . . oh hell! Even if I made a big mistake?"

"Of course you might. But that's the chance one takes. No matter what course you pursue, you take that chance always." Smiling, she stood up and took hold of his arms, giving him a little shake. "You know what's worried me more than anything where you're concerned? That you might always be inclined to follow in my steps. And you can't. It's no way of life for a man. Now, don't you think you've enough to sleep on and think about? And wouldn't you care for a cup of coffee?"

"Coffee. Sure, fine." Mark gazed at her for a long, wondering moment. "You know, 'Retha, we've known each other all our lives —"

"All your life, boy, don't you mean?"

"I guess I do," he said dryly. "What gets me is that after all that time, you can still fetch me a mighty surprise."

The group around the fire broke up. The kids straggled back to the wagons and made their preparations for sleep. Laban and Bije carried Myra Mae to their wagon and put her inside in a nest of blankets. Stella climbed into the wagon beside her, saying that she couldn't sleep anyway so she might as well sit up and watch over her sister.

Creed Jacks told Lazlo Kusik to turn in too; he made sure that Lazlo spread his soogans close to a fire where Jacks could readily keep him in sight.

Laban had a bad case of the shakes as he hunkered down by a fire and took a drink from his flask. For once, he had a good reason for slugging it down other than the fact he just liked to drink. It was too much for a man to take in all at once, he thought miserably. Who would have believed that so many things could become turned around in a few short hours?

He owed Lazlo Kusik for Stella's life. On Myra Mae's account, there was Aretha Bly to thank. And her brother too.

None of it, Laban knew in savage self-recrimination, need have happened. If only he hadn't kited off after Kusik in a frenzy for revenge . . . and Kusik's gold. Otherwise they'd be well out of this desolate frozen country by now. Back to a better climate where, providentially, a sound treatment for Myra Mae's illness might still be found.

Laban groaned aloud and pounded a gloved fist on his knee.

"Thinking on this 'n' that, are you, partner?"

Creed Jacks spoke lightly, settling on his haunches on the other side of the fire. He rubbed his hands together and held them to the heat, palms out. His eyes were lambent in the orange light.

Laban took another pull at his flask. "You might say that, Mr. Jacks."

Creed Jacks glanced at Hutch and Bije, who were standing a little way off, sullenly eyeing the two of them. Robert Topbear was nearby, his moon face an inscrutable mask.

"Very well, Colonel. Would you care to say your piece here and now in front of all concerned?"

"If you want."

"I want."

Creed Jacks beckoned to Hutch, who shambled over and stood by the fire, his eyes bloodshot and surly. Slowly now, Bije drifted up beside Hutch and in another moment so did Robert Topbear.

"Now," Creed Jacks said pleasantly, "we're all friends here, *bueno compadres,* partners and fellow conspirators. That sort of thing, eh? Let's have it straight out, Colonel. With a title like that, you should exert a voice of authority. Pipe up right now, won't you?"

Even in his fog of liquor, Laban felt a

needle of fear as he met Creed Jacks's show-nothing eyes. But a core of determination hardened in him.

"I want to call our deal off, Jacks. Things have changed. These people . . . I am grateful to them."

"I would fancy so." Creed Jacks picked up a stick and poked at the embers, his face sallow in their glow. "Kusik and his friends saved your daughters' lives. Ergo you are prepared to forgive his killing of your nephew. And to forgo your designs on his gold. I can even comprehend why such trivia weigh so heavily with you."

Creed Jacks paused, smiling gently. "Regrettably none of it matters to me. Not by the tiniest pinch of mouse dung. Why should it?"

"Jacks — !"

"Colonel," Creed Jacks's voice cut as quietly and surely as a knife, shutting Laban off, "let us take a vote, shall we?" He glanced at Robert Topbear. "How do you feel about it, Chief?"

Robert Topbear said tonelessly, "I will go as the colonel does."

"My, what a surprise." Creed Jacks shuttled a mild glance at Hutch. "Mr. Prouter?"

"All I want," Hutch rumbled, "is to

carve that hunky bastard's liver out. And that is God's truth."

"Mr. Willet?"

Bije hesitated, shifting from one foot to the other. He sent Laban an owlish and uneasy look.

There were two kinds of family loyalty, Laban thought obscurely. One kind went to your next-to-nearest kin, the other to your nearest. Lazlo Kusik had killed Bije's brother. That would be all of it for Bije, Laban knew, even before Bije muttered, "Reckon I will side with you, Mr. Jacks."

"Fine. Fine!" Creed Jacks showed all his teeth in a smile that made Laban think of bared bone. "It would seem you're out-voted, Colonel. Not, understand, that it makes a whit of difference. Just wanted to be sure you get the whole picture in, shall we say, balance. We struck a bargain at the outset, my friend. And you are going to stick to it. Right to the end of the line."

CHAPTER 18

Before the wagons started out the next morning, Lazlo walked off into the brush to relieve his bladder. He'd just finished up when a mild and sardonic voice spoke from a few yards behind him, giving him a bad start.

"Ah there, hunky! Glad to see you weren't planning to take a long walk out on us. Or, perhaps, cooking up a foolish *coup* that would only get you, and possibly some of your companions, killed. Of course," Creed Jacks added with a mild chuckle, "not being a mind reader, I can't really be sure about that last, can I?"

Lazlo shook his head. "No, not even you. Now, Mr. Jacks, you want to relieve yourself too?"

"Oh, I'm relieved, hunky. You just did it for me."

Creed Jacks stepped back and clear of the wands of brush, motioning Lazlo out too. He was very careful always not to let Lazlo get within reach of him. He followed at a distance of several yards as Lazlo tramped back toward camp.

It dovetailed with the whole animal-quick alertness of the man. Even after you turned in at night, you couldn't be sure whether Creed Jacks was asleep or pretending to be. He'd lay on his side facing you, a safe distance away but not too far, hat tilted on the side of his head to keep his face in shadow. And you could be sure — or could you? — that a gun was clamped in his fist under the blanket.

Creed Jacks was only flesh and blood. He had to relax his vigilance sometime. But how could you know when? Even if he were willing to gamble his own life, Lazlo couldn't bring himself to jeopardize the lives of all these kids who had a hope of something better for the first time. Just as surely he couldn't endanger the lives of the Blys or the Ruddys by any action of his.

There was a penalty, he thought heavily, for getting involved with other people. It whittled away a man's own options almost to nothing . . .

As the wagons inched down the crooked switchbacks out of the mountains, the going became easier in some respects, harder in others. A lot of snow had accumulated in the lower passes. Not only had it pelted down more fiercely on this side of the peaks, filling the trails deeply in some places, it had also banked thickly along the rims and walls of the narrow canyons through which the trails wound. The early daylight was gray, unrelieved by even a hint of sun. It had an eerie, dispiriting effect. Closed in by canyon walls, fighting their slow way through drifts, both the children and grown-ups felt a depression that weighed on their minds and muscles.

Then they were on the last rough rising contour of country that remained before the trail dipped off into the level basin where Carson's Crossing lay. From here on they should have easier going.

Alone of the party, Robert Topbear appeared to be on top of the world. He was clear-eyed and sober, and getting more so by the hour. He was still in flabby condition; it would take months of drying out to flush the dregs of heavy boozing out of his system if he kept to his resolve. Right now it gave Lazlo a good feeling to watch him slogging doggedly through the drifts and, wherever the wagons bogged down, lending all the strength he could to helping them inch ahead.

Close to midday, a misty orb of sun showed above the rimrock on their left side. The gray sky turned to a lighter gray. Not a very auspicious token, but enough to pick everyone's spirits up a little. And the wagons were on a stretch that promised easier travel.

Sureshot Stell had been riding in a wagon. Now she clambered down and tramped ahead, falling in beside Lazlo. He was surprised at how perky she looked, even with the broken arm, splinted and muffled and hugged awkwardly close to her middle. Her skin was brightly flushed, but apparently from the cold and not from fever.

Politely, Lazlo wondered aloud if her arm wasn't giving her some pain.

Stella laughed. He hadn't heard her laugh before. It was a rich and satisfying sound. Sure the arm was hurting a little, but Miss Bly had splinted it up real dandy. Long as she took it easy — and who could walk very fast in all this snow? — it should be all right.

"I feel fine as froghair, otherwise. Anyways, I couldn't abide another damn minute rocking along in that wagon with a busted arm. Every time them wheels hit a jolt, a body catches it clear to her toes. How you doing, Buster?"

"I am doing all right."

Afterward, sort of tentatively, they began to draw each other out, talking about this and that. Was all of it just aimless talk? He wasn't sure at first.

One thing Stella wanted to make damn sure he understood was that after what her pa had told her a little earlier, the battle lines were clearly drawn. She and her pa and Myra Mae and Robert Topbear were all on his side.

"I had thought as much," said Lazlo. "I thank you all. But how far will this go? You might have to fight Jacks and Hutch and your cousin."

Stella laughed shortly. "Jacks fixed that. Soon's he was sure how the wind was blowing, he got hold of all the guns we had and shed 'em back on the trail somewhere. All 'cept the ones him and Bije and Hutch are toting."

"Then we are in the same boat. But they won't hurt you or yours unless any of you takes up for me. So don't do it, Stell."

"Stella, damn it!"

"Stella. I am sorry. It's a good name."

"Sure it is. Yours now, Lazlo, that sounds sort o' funny. How you spell it?"

Lazlo smiled. "In English, it is supposed to be L-a-s-z-l-o. But nobody ever got it right. When I came to this country as a kid, the immigration people spelled it wrong on my papers, and everyone has spelled it wrong since. So I myself go along with it and drop the 's.' "

"L-a-z-l-o, huh? Don't have a bad ring to it, at that."

Stella talked a little about her early life, how her pa had hoped for a son and had never made a secret of his bitter disappointment at not having one, and how out of her own hurt she'd taken to acting like a boy just to mock and anger him.

"Worked real fine," she added pensively, "so good I never sprung loose of the habit. Never really wanted to, I reckon."

"I would think your mother would put a stop to this. Didn't she ever take you in hand?"

"She tried to, for a spell. But Ma died right after Myra Mae was born. Then I took my head like I wanted and bedamned to what Pa liked or didn't."

Lazlo nodded. "It all starts there," he said thoughtfully, "when we are kids. Everything we are comes from back then."

"Ain't it the truth." She eyed him askance. "How about you, Buster?"

Lazlo told her a few things. About the early death of his father. Growing up with a mother whose grand self-puffery was her alleged descent from a great nobleman. Filling her only child with dreams of his own, a kind of silent shout flung in the teeth of the grinding poverty he'd always known.

He was sparing of details, but Stella got the idea right away.

"So finding all that gold meant a mighty heap to you, didn't it?"

"The long and short of it, Stella, is that I am a greedy man. But that, I guess, is why. Yes."

"Well, there's no pure people on either side of any fence. Leastways none I ever knew of." She laughed briefly, gazing off toward a mountaintop. "I sure ain't, myself."

"What does that mean?"

"What do you mean, what does that mean?" Her glance switched back to him, so quickly and fiercely that he knew he'd unwittingly hit a nerve. "Just what the hell you think purity *is*, Buster?"

"Well, I, uh . . ." God, how did a man get into this sort of an impasse? And once in it, how did he get himself out? "I mean," he said doggedly, "a woman is pure or she is not pure. That is all."

"It ain't by a blamed sight!" Stella balled her good hand into a fist and hit him on the shoulder hard. She was genuinely angry. "You don't know diddly-squat about anything, do you, Buster?"

Lazlo rubbed his shoulder. "Not about women," he agreed sourly. "Them I must learn more of."

"You ain't learned half by yet, that's damn sure!"

They tramped along in flinty silence for a full minute.

Then Stella, looking straight ahead of her, said tonelessly, "There was a man I met back when I was going on nineteen. He sweet-talked me a good deal and turned my head a lot. We was supposed to be wed. Then he called it off."

Lazlo shook his head, honestly mystified. "Why would he do that?"

"Why d'you *think*, damn it! Because he'd got what he wanted!"

Lazlo said, "Oh," and wisely said no more.

After another minute of tramping silently alongside him, Stella said tensely, "Anyway, I've had no use for men since then. But let me tell you, Buster. If I ever *did*, and if any man done that to me again, I would hunt him down and gutshoot him. By the Lord Harry, I would." She snapped her fingers. "Just like that!"

"It would be just," Lazlo said respect-fully.

"Damn right it would. And what the hell are you *grinning* about, anyway?"

Lazlo straightened out his face. "I did not mean to grin. I was just thinking."

"Devil you was. What about?"

"About a breed of independent woman there is coming to be. Not many yet. But a few. Miss Aretha Bly is one kind; you are another. Very different kinds, I think. You are —" He paused lamely. "You are not the same at all."

Lazlo braced himself, thinking she would likely get mad all over again.

Stella only shook her head, gently puckering her lips. "No, don't reckon so. I'm noways like that lady. She is the sort will give her whole self to som'at she believes in. Am I right or not?"

"I think it is so."

"Well, that ain't me." Her gaze was set ahead, straight and hard. "There is room in my life for a man. A good man, if I ever knew one. And for having kids and raising 'em. But I tell you this." A long pause. "I won't never stand for any man telling me how I can think or say or act. Bedamned if I will!"

"I think there is room for both those

things in the life of a good woman," Lazlo said gravely. "To have a family and to have her own mind too."

"You do?"

"Yes, I think so."

For quite a while they swung along the trail with no more talk. But they stayed side by side, and to both of them it felt right.

Around noon the wagons turned a jutting angle on the trail. A little farther on, they paused on the final upland lift before the long descent off the heights.

By now, just about everyone's mood was high from the increasing warmth of the sun. At the same time, busy watching their footing where melting snow and ice had turned the rock dangerously slick, they emerged onto the panoramic view almost before they knew it.

And there they came to a halt. They did it unthinkingly, involuntarily. It was a gala moment.

They were on a stretch of trail that followed a broad sweep of ledge. On one side, to their right, rose the broken spine of a granite cliff that was laced with irregular shelves of rock, rotted and crumbling. Over all of it, gleaming crests of snow had been stiffened by wind and cold into weird outthrusts of their own. On the other side, the ledge fell away in a long sheer drop of more crumbling rock faces for a hundred feet or more.

Lazlo, in spite of his own situation, couldn't blame the younger folk for their jubilant surge of spirit. From here, at last, they could see into the verdant basin of their destination. At this height everything stood out with an incredible clarity. One could make out, distantly, like a tumble of children's blocks, the flat dark shapes of buildings in Carson's Crossing and of outlying farms and ranches.

The kids were wildly excited. Some of them showed it with childish exuberance, laughing, running, and slipping on the slick rock. Others just gaped and gazed. A few solemnly stood and looked and rubbed tears out of their eyes.

Excited or not, everyone needed the usual nooning. They needed to rest and eat. Usually they nooned with cold food. Today, Miss Aretha decreed, they would have a hot meal, for it was a celebration of sorts. She dispatched the kids in each direction, both up and down the trail, to hunt fuel for the fires. Even scrub brush grew scantily in this high, stony desolation, and it took them awhile to scratch up enough.

But that didn't matter. Haste was no longer important. The weather was bright, the season's first fall of snow melting away fast, and travel on the downslopes ahead would be easy. By this time tomorrow, they would be in the soft roll of hills that edged the basin.

The kids straggled back from their brush-rustling in twos and threes, and the fires were lighted.

Lazlo and Stella had stayed together, not making a great thing of it but keeping sort of close, talking a little as they poked around picking up a few sticks. They almost forgot everything else. In fact the two of them were downright startled when Miss Aretha came up to them, saying crisply, "Mr. Kusik, have you noticed my brother about?"

"No, ma'am, I have not."

"Well, he hasn't come back. He and young Cissie were gathering wood, I don't know which way, and nobody has seen them. I wondered if you had. Or you, Miss Ruddy?"

Lazlo's first embarrassed thought was that Mark and the girl were off spooning somewhere, but Stella's reply squelched it.

"No," Stella said slowly. "I seen one thing, though. That big pard o' yours, Lazlo. He went lumbering off up the trail a spell back. I didn't take much notice at the time, but . . . I don't think he's come back."

Both Lazlo and Miss Aretha looked at her blankly.

Stella shrugged. "Maybe it don't mean som'at. But that Hutch fellow is bad medicine. I reckon you both know it. Drunk all the time. Acting like he is gone out of his head. Was eyeing that young 'un, Cissie, pretty fierce and ugly a lot of the time."

"Oh God, he was," Miss Aretha whispered. "Mr. Kusik . . . !"

Lazlo said, "*Up* the trail it was, Stella?"

"Yes."

"Stay here, both of you. Say nothing."

As he spoke, Lazlo was already moving away from them, quickly and quietly. If nothing was amiss, no sense alarming the whole camp. If something was wrong, he must lose no time.

Damn! He should have kept an eye on Hutch as he'd resolved. His growing awareness of Stella Ruddy had caused his attention to stray.

One good thing, though: It had also caused Creed Jacks to relax his watch on

Lazlo. At just the moment Lazlo was wondering where the gunman was, he saw Jacks ahead of him. He was sitting on his heels on the sunny side of a wagon, his back propped against the wheel.

Lazlo pulled to a halt. Was Jacks feigning again? He really seemed asleep, his head lolling back against the wheel felloe, mouth slightly open. This last tiring stretch of trail might have caught up with Jacks's frail constitution . . . or he might simply be bored with the sudden run of festive proceedings.

For a wild moment Lazlo thought of swiftly crossing to him and overpowering him. Just as quickly he discarded the notion. Jacks was too far away; he might snap back at any moment, and there was no time to waste. Lazlo slipped past him, giving him a wide berth, past one last wagon too, and then he raced up the trail.

Reaching the sharp bend around a bulge of rock, he heard Jacks call out warningly, "*Kusik!* Hey!"

Lazlo threw a glance over his shoulder. Jacks, somehow aroused, was starting to his feet. Lazlo shook his head and didn't slacken his run. He kept looking backward though, seeing Jacks's face distort palely, his hand slashing back the skirt of his coat.

That was as far as he got in pulling his gun. Suddenly Robert Topbear came around the wagon. He sprang at Jacks from the side and back, flinging his arms around the gunman. His rush and his weight bore Jacks to the ground.

That was all Lazlo saw. Scrambling around the bend now, he was cut off from them. Keeping up a full, driving run, he put all his attention ahead of him. His heart was pumping wildly at the end of what was maybe a hundred-yard dash along the angles of a crooked, cliff-hugging trail. Then he came to a dead stop.

He saw Mark Bly sprawled on the ground, limp and silent. A sinking dread filled Lazlo, for he was sure what else he would find.

CHAPTER 19

Mark lay in a crumpled, twisted position. At first glance he looked dead. But he wasn't. He'd been fetched a wicked blow that had mashed a great strawberry mark along the whole side of his face. Even as Lazlo bent above him, Mark moved his head and let out a faint groan. He'd be all right.

Lazlo plunged away along the trail, his boots driving fiercely at the scatter of rubble that had fallen from the rim above. Another bend was ahead. He veered around it and came on Hutch and Cissie.

The girl lay unconscious on the granite rock, most of her clothes torn away. Hutch, kneeling beside her, was tearing away the rest of them. His face was red, bloated, crazed. When he looked up, surprised at Lazlo's approach, his eyes were like raw gleaming sockets, bloodshot and out of focus.

His beard split in a great laugh. "Why howdy there, little pard! I vow, I 'uz just —"

As he said it, Hutch was swaying to his

feet, pawing at the Walker Colt shoved into the waistband of his pants. Lazlo hadn't even paused. His legs pounded with a straining fury across the few yards remaining between them. Although it took him only a few seconds to reach Hutch, it seemed like an agonizing splinter of time wrenched from out of eternity.

Hutch had just dragged the Walker Colt free of his pants — he had it cocked but not yet pointed — when Lazlo's full weight slammed into him.

It was like plowing into a brick wall. Hutch's vast bulk seemed hardly to budge under the impact. In the same moment Lazlo struck blindly at the upswinging gun, caught its barrel, and gave it a desperate twist sideways as the weapon went off.

He felt the scorch of exploding powder along his cheek. The thunder of the shot, almost in his face, deafened him. The echoes clattered back and forth along the crumbling cliffside. They brought down a scatter of small debris that rained over the two men.

Clutched momentarily against Hutch's unswaying bulk, off-balance and unable to pull quickly away, Lazlo expected the sudden crush of Hutch's great hands on him. Even as the taste of despair crowded into his throat, he realized that Hutch, incredibly, was toppling backward.

Maybe it was a residual effect of Lazlo's collision with him. Or maybe it was just the final effect of all the booze he'd consumed. Whatever — Hutch was going down. And in the same instant, Lazlo thrust away from him and scrambled sideways, out of his reach.

Hutch crashed heavily on his back. But the fall seemed to clear his head, and he had retained a hold on his Walker Colt. Even as Lazlo was coming back to his feet, Hutch was climbing to his knees, cocking the Walker, swinging it up to bear. His teeth were bared, his hair dripping over his face in limp straggles.

Lazlo was half-upright before he realized how quickly Hutch had recovered. Not hesitating, Lazlo closed a fist over a hefty piece of rock and flung it as he was still in the act of getting his feet under him.

The rough-edged chunk caught Hutch squarely in the face. He let out a yowl and dropped his gun, clapping his hands over his shattered nose. He took two wobbling steps backward.

Lazlo made a wild dive for the Walker Colt. Just as wildly he grabbed it up, closed a fist around it, and, sprawled flat on his stomach, brought it up to line on Hutch.

There was no need. Hutch had staggered back a foot or so too far. Suddenly his feet were skidding away from under him. He threw himself forward, clawing wildly at the rimrock. But it was slick with ice, and he kept slipping backward.

Lazlo's last blurred glimpse of Hutch was seeing him skate helplessly on the brink, arms flailing, his beard parting in a wild shriek. Then he went over and down.

Numb and sick, Lazlo crawled over to the liprock. From there he could see the dark imprint of Hutch's body at the base of a snowy chasm far below. He must have bounced at least twice off protrusions of rock. From there on, it was a straight fall to the bottom . . .

Lazlo climbed shakily to his feet. He looked almost blankly at the Walker Colt in his fist. Then he turned to Cissie.

Apparently she wasn't really hurt; no bruise showed on her tender flesh. She must only have fainted, and already she was coming to, making soft little moans as her head turned from one side to the other. The crumple of her clothing that Hutch had torn off lay beside her, and it would be as well to let her rearrange it herself. She would not welcome the sight of any man near her as she revived.

And there was still Creed Jacks. What had happened after Robert Topbear had jumped him? No shot had been fired . . . no gun had gone off except Hutch's.

Lazlo stared at the vintage Colt. What could he do with a pistol? He'd hardly ever fired one. But at least he was armed again.

He started back down the trail at a hard trot. He came to where Mark had fallen. The youth was on his feet now, clutching at the cliff wall for support, rubbing a hand dazedly over his face.

He stared at Lazlo. "Cissie?" he said hoarsely.

Lazlo said tersely, grimly, "I think she is well enough. Hutch is dead. He did not hurt her, but he tore off her clothes. Give her a little time to cover herself; then go to her. But then you both wait, understand? Don't either of you follow me back."

Mark gave a slow, vague nod, and Lazlo went on.

He did not know what would be ahead of him, but likely it would mean shooting. He did not want Mark or Cissie in line. Christ — what chance would he stand with this antique piece of Hutch's, assuming that he could hit anything with a pistol?

Lazlo knew one thing: He would not give up again, not while he had a gun in his fist and the strength to pull the trigger.

As he drew near the campsite, Lazlo slowed his pace on the crooked bends of trail. He went forward slowly and warily, his body sunk in a half-crouch. His nerves were so keyed that he was set to shoot at the shadow of a movement.

Skirting a sharp angle of rock, he came on Creed Jacks quite suddenly. The gunman, too, was edging around a rock shoulder in the trail, working carefully toward him.

They saw each other at the same time. Creed Jacks's gun flashed in his fist. He fired just as Lazlo jerked back to cover. The bullet scored rock so close to his face that he felt a sting of rock dust.

The shot echoes dislodged rock chips from the crumbly cliffside above. Lazlo felt them rain down on his head and shoulders.

Nevertheless he didn't hesitate. Jacks had also pulled back to shelter just after he'd fired, and in the following instant Lazlo whipped around the rock angle and flattened himself against the slight hollow beyond it, holding his cocked pistol ready.

A moment later Jacks did the same, stepping into plain sight for a moment as he came around his sheltering corner, and Lazlo fired. Not surprisingly, he made a clean miss. And now Jacks too was hugging a small hollow and cut off from Lazlo's view.

His light laugh and faint shout reached Lazlo plainly, "How do you like it now, hunky?"

Lazlo didn't like it at all. The two of them were at a standoff. The perhaps two hundred feet of distance between them was laced with abrupt outthrusts of rock and short pockets of cover. If a man were agile enough, he could either work nearer an opponent or retreat from him, dodging around the rocky projections and into the shallow depressions.

But Creed Jacks was the pistolman. Lazlo was not. Hutch's big Walker Colt felt like an unwieldy chunk of lead in his fist.

It does not matter. Now it will be one of us or the other.

Lazlo and Jacks made the same decision in the same split instant. Both men came lunging fast away from their shelters into the hollows just beyond. Both fired and both missed.

But Lazlo had missed by a couple of feet or so. He knew it by the *feel* of the shot.

And Creed Jacks, again, had come close enough to dust him with rock splinters. Now both men were cut off from one another once more.

Jacks's mocking laugh drifted to him even through the clatter of rubble falling from the granite overhangs. Lazlo shrank into his skimpy shelter, hardly aware in his panic of his own slugging pulse and the ooze of his sweat.

God. A few more shots — or even one — might bring the whole shuddering mass of age-rotted rock down on them.

Creed Jacks made the next move, springing around his shoulder of rock and firing simultaneously. His bullet screamed off a rock close to Lazlo's head, and Lazlo followed up at once, firing at Jacks as he pivoted around his own rocky angle into a fresh position.

And then it no longer mattered.

The echoes of gunfire had started to reverberate along an ever-broadening stretch of pitted cliffside. No small trickles of rubble now. Big chunks of loose rock sloughed away from the quaking escarpment and crashed downward.

Both Lazlo and Creed Jacks ducked out and away from their meager cover to avoid the falling rock. At the same time, instinctively, they fired at one another again. The merging slam of gunshots brought a thunderous groan of reply from the whole section of eroded cliff. Now, in one continual roar, a great piece of it gave way.

The main slide of rock and dirt and snow was funneling down toward Creed Jacks. Lithe as a snake, he dodged away from its path, but then he tripped and went down. The avalanche thundered over and around him. A mist of reddish dust shrouded everything.

The roar of cascading rock dwindled away.

Lazlo stood swaying on his feet. He was bleeding from a few cuts and coughing from the gritty fog that mushroomed around him. As the dust began to settle, he stumbled forward, his gun pointed ahead of him. Suddenly he glimpsed Creed Jacks on the ground through the reddish haze and drew a quick bead on him.

The Walker Colt snapped on a dead chamber. Frantically he pulled the trigger again. Nothing.

Lazlo came to a stop now, staring dully at Creed Jacks as the dust cleared away and he realized what had happened. Jacks was pinned flat, buried from the waist down in a mass of debris. He too was coughing on rock dust, and it must have got in his eyes; he was groping blindly for his pistol.

Tramping forward, Lazlo saw Jacks's gun in the rubble, maybe a yard from his out-flung arm. He bent and picked it up. A finely hand-crafted weapon, it was ruined, smashed beyond repair. A falling rock must have done it. Lazlo threw the gun aside and, not sparing Jacks another glance, climbed onward over the heap of rubble.

The fallaway of crumbling granite nearly choked the trail for another hundred feet; then it tapered off, and he was hurrying on, breaking into a run as he neared the camp.

What had happened back there?

Coming hard around the last bend above the camp, he saw all of it at once. Bije Willet was holding a rifle on everyone.

He stood with his back to Lazlo's vantage, keeping all of them covered. Laban Ruddy was at the front, with Stella and Robert Topbear close to him. Behind them, watching tensely, were Aretha Bly and the gang of orphans.

It was plain enough what had happened. It crossed Lazlo's mind as a fleeting image. Bije had rescued Creed Jacks from

Topbear, and then Jacks had ordered him to hold the rest of them at bay while he went ahead to deal with Lazlo.

The scrape of Lazlo's boots pulled Bije around fast, his rifle swinging with him in a cramped arc. Lazlo came to a halt. He saw the squeeze of fear, desperation, and anger in Bije's face.

Bije had come only halfway around. He couldn't cover both Lazlo and the others at the same time. The panic of indecision showed in his stupid face.

Lazlo did not raise the Walker Colt. Holding it down at his side, he said in a steely, positive voice, "Throw it away, boy. Don't make me kill you."

The Walker was jammed, or a chamber was fouled, or the loads were spent. It didn't matter which. The gun was useless, and his words were a bluff.

Bije hesitated and then swung the rifle toward him, bawling, "Go to hell, you hunky sonbitch!"

"*Bije!*"

Laban Ruddy's voice cracked like a whip. He took one long step forward, causing Bije to swing the rifle back on him. "Don't try it, Bije. If you shoot Kusik, you'll have to shoot me too."

"That goes for me too, Bije," Stella said

311

quietly. "Don't reckon you hone to wipe out all the kin you got left, do you?"

Robert Topbear put in mildly, "Nor me either. I don't think you'll do that, Bije."

Bije stared wildly from them to Lazlo and back again. He lifted the rifle high in his trembling fists and then dashed it to the ground. A kind of sob broke in his throat. "Aw right, Uncle Labe! Aw right, damn all your eyes!"

CHAPTER 20

It was not a long nooning. All of them were glad to be away from the place and to begin their last descent toward the foothills that edged the fertile basin. By sunset, as the last burn of daylight ruddied the western rim of land, they made camp in the lowland hills.

As preparations for the evening meal got underway, Lazlo tramped over to one of the covered wagons. He looked into its dimness. Creed Jacks lay on his back on a pallet of blankets, his slight body loose and sprawled. He couldn't stir a muscle below the lowest point of his spine, and he felt no sensation at all from there on down.

"Ah, hunky." Creed Jacks's face was like a blob of gray suet in the bad light, but his voice was still cool and mocking. "Come here to crow a bit, have you?"

Lazlo shook his head. "I would not do that. I think you would have got me if the cliff had not come down on you. I am sorry for it, Jacks."

"What for? I was set to get you. You were set to get me right back."

"Not this way."

It had taken most of an hour to extricate Creed Jacks from the pile of fallaway rock that had emprisoned his legs and hips. As they'd cleared away the rubble, more of it had slid down from above. At last, working with infinite care, they had freed him. Creed Jacks was in a sorry way. Both of his legs were crushed, broken in several places, and they might heal after a fashion. But the damage to his spine that had eliminated all mobility and feeling through his lower body was something else. Probably he would never walk again.

"I believe not." Creed Jacks gave a febrile chuckle. "In any event, my working days are over . . . come what may."

"Miss Bly says there is a good hospital in Carson's Crossing. We will be there by about noon tomorrow. Maybe —"

"Quit it, hunky." Creed Jacks's grin was twisted and weary. "I'm a gambler. Been one all my life. This time I overplayed my hand. The gambler ran out his string. Happens to the best of us. Or the worst . . ."

Walking a slow circle of the camp now, Lazlo thought heavily that he should not waste sympathy on the man. But he felt a powerful depression all the same.

Miss Aretha, kneeling by a fire as she expertly fed sticks into it, looked up at his approach.

"Well," she said with a pleasant nod, "you look as though you'd lost your best friend, Mr. Kusik. I can't see why. You have gotten your gold through. From what I've gathered, it — along with what remains in your 'cache' back in Bozetown — should make you a man of moderate wealth."

Lazlo searched her words for a hint of mockery, but there was none. Her smile was sober and friendly and a little quizzical.

"Yes," he said gravely, "there is that."

"Is it Mr. Prouter? Of course you were friends —"

"No," Lazlo said wryly, "we were never that. Even if it looked so at first."

"That fellow in the wagon, then? Jacks?"

"I guess that is it. A bitter thing for a man."

Miss Aretha stood up now, her small face very serious. "It was you or him, Mr. Kusik. What he got, he asked for. 'The wages of sin . . .' Do you know?"

"Yes. But that is death. This is worse than dying, I think. There is another saying from that book. It has to do with not judging."

" 'Judge not . . .' " She paused with a prim nod. "Quite so, Mr. Kusik. I should not need reminding."

Her serious look broke in a sudden smile, making him think once again: *This woman is not plain. Not ever!* "Speaking of sayings," she went on, "there was a man of my region, a man named Thoreau. He once wrote of a friend, 'We are of different tribes, and we are not at war.' That is how you and I are."

Lazlo nodded, returning her smile. "I think it is so."

He felt less depressed, a little less tired, as he moved off and away, through the scatter of fires coming to life against the chill of night. Around them children played and laughed shrilly. Cissie O'Halloran was not frolicking. She crouched beside a fire with her arms folded around her knees, gazing across the camp.

Cissie looked up, giving him a quick shy smile that said her thanks all over again.

Lazlo solemnly touched his hat and walked on, briefly following Cissie's glance. Mark Bly was leaning his crossed arms on the tailgate of a wagon, talking to

316

someone inside it. That was Myra Mae Ruddy, still weak from her illness.

A lot of things did not turn out as you might wish. Later on, you might smile about it, but it was never funny at the time. Least of all when you were young. Lord, the pain of being young! Goldenly reminiscing, people forgot all of it too soon . . . too easily.

Over by another fire, Laban Ruddy and Robert Topbear and Bije Willet were sitting side by side, passing a bottle (produced from God knew where) back and forth. Spotting Lazlo, both Laban and Topbear hailed him in loudly amiable tones, inviting him over to have a drink. Bije only scowled and took a long pull of whiskey.

Lazlo smiled and shook his head and walked on.

Nearly all the resolutions that men made turned out to be worth just that much, in the end. Still, you never knew. Perhaps since they'd all come through a fierce time, the colonel and Topbear merely felt that a little celebrating was in order. Or they were just hopeless drunks. Each was a good man in his way. Maybe that was what mattered most.

Stella was sitting with her back against

the wheel of the last wagon in line, pulled up at the outer edge of darkness that rimmed the camp. It seemed to Lazlo that she was quietly waiting. Not asking for anything, not particularly expecting it either. But waiting all the same.

As Lazlo came up to her, she raised her eyes and said, "Howdy. Bet *you* ain't been that way a whole lot either."

Lazlo gazed at her, baffled. "What way?"

"No rifle. You ain't toting one about you anywhere I can see."

He laughed heartily. (How long since he'd given out a laugh that felt genuine? He couldn't remember.) He dropped to his haunches beside her, gazing aimlessly around the camp. Looking anywhere but at her.

"Maybe," he said carefully, "there is not the need anymore. Stella, can I ask —"

A smacking blow on the back of his neck made Lazlo swear furiously, swiveling around on his heels. The dark form of one of the kids was running off, and behind it trailed the taunting laugh of Cyrus.

Now it was Stella's turn to laugh.

"Say, listen. If the folks that boy is supposed to hitch up with at Carson's Crossing don't fancy him, maybe *you* could take him on. How'd that be?"

Lazlo rubbed his neck and glared at her. "I could ask you the same. What do *you* think of it? It would have to be all right for both of us."

Stella laughed again. Then she caught his meaning; the laugh faltered and died on her lips. "Listen, Buster, do you mean . . . ?"

Apparently she couldn't bring herself to say it all. But Lazlo, meeting her gaze straight on, knew once and for all that a man could find better treasures than any gold strike could offer. And it was he who said the rest.

"I mean for always," he told her.

ABOUT THE AUTHOR

T. V. Olsen, who lives in Wisconsin, is the author of many Westerns, including *The Stalking Moon, Eye of the Wolf, There Was a Season, Summer of the Drums,* and *Track the Man Down.* His novel *Arrow in the Sun* was made into a film, *Soldier Blue,* as was *The Stalking Moon,* which starred Gregory Peck.